MW00809725

# Trees and Shrubs
# Of New Mexico

# Trees and Shrubs of New Mexico

Jack L. Carter

Illustrations: B. Dennis,
Marjorie C. Leggitt
& W. J. Underwood

Johnson Books, Distributor: Boulder, CO

Copyright © 1997 by Jack L. Carter
Mimbres Publishing
Plant Drawings Copyright © 1997 by the illustrators

All rights reserved. No part of this work may be reproduced or
transmitted by any means, electronic or mechanical, including
photocopying or recording, or by any information storage
or retrieval system, without permission in writing from the author.

ISBN 0-9658404-0-9

Library of Congress Catalog Card Number : 97-93998

Distributed by Johnson Books
1880 South 57th Court
Boulder, CO 80301
1-800-258-5830
(303) 443-1576
and
Jack L. Carter
Box 1244
Silver City, NM 88062
(505) 388-9221

Cover :  Howell Graphic Design
Silver City, NM 88061

Cover illustration:
NEW MEXICO RASPBERRY
*Rubus neomexicanus*

# Table of Contents

# PREFACE

This book has been written for the educated layperson who wishes to become more familiar with the woody flora of New Mexico. It has been designed so those who want to learn more about the flora of their local community, the life zone in which they live, or the ecology, evolution and distribution of the vegetation of New Mexico, can start their personal learning experience just outside their front door. Although this publication contains considerable scientific information, professional training in botany is not required to learn the common names of the local trees and shrubs in your neighborhood. However, like all learning it does require a visceral enthusiasm to examine some part of the botanical world and some messing about in the botanical sciences. The book is structured so that each individual may have a personal experience with plants. If we have done our job well, we have freed the student from the teacher so he or she may become a self-directed learner.

Why is the study of plants so extremely important to the future of humankind? Probably less than ten percent of the citizens living in the State of New Mexico could describe in 100 words or less their biologic relationship to green plants. While thousands of yet to be identified species of plants are being lost each year, we take for granted these vital organisms that through photosynthesis are the alpha and omega of human existence. After more than a billion years of evolution, animals, including *Homo sapiens*, still rely on the coming together of carbon dioxide and water in green plants to produce the sugars, starches and oxygen required for their survival.

Up until the last two centuries there were so few *Homo sapiens* and the world's flora seemed so vast and diversified that no one thought we would ever have a problem maintaining the vascular flora of planet earth. Today conditions have drastically changed. As the world's human population has continued to increase at a geometric rate, we have rapidly destroyed a large part of the world's flora. Because we live very short lives and have trouble seeing ourselves as part of the living world, we have in the past 200 years thoughtlessly destroyed forests and prairies that required millions of years to evolve, and several hundred years to develop to maturity. As we look to the future we recognize that as long as so many individual members of the human race go into our forests, and each day destroy so many trees that required 50 to 300 years to reach maturity, or plow or scrape off millions of acres of prairie around our cities, we are literally forcing the demise of countless animal species, including *Homo sapiens*.

Today we are starting to see signs of change in the way we interpret our relationship to planet earth. As part of this learning process an ever increasing segment of society is involved in identifying many important issues related to plants in our lives. We are encouraged to use native plant species in our lawns and gardens, to xeriscape where possible and to conserve water. More and more people want to know what species of trees, shrubs and grasses are appropriate for their personal property and what plants are being planted in their city parks and along the local streets. In the Southwest we are involved in making decisions and casting our vote concerning the logging of regional timber, the grazing of cattle on public lands and where mining activities will be permitted. More people than ever before want the native flora and fauna of our state and national parks and forests protected now and in the future.

There are a wide range of organizations such as the Native Plant Society of New Mexico, The Nature Conservancy, the Audubon Society and all of the affiliated chapters of these organizations that have educational programs. Closely associated are the many state and federal agencies that play a role in challenging citizens to learn more about the natural history of New Mexico.

Teachers have a vital role to play in returning the study of plants to the curriculum. However, if we examine the major concepts that are today included in biology courses in our schools and colleges, we find the class time devoted to the study of botany has been continuously reduced over the past 50 years. Field studies, where students have an opportunity to work with the local flora and fauna, are practically non-existent. It is not uncommon for teachers of biology at all levels to identify their limited knowledge of the local flora, and the fact that they are not comfortable taking students on field trips. Obviously this is not true of all biology teachers, and there are those teachers who do make the study of plants a major objective in their courses. But until this larger problem is corrected there is no way we will have students leaving our schools and colleges with a knowledge and appreciation of the local flora that will allow them to make the decisions necessary to conserve the natural world. We know we can and must do better.

New Mexico is a beautiful state that offers wonderful opportunities for each of us to learn more about our relationship to plants. We see this book as a tool that can be used by every citizen to learn to enjoy their local flora and to better understand the natural world.

Jack L. Carter
May 1997

# ACKNOWLEDGEMENTS

This book is the result of 14 years experience teaching field botany, systematic botany and plant geography in the Southwest, seven years of field work, considerable collecting, a great deal of encouragement from my friends, and a personal desire to assist those who wish to know more about the vascular flora of the region. In all honesty, as I examine the end product of this endeavor I am drawn to two conclusions. First, I think the original plan got completely out of hand, and second, I now realize how much fun an eccentric old geezer can have in retirement.

I like to lay the blame for this book on others. If those several hundred intelligent and enthusiastic Colorado College students who enrolled in my courses and traveled with me throughout the Southwest would not have been so anxious to learn and would not have asked so many important questions, this publication never would have been produced. Or if my wife, Martha, would have just said, "Stop this crazy activity, we are not supposed to devote our retirement years to collecting all over the State of New Mexico, examining herbarium materials, developing databases, learning about 600 dpi printers, scanners and computer technology," again, none of this would have happened. Instead of calling a halt to the work, Martha made the serious mistake of joining me in this adventure and has consequently developed into a knowledgable field botanist and a very fine desktop publisher. She has become an involved and committed partner, in fact, a driving force in these botanical exploits.

From the start college and university students and faculty, as well as U. S. Forest Service staff and many friends, were anxious to work with us. With financial support in 1991 from The Colorado College, through the Southwest Studies program and a Howard Hughes grant, Sheila George and Amy Chadwick, biology majors at Colorado College, participated in the field work and assisted in the production of over 900 herbarium specimens. With similar continued support from the College in 1992 we were able to enlist the assistance of Sheila Christy and Charles (Chuck) A. Huff, talented students of botany at Western New Mexico University, to join in our studies. Not only was Chuck a fine botanist, but he brought to our work considerable knowledge and enthusiasm for computers that we were able to use in maintaining collection records and improving herbarium label programs. Our field work continued through 1993 and by the end of that growing season we had made over 1,800 collections and produced 2,100 herbarium sheets. In 1994 Diego Villalba (WNMU) and Vandy Johnson (Stanford University) joined with us and we received financial support from the USDA Forest Service, Gila National Forest, to gather baseline floristic information on the Negrito ecosystem of the Gila National Forest. This work continued through 1995, and in 1995 and 1996 we added field studies in the Hermosa, north Palomas and Seco ecosystems of the Gila. Also, Owen Williams, Donna Stevens, Adrian Acosta, Nancy Deever and Lori Weber, all of WNMU, joined in various aspects of our studies. In the past year Donna Stevens has brought her knowledge of botany and her expertise in grammar together to become a fine copy editor. Throughout these several years additional field trips were taken into the Cibola, Santa Fe, Apache-Sitgreaves, Coronado, Carson and Lincoln National Forests. By the end of 1996 over 2,800 herbarium sheets had been prepared and distributed among the herbaria of the Gila National Forest, New Mexico State University, The University of New Mexico, The Colorado College and Western New Mexico University.

Some years ago I recall reading a study that reported that the first year college student of science must learn more new terms than the first year student of a foreign language. Botany, like all areas of science, is closely tied to terminology and language and we have provided an extensive glossary. But we have one additional tool that is extremely helpful and that is the illustrations of most of the included species. Without these illustrations this book might appear to the neophyte as a well arranged glossary of botanical terms. However, through the excellent work of three principal illustrators and several other people who participated in a lesser but important way, the publication will be of use to a much wider audience. Beth Dennis, illustrator in the Department of Biology at The University of New Mexico, has made a major contribution to this publication and has here demonstrated why she is one of the very best illustrators of biologic materials in New Mexico. Marjorie C. Leggitt, a friend and former student at Colorado College, who so skillfully illustrated *Trees and Shrubs of Colorado*, continues here to demonstrate her ability to interpret the vascular flora of the Southwest. She is today recognized as the foremost botanical illustrator in Colorado. William Underwood came to the project with considerable experience as an illustrator and artist, but with little experience in illustrating plants. We soon recognized his skills and could see he had the ability to describe in pen and ink exactly what he was observing. He, along with the other two major illustrators, has made this book a much more powerful publication for the beginning field botanist. Also, in the key to the mistletoes (Viscaceae) we must recognize the excellent work of Sharon Harris who illustrated the enlargements of the reproductive structures of the dwarf mistletoes for the Agriculture Handbook No. 401. Beyond these four people we are pleased to include illustrations by Harry M. Stover, Charles A. Huff, Susan Rubin and Marilyn Huggins.

I express my deep appreciation to Colorado College Professors Richard Storey, Sylvia (Tass) Kelso and Joseph Gordon and staff member, Caroline Noble, for their continued interest and support of this project. Professor Terry Heiner provided important administrative assistance by arranging for us to use the herbarium, laboratory space and business office facilities at Western New Mexico University. Of even greater importance, it was he who identified several of the serious students of botany who have contributed so much to this work. Also, special thanks must go to Professor Richard Johnson, WNMU, for being our personal teacher and guide as we developed the computer skills vital to producing the final product. He was always anxious to help when we needed his expertise. In addition, Laura Howell was of assistance in getting the final proofs ready for publication.

I am grateful to the Gila National Forest staff and especially Paul Boucher, Forest Biologist, not only for supporting us in this work, but for directing us to many plant species we might have missed without their assistance. Also, we thank Professor Emeritus Dale Zimmerman, WNMU, for assisting us in locating and identifying several critical species in this study. We have relied heavily on Professor Timothy Lowery and Assistant Curator Jane Mygatt of the herbarium at The University of New Mexico for their continued assistance. Richard Spellenberg, Professor & Curator of the Herbarium, Department of Biology, New Mexico State University has been an important contributor to this study and has been especially helpful in our work with the genus *Quercus*. Then there were all those special friends who joined us on field trips, called our attention to interesting collection sites or to taxa we should give special attention, such as Mr. Thomas Wootten, Professor Kelley Allred, Professor Richard Worthington, Dr. David Anderson, Mr. Robert Denham, Mr. Chris Frazier, Mr. Robert Sivinski, Mr. Laird McIntosh, Mr. Ron Flemke, Mr. Ralph Fisher, Mr. Reggie A. Fletcher, Professor Robert P. Adams, Professor A. Michael Powell, Ms. Debra Swetnam and Ms. Margaret Kirkeminde.

We are pleased to recognize all those individuals who have contributed so much to this book. At the same time we hope those we may have failed to mention will forgive us this shortcoming. Beyond this, I accept full responsibility for the errors and omissions within the pages in this book.

This is the first edition and first printing of this book. One important result of the methods we have used to produce this publication is that it will be easier to update names, add species and make corrections. As problems are identified please send us your suggestions.

Jack L. Carter<br>
June 1997

# INTRODUCTION

Almost daily someone calls on the telephone, drives into the yard, stops me in the hall at the university or at the post office to ask a question about a plant they have seen on a hike, that is growing in their yard, or that they have observed in a nursery. After an exchange of questions and answers we can almost always make a pretty good guess concerning the name of the plant in question. The questions I ask the interested party are always about the same. Where was the plant growing? Were the leaves simple or compound? Were they alternate or opposite, entire or toothed? Were spines or thorns present? What color were the flowers? How tall was the plant? These are the characteristics of flowering plants we must consider if we hope to identify a particular plant. These are the basic questions around which this book is designed.

I like these folks. It tells me they are observant, intelligent and thoughtful people who wish to learn more about the local flora. There is no such thing as a silly question raised by these friends. In fact they have great courage, because they are willing to expose their limited knowledge of plants in order to learn more about their natural world. Certainly the major objective of education at all levels is to produce a world of people who will ask questions. I should add that nothing thrills me more than to be able to tell them that I do not know the name of a plant, and that we need to go take a look at it to gather additional information. At this point we are all learners. We dedicate this publication to all these friends who in a formal classroom setting, on a field trip or in a cafe, bar or restroom said, "Carter, I want to ask a question about this plant I found."

This book is basically an illustrated dichotomous key that has been designed to assist beginning students in becoming familiar with the woody plants, including trees, shrubs and woody vines, that occur in New Mexico. We include here the native species as well as a number of cultivated and other adventive species. Also, a number of borderline "woody" species are included that are large succulents, semisucculents or woody at the base.

Probably to the chagrin of professional botanists and plant systematists the preliminary key in this book is not strictly a key to plant families as we usually find in similar treatments. We know a key to families makes the very best sense to those of us who have received some training in botany because it provides a structure for organizing our knowledge. However, years of experience in teaching field botany to beginning students, those who have never had a course in botany, has taught me that plant families are an enigma to this audience. At this stage in their botanical career they are just not interested in such

terms as Scrophulariaceae, Fabaceae and Lamiaceae. What most neophyte botanists want to know at this particular time is the common name of the plant of
interest to them. This book is designed so that after finding a common name for
a plant and a scientific name, the lay person may then, if they are interested,
learn the name of the plant family.

What is a dichotomous key? Keys are devices useful in identifying unknown objects, i.e., plants, animals, rocks, etc. The conventional type key to
unknown objects is the dichotomous key. The term "dichotomous" denotes two
divisions or two choices. This means the specimen under consideration should
be described in one of the two number ones in the first couplet at the beginning
of the key. If the plant you hope to identify is described in the first number "1"
you should proceed to number "2" at the end of the couplet, but if the plant is
described in the second number "1" you should by-pass number "2" and proceed
to the number at the end of the second portion of the couplet. At the end of each
couplet you are directed to the next couplet appropriate to the specimen you are
attempting to identify. Always carefully read both numbers of the couplet. Keep
in mind, studying a dichotomous key in the library will probably be of little
value, and keys make poor late night reading material. Keys function best at the
interface of plants and people in the field or in the laboratory.

We hope that through the glossary of terms and the illustrated glossary
the beginner will start to expand their vocabulary and ability to conceptualize
woody plants. We consider the index of common names an important tool that
can be used to get the learner closer to identifying the plant under consideration.
For those with more knowledge of plants the indices of scientific names and
family names will be helpful. Also, distribution maps for each species will become an important tool in identifying individual species and for establishing a
flora for your area.

We encourage the use of the illustrations as a picture book for making
determinations. I always encourage students to carry a set of colored pencils
into the field so they can color the plants they come to recognize in their personal copy of the book. Other helpful tools include a small notebook, pencil,
10x handlens, a millimeter/centimeter ruler and a pocket knife. Inside the back
cover of this book is a small mm/cm ruler that will be helpful in the field.

A word about plant names. As you identify a plant you will find a common name or several common names in bold type. If this is all you wish to know about this particular plant you may stop at this point. For those who are interested, the common name or names will be followed by the single best scientific name, and this will be followed by the plant family to which this species belongs. The scientific name is made up of a binomial, or two names, the generic name (genus) and the specific name (specific epithet). These two terms form the scientific name of that particular species and are in italics. The binomial will be followed by the name of the "authority", or the person who is responsible for describing this plant and giving it this particular scientific name. You will occasionally find the name of a person in parentheses followed by the name of the most recent authority. The name in parentheses is referred to as the "parenthetical authority" or the original author who described this species. You will also find we have added some synonyms (Syns.) following the correct scientific name. These are names that were at one time the correct scientific name for this species, but for any of several reasons the name has been changed to a new name or has reverted back to a previous name. We have added some of the common synonyms in this publication for those folks who may have originally studied a plant under a previous scientific name and learned to recognize it by that earlier name. It is important to note that scientific names are continually in a state of flux, not to confuse the student, but because science is always in an uproar. Serious students of systematic botany are continuously studying the ecology, geography, biochemistry and genetics of the world's flora and producing new information that the scientific community respects and brings to the literature. This is as it should be and this is what makes science so much fun. So please believe me; scientific names are not being changed to make students of natural history miserable.

With some understanding of plant names, it is now important that we consider the term "species". Before the concept of evolution was accepted, it was generally believed that each organism owed its origin to *special creation,* that species never change, are immutable and once described would always be the same. It followed that if hybrids were formed they were sterile.

In the early 1800's plant scientists started to recognize signs that this is not exactly true. It soon became obvious that species are not immutable, that they are extremely variable within a population and that some hybrids produce fertile offspring. However, it was the work of Charles Darwin, Alfred Russel Wallace and Gregor Mendel, building on the research of those who went before them in the early 19th century, that produced a new species concept based on change over time in the environment and changes in the genetics of individual

plants. In 1859 Darwin published *The Origin of Species* and that one book re-
sulted in a scientific and social revolution that remains with us to this day. The
social implications are not of serious consequence to this book, but the biologic
implications are critical.

As you attempt to identify a single plant by following the steps in each
dichotomy, you must always keep in mind that the plant you are studying is just
one member of a population. It is the sum total of the characteristics of the
population that describes the species. Also, never forget that plants produce fertile hybrids, especially as you study some rather confusing genera such as the
Oaks, (*Quercus*) or the Willows (*Salix*). A key of this type can only describe the
central tendency of the scientifically established species within its range, including the illustration, and the variation in such factors as leaf width, leaf length,
flower color, fruit size and color, etc. Those of us who study living systems learn
to live with tolerance for variation within species. Perhaps if we come to better
understand this variation within plant species we will learn to better understand
and enjoy the variation in *Homo sapiens*.

## NEW MEXICO

New Mexico is a state of great diversity. This diversity extends to the
climate, geology, flora and fauna, and human history. With a total area of over
121,000 square miles and a range in elevation from 13,160 feet on Wheeler
Peak in the northcentral part of the state, to 2,876 feet in the southeast corner of
the state, just getting to know New Mexico can become a lifelong pleasure.

It is possible, in a very general way, to divide New Mexico into five
floristic regions. These include the Rocky Mountain influence in the northcentral
portion of the state, the Great Plains influence in the northeast and on the eastern
side of the state, the Great Basin influence in the northwest corner of the state
and the Four Corners area, the Mogollon Plateau influence in the westcentral
portion of the state, and the Chihuahuan Desert influence that covers the southern portion of the state and extends into the central area of the state along the Rio
Grande. Beyond the realm of this book, each of these regions may be identified
by old volcanoes and mountain ranges, rivers and their adjacent riparian zones,
dunes and lava beds that all add to the biodiversity. The distribution maps and
descriptions included with each species will help to define the range of that
species and the habitat in which it occurs.

Each of these regions have a characteristic flora and fauna. However, it is important to note that within all of these regions there are continuous intrusions and human disturbances such as grazing, timbering, agriculture, mining and, of course, the ever increasing size of the human population. We know this process has been going on for centuries and will continue, but with the rapidly growing human pressure much of this place we call New Mexico is losing its unique biologic integrity.

DISTRIBUTION MAP SHOWING NEW MEXICO COUNTIES

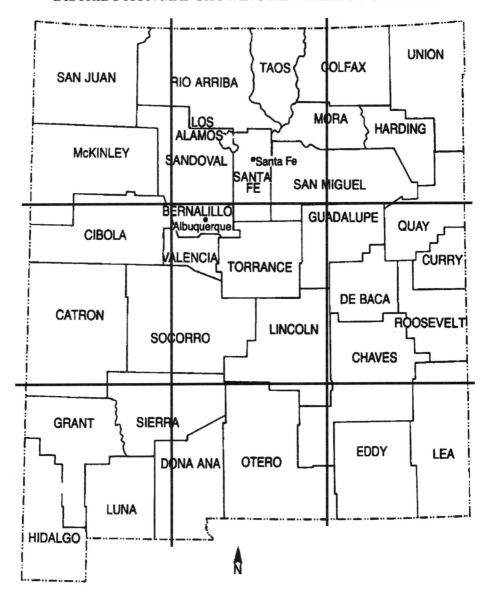

## TREES, SHRUBS AND WOODY VINES OF NEW MEXICO

## PRELIMINARY KEY

1.    Woody plants with needle-like, overlapping, or scale-like leaves, somewhat deciduous with age in *Ephedra*; fruit a cone, small strobilus with several thin scales, or berrylike; plants not producing true flowers with sepals and petals; seeds borne externally and exposed on cones or small strobili ............................................... 2.

1.    Woody plants with broad leaves; leaves seldom needle-like, or scale-like and rarely evergreen, usually deciduous in winter; fruit variable but not a cone or small strobilus; plants producing true flowers with basic flower parts including sepals, petals, stamens and pistils in various combinations; seeds enclosed in the ovary and fruit ........................................................................................... 3.

2.    Leaves needle-like or overlapping as green shingles, conspicuous and evergreen; stems not jointed; fruit a true cone or berry-like; includes conifers, pines, firs, junipers, gymnosperms and their allies ......... (Genera including *Abies, Juniperus, Pinus, Picea,* etc. Division CONIFEROPHYTA) ................................................................................ KEY I. Page 13

ARIZONA CYPRESS
*Cupressus arizonica*

CHIHUAHUA PINE
*Pinus leiophylla*

2.      Leaves scale-like, sometimes inconspicuous, occurring
        only at the nodes, opposite (2) or whorled (3) at each node,
        not evergreen, but often becoming deciduous with age;
        stems jointed; fruit small with a few scales; includes
        Mormon tea and related species (Genus *Ephedra,*
        Division GNETOPHYTA).............................................KEY II.
                                                                    Page 35

BIG JOINT-FIR
*Ephedra trifurca*

3.      Leaves with parallel veins from the base; flower parts in threes
        or multiples of three, including sepals, petals, stamens and pis-
        tils; vascular bundles in stems on several radii, appearing scat-
        tered, thus no annual rings produced; includes yuccas, agaves
        and their allies  (Class MONOCOTYLEDONEAE,
        Division ANTHOPHYTA)........................................ KEY III.
                                                                    Page 43

BANANA YUCCA
*Yucca baccata*

3. Leaves and leaflets with a single mid-vein, the lateral veins branching toward the margins and often netted or absent in the cacti, some Chenopods and the Crucifixion Thorn; flower parts in twos, fours, or fives, or multiples of four or five, including sepals, petals, stamens and pistils; vascular bundles in the stems on a single radius, thus annual rings produced each growing season in woody species (Class DICOTYLEDONEAE, Division ANTHOPHYTA) ................................................................. 4.

4. True leaves absent in mature plants; stems fleshy and succulent with watery sap, flattened, ribbed, or cylindrical with tubercles; plant spines occurring at areoles and in some species surrounded by many fine, small barbs called glochids; fruit a berry, usually bearing spines with many seeds in each fruit; includes the true cacti (Cactaceae) KEY IV. Page 61

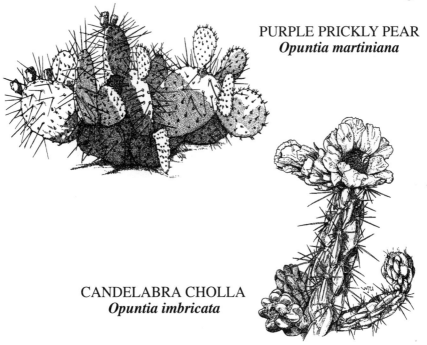

PURPLE PRICKLY PEAR
*Opuntia martiniana*

CANDELABRA CHOLLA
*Opuntia imbricata*

4. True leaves present in mature plants; stems woody and lacking abundant watery sap, cylindrical but lacking tubercles, not ribbed or flattened; plants with or without spines and thorns, these often occurring at nodes; glochids absent; may be parasitic; fruit variable, seldom bearing spines, number of seeds in each fruit ranging from one to many ................................................................................................ 5.

5.    Plants aerial parasites on the stems of gymnosperms or deciduous trees or shrubs, forming small shrubs or perennial herbs; roots modified to form haustoria that penetrate the host plant; leaves opposite, simple, leathery to succulent, with parallel veins, evergreen or scalelike or occasionally absent; plants monoecious or dioecious; flowers unisexual with an inferior, 1-celled ovary or with stamens the same number as the perianth parts; fruit a berry and sticky to the touch; includes the mistletoes (Viscaceae) ..... KEY V.
Page 76

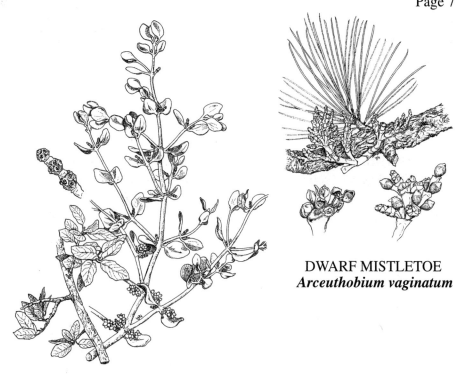

DWARF MISTLETOE
*Arceuthobium vaginatum*

MISTLETOE
*Phoradendron villosum*

5.    Plants not parasitic, but typical trees, shrubs or woody vines; roots in the soil and not forming haustoria in the stems of host plants; leaves opposite, alternate or whorled, rarely with parallel veins; flowers and fruits variable .................................................... 6.

6.    Leaves, stems and buds opposite or whorled ......................... 7.

6.    Leaves, stems and buds alternate ............................................ 8.

7.    Leaves simple ......................................................................... KEY VI.
                                                                                        Page 89

BLUE SAGE OR
SHRUBBY SALVIA
*Salvia pinguifolia*

NEW MEXICO FORESTIERA
OR NEW MEXICO OLIVE
*Forestiera pubescens*
var. *pubescens*

7.    Leaves compound ................................................................ KEY VII.
                                                                                        Page 159

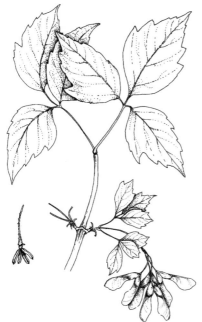 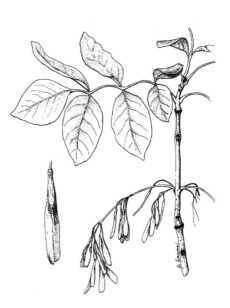

BOX ELDER
*Acer negundo*

VELVET OR ARIZONA ASH
*Fraxinus velutina*

8.   Leaves simple ............................................................ KEY VIII.
Page 185

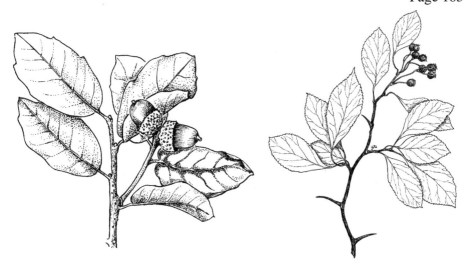

GRAY OAK
*Quercus grisea*

RIVER HAWTHORN
*Crataegus rivularis*

8.   Leaves compound ......................................................... KEY IX.
Page 424

SHRUBBY CINQUEFOIL
*Pentaphylloides floribunda*

BARBERRY
*Mahonia trifoliata*

# THE GYMNOSPERMS

The most commonly recognized gymnosperms in the Northern Hemisphere are the pines, spruces, firs and junipers. Their needles and scale-like leaves, as well as their woody and berry-like cones make them easy to identify. In comparison to the angiosperms or flowering plants, they are true survivors, originating in the early Triassic Period of the Mesozoic Era over 230 million years ago.

This extremely successful group of plants dominated the Earth's flora for over 150 million years and evolved a number of morphological characteristics that have allowed them to remain a vital part of the flora. Today they compete very well with the more recently evolved flowering plants and continue to form an important ecological and economical portion of the tree flora in the arid Southwest.

The gymnosperms form a neat evolutionary package in New Mexico. They are confined to two families, the Cupressaceae and the Pinaceae, and defined by 23 species. They occur in a wide range of elevations, from 3,500 to 12,000 ft., and are commonly used to identify the life zones throughout the southern Rocky Mountains. By simply studying the pines and their allies one can learn a great deal about the ecology, morphology and evolution of plants in western North America.

## GYMNOSPERMS

1.      Leaves small, awl-like, scale-like or imbricate, not needle-like;
        fruit a berry or a round, woody cone with 6 to 8 flattened plates ........ 2.

1.      Leaves needle-like, separate or in clusters,  not scale-like or im-
        bricate; fruit a cone at maturity,  usually of flat open scales .............. 9.

        2.      Mature female cones dry and woody, orbicular and per-
                sistent, opening by several sutures at maturity, commonly
                more than 1.5 cm in diameter; becoming large monoe-
                cious trees to 24.0 m in height; occurring at 5,000 to 7,300
                ft. (1,520 to 2,230 m) in elevation. A tincture of fresh
                twigs of *Cupressus arizonica* was used by Native Ameri-
                cans to treat all skin fungus infections including ringworm
                and athlete's foot.

        **Arizona Cypress**, *Cupressus arizonica*  Greene

                                                                    Cupressaceae

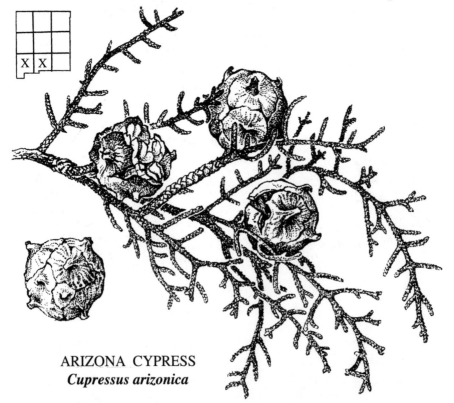

ARIZONA  CYPRESS
*Cupressus arizonica*

2.    Mature female cones fleshy and berry-like, sometimes mealy, indehiscent at maturity, less than 1.5 cm in diameter; monoecious or dioecious trees or shrubs; several species widely distributed over the State .............................. 3.

3.    Leaves on mature branches awl-shaped, not imbricate, 5.0 to 15.0 mm long, appearing whorled; fleshy cones bearing 1 to 3 seeds; shrubs usually less than 1.0 m in height, spreading and prostrate; common over the northern third of New Mexico, occurring at 8,000 to 11,500 ft. (2,440 to 3,510 m) in elevation. The berries of this dwarf juniper are the principal flavoring agent in gin and alcoholic bitters.

**Common Juniper**, *Juniperus communis* L.                    Cupressaceae

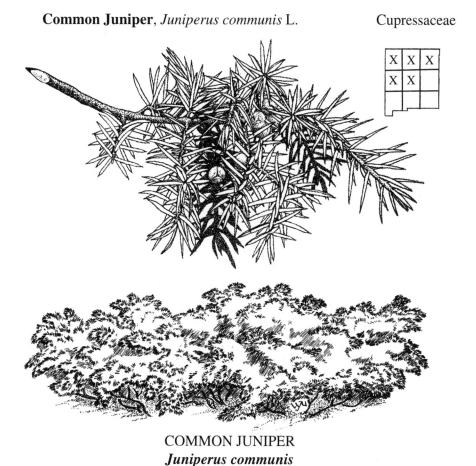

COMMON JUNIPER
*Juniperus communis*

3.    Leaves on mature branches imbricate and scale-like, not awl-like, less than 6.0 mm in length; trees and shrubs usually more than 1.0 m in height; growing upright .............................. 4.

4.      Bark of older branches and the trunk divided into rectangular or square plates resembling the back of an alligator, thus the common name; mature foliage characterized by white resinous dots of exudate; female cones producing 3 to 4 seeds, usually 8.0 to 18.0 mm in diameter; trees of 8 to 12 m are not uncommon with some specimens reaching 14 m or more. Although the species occurs throughout the State, it is more common in the central and southern portions at 6,000 to 8,000 ft. (1,830 to 2,440 m).

**Alligator Juniper**, *Juniperus deppeana* Steudel

Cupressaceae

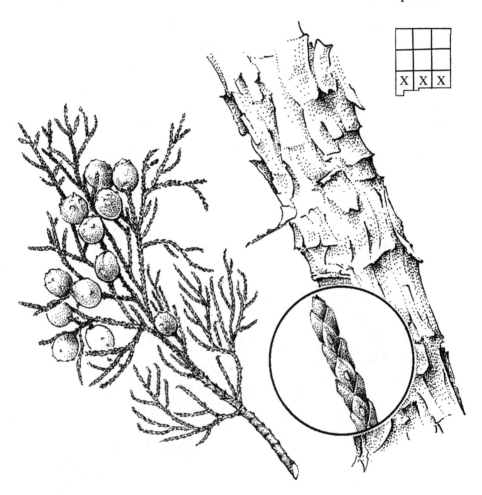

ALLIGATOR JUNIPER
*Juniperus deppeana*

4.      Bark of older branches and the trunk in strips, fibrous
        and shredding the length of the tree; mature foliage not
        characterized by white resinous dots; female cones pro-
        ducing 1 to 3 seeds. .............................................................. 5.

5.      Leaves entire, occurring in pairs under a hand lens; younger
        branches appearing weak, slender and drooping at the end; heart-
        wood dark reddish brown or purple; this small tree, reaching a
        height of 8.0 m, is dioecious; mature fruit 4.0 to 6.0 mm in diam-
        eter, glaucous-blue in color, commonly producing 2 seeds, with
        1 or 3 seeds not uncommon; common over most of New Mexico,
        occurring at 6,500 to 9,000 ft. (1,980 to 2,740 m). (A closely
        related species, the **Eastern Red Cedar**, *Juniperus virginiana*
        L., is introduced and cultivated in lawns throughout the State and
        will also key to this species, and may have a common origin.).

**Rocky Mountain Juniper**, *Juniperus scopulorum* Sargent

Cupressaceae

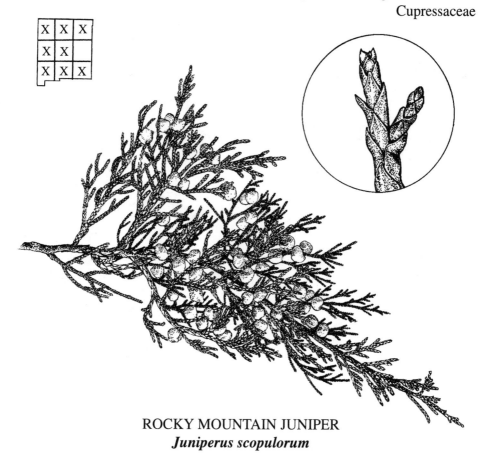

ROCKY MOUNTAIN JUNIPER
*Juniperus scopulorum*

5.      Leaves minutely denticulate, occurring in pairs or whorls under
        a hand lens; younger branches appearing shorter, stout and stiff
        at the end; heartwood light orange to yellowish brown; mature
        fruit commonly producing 1 or 2 seeds ............................................. 6.

    6.      Mature fruit 8.0 to 16.0 mm in diameter, mealy becom-
            ing fibrous, purple to reddish brown in color; conical, mo-
            noecious trees to 7.0 m in height, usually growing from a
            single trunk rather than branching at or below the ground;
            occurring on rocky slopes and over rolling hills; restricted
            to the western and northwestern portion of New Mexico,
            at elevations of 6,200 to 7,500 ft. (1,890 to 2,290 m).

**Utah Juniper**, *Juniperus osteosperma* (Torrey) Little

Cupressaceae

UTAH JUNIPER
*Juniperus osteosperma*

6.     Mature fruit 4.0 to 8.0 mm in diameter, fleshy to succu-
       lent, purple, blue, red, pink to copper-orange in color; trees
       small, variously shaped, dioecious, usually less than 5.0
       m in height, with several branches arising at or below the
       soil level or from a single trunk ............................................. 7.

(The distribution, geography and evolution of the following three
species are not completely understood and further study will be
necessary to determine their relationships.)

7.     Mature fruit blue to blue-black, sometimes dark reddish blue in
       color; few, less than 15 per cent, of the elongate and flat, whip
       leaf glands with a white exudate under a hand lens; appearing as
       a tree or a shrub with the main branches arising at or below the
       soil level, with the bark shredding or splitting into strips; one of
       the most widespread woody plants in New Mexico and the South-
       west at 5,000 to 8,000 ft. (1,520 to 2,440 m) in elevation.

**One-seeded Juniper**, *Juniperus monosperma* (Engelmann)
                              Sargent              Cupressaceae

ONE-SEEDED JUNIPER
*Juniperus monosperma*

7.    Mature fruit red, pink, rose or copper in color; most of the whip
      leaf glands with a white exudate visible with the naked eye or
      under a hand lens .................................................................. 8.

8.    Mature fruit copper to red or reddish brown in color, but
      bright and not covered with a bloom; trees more com-
      monly branching at the base appearing as a shrub; distri-
      bution is in the southeastern portion of New Mexico with
      isolated areas of possible hybridization with the **Rose-
      Fruited Juniper**; occurring at 4,000 to 5,000 ft. (1,220
      to 1,520 m).

**Pinchot or Red-berried Juniper**, *Juniperus pinchotii*
                              Sudworth     Cupressaceae

8.    Mature fruit rose to pink, sometimes tending toward red-
      dish-blue, especially when covered with a dull bloom;
      trees more commonly appearing to grow from a central
      trunk; distribution in the southwestern portion of New
      Mexico; occurring at 4,000 to 5,000 ft. (1,220 to 1,520
      m).

**Rose-fruited Juniper,** *Juniperus erythrocarpa* Cory
                                        Cupressaceae

9.    Base of the needles surrounded by a sheath, at least when young;
      needles in clusters or fascicles containing 2, (seldom 1) or more
      needles .............................................................................. 10.

9.    Base of the needles not surrounded by a sheath; needles separate,
      not in clusters or fascicles .................................................. 19.

10.    Needles in clusters or fascicles of 5 .......................................11.

10.    Needles in clusters or fascicles of 1, 2 or 3 ......................... 14.

11.    Needles longer than 10.0 cm in length, commonly reaching 14.0
       to 20.0 cm; usually 5 leaves in a bundle, however 3 or 4 to the
       bundle may occur on the same tree; found north of Mimbres,
       NM, in Rocky Canyon, but occurring commonly in the Chiricahua
       Mountains of Arizona, uncommon in the montane at 6,000 to
       9,000 ft. (1,830 to 2,740 m).

**Arizona Yellow Pine**, *Pinus ponderosa* var. *arizonica*
                                (Engelmann) Shaw        Pinaceae

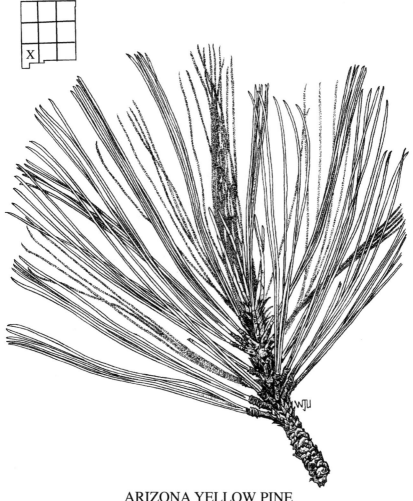

ARIZONA YELLOW PINE
*Pinus ponderosa* var. *arizonica*

11.    Needles averaging less than 10.0 cm in length, commonly ranging from 2.0 to 8.0 cm ...................................................................... 12.

    12.    Needles less than 4.0 cm long, curved, distinguished by gray-green resin spots, sticky to the touch; cone scales with exserted prickles; seeds winged; occurring in the upper montane to subalpine, 9,500 to 12,500 ft. (2,900 to 3,810 m); over the northern part of New Mexico. The oldest surviving **Bristlecone Pine** has been radiocarbon dated as being at least 4,600 years old.

        **Bristlecone** or **Foxtail Pine,**  *Pinus aristata* Engelmann

                                       Pinaceae

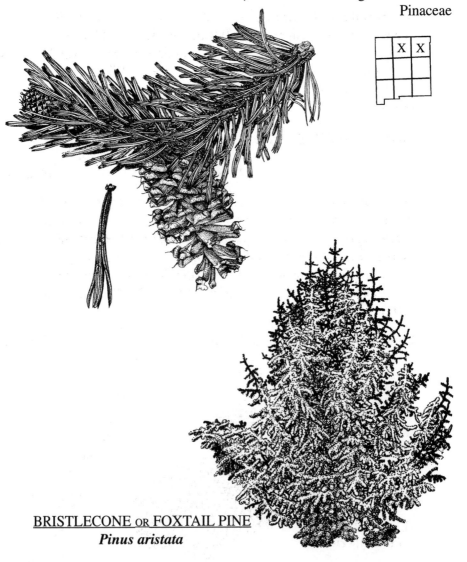

BRISTLECONE or FOXTAIL PINE
*Pinus aristata*

12.    Needles more than 4.0 cm in length, straight or slightly curved, not sticky to the touch; cone 7.0 cm or more in length, the scales lacking prickles; seed wings rudimentary or absent ....................................................... 13.

( The relationships among the following two species, including the **Limber Pine**, (*Pinus flexilis* James) and the **Southwestern White Pine**, (*Pinus strobiformis* Engelmann) and in addition, the **Eastern White Pine**, (*Pinus strobus* L.) are not well established. Several authorities consider the **Limber Pine** and the **Southwestern White Pine** to be a single species.)

13.    Scales of the cones strongly reflexed and narrow toward the apex; cones slender and longer in profile than in the **Limber Pine**; leaves bluish green; trees at maturity tall and straight; frequent over the southern, especially the southwestern portion of New Mexico at 6,500 to 9,500 ft. (1,980 to 2,900 m). (As the name implies this species may be closely related to **Eastern White Pine**.)

**Southwestern White Pine**, *Pinus strobiformis* Engelmann
Syns. *Pinus flexilis* var. *reflexa*
Engelmann           Pinaceae

13.    Scales of the cones not strongly reflexed but broadly truncate at the apex; cones wider and shorter in profile; leaves yellowish green; mature trees not generally as tall as the **Southwestern White Pine**, appearing shorter and more robust; extending over the northern mountainous portion of the State, down the higher mountains into southern regions at 7,500 to 12,000 ft. (2,290 to 3,660 m).

**Limber Pine**, *Pinus flexilis* James           Pinaceae

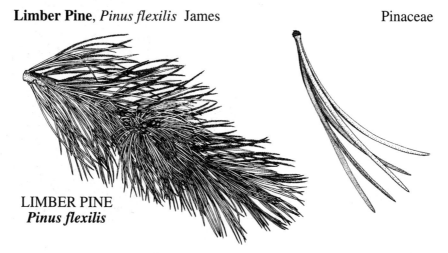

LIMBER PINE
*Pinus flexilis*

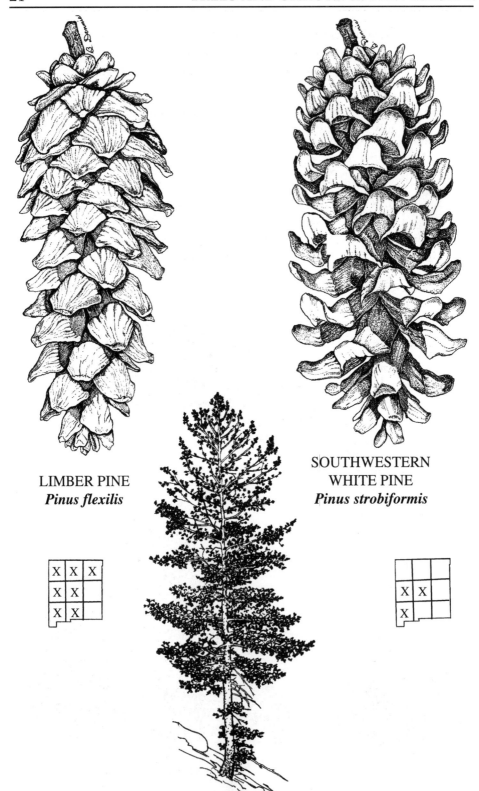

LIMBER PINE
*Pinus flexilis*

SOUTHWESTERN
WHITE PINE
*Pinus strobiformis*

14.     Needles mostly 1 or 2 in a cluster or fascicle; trees small, usually less than 12.0 m in height at maturity, often appearing shrub-like in growth habit ..................................... 15.

14.     Needles mostly 3 in a cluster or fascicle; trees larger, usually reaching a height of more than 14.0 m at maturity, growing as trees or shrubs ..................................................... 16.

15.     Needles commonly 2 to the cluster or fascicle, occasionally 1 or 3 per cluster, channeled but only slightly terete; sheaths deciduous; a straggly small tree or shrub; widely distributed and common over New Mexico in dry habitats, often with one of the junipers, at 4,500 to 8,000 ft.(1,370 to 2,440 m) in elevation.

**Piñon Pine,** *Pinus edulis* Engelmann                              Pinaceae

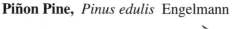

PIÑON PINE
*Pinus edulis*

15.    Needles commonly one to the cluster or fascicle, occasionally 2
       per cluster, terete; occurring in extremely isolated habitats simi-
       lar to the **Piñon Pine** in the southwestern corner of New Mexico
       at elevations of less than 4,500 ft. (1,370 m). The single needle
       per cluster results in the tree appearing thin and weak. Consid-
       erable disagreement exists as to whether this is a distinct spe-
       cies, a subspecies of the common **Piñon Pine**, or a disjunct spe-
       cies related to the **Single-needle Pine** of southern California and
       Nevada.

**Single-needle Piñon,** *Pinus edulis* var. *fallax* Little
                    Syns. *P. monophylla* Torrey & Fremont          Pinaceae

SINGLE-NEEDLE PIÑON
*Pinus edulis* var. *fallax*

16. Needles 2.0 to 6.0 cm in length, 3 in a cluster (occasionally 2 per cluster), sheaths seldom persistent or if present then strongly recurved; trees small, sometimes appearing as a shrub, seldom reaching 12.0 to 15.0 m in height, usually less than 10.0 m; mature female cones globose to somewhat flattened and ovoid, seldom over 3.0 cm in length, producing large nuts with extremely hard shells; confined to the southern portion of New Mexico at 5,000 to 8,500 ft. (1,520 to 2,590 m) in elevation. It is important to note that this species may also be evolutionarily related to the **Single-needle Piñon** and the **Piñon Pine**.

**Mexican Piñon,** *Pinus cembroides* Zuccarini    Pinaceae

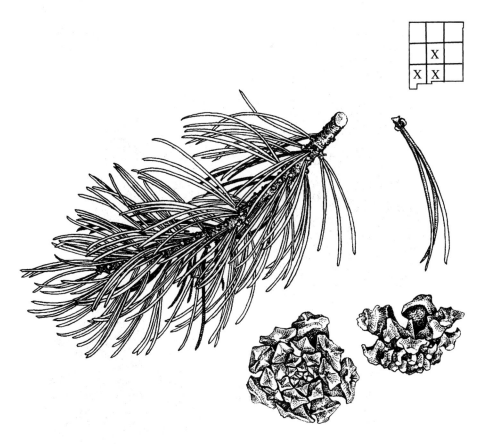

MEXICAN PIÑON
*Pinus cembroides*

16.    Needles 6.0 to 40.0 cm in length; mature trees 15.0 to
       40.0 m in height; mature female cones globose to elon-
       gate, usually 4.0 to 12.0 cm in length ................................. 17.

17.    Needles  5.0 to 11.0 cm in length, sheaths deciduous as leaves
       mature; female cones conspicuously stalked and persistent on
       the tree, 4.0 to 6.0 cm in length; mature trees occasionally reach-
       ing to 14.0 m in height, but usually averaging 9.0 to 12.0 m;
       confined to the southwestern corner of New Mexico, frequent at
       5,000 to 7,500 ft. (1,520 to 2,290 m) in elevation.

**Chihuahua Pine**, *Pinus  leiophylla*  Schiede & Deppe var.
                 *chihuahuana*  (Engelmann) Shaw          Pinaceae

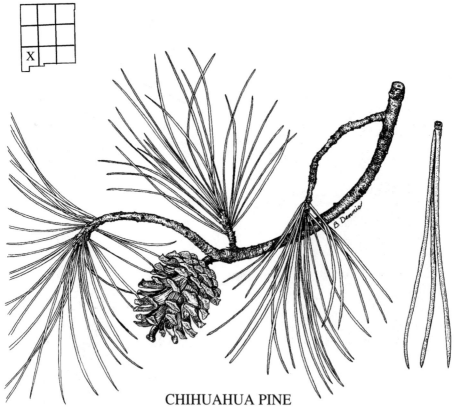

CHIHUAHUA PINE
*Pinus leiophylla* var. *chihuahuana*

17.    Needles 11.0  to  36.0 cm in length, sheaths persistent as leaves
       mature; female cones not conspicuously stalked, usually falling
       with age, 6.0 to 12.0 cm  in length; mature trees commonly over
       15.0 m in height ............................................................. 18.

18. Needles 11.0 to 22.0 cm in length, sheaths 10.0 to 20 .0 mm in length; mature female cones ovoid or ellipsoid, averaging 6.0 to 9.0 cm in length, borne singly or in clusters of 2 or 3; mature trees commonly reaching 20.0 m or more in height; common tree from montane to subalpine throughout the mountains, from 6,500 to 9,500 ft. (1,980 to 2,900 m) in elevation.

**Ponderosa Pine** or **Western Yellow Pine**, *Pinus ponderosa* Lawson var. *scopulorum* Engelmann

Pinaceae

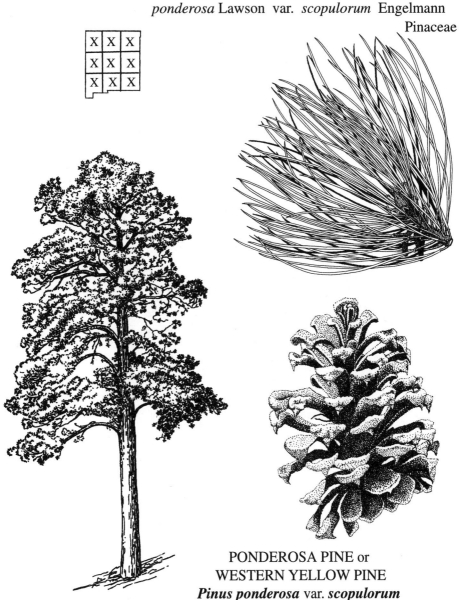

| X | X | X |
|---|---|---|
| X | X | X |
| X | X | X |

PONDEROSA PINE or
WESTERN YELLOW PINE
*Pinus ponderosa* var. *scopulorum*

18. Needles 24.0 to 36.0 cm in length, sheaths 24.0 to 38.0 mm in length; mature female cones ellipsoid to linear, averaging 8.0 to 10.0 cm in length, seldom borne in clusters; mature trees seldom reaching 20.0 m in height; frequent tree throughout the mountains in the southwestern portion of New Mexico at elevations of 6,000 to 8,000 ft. (1,830 to 2,440 m).

**Apache Pine**, *Pinus engelmannii* Carriere            Pinaceae

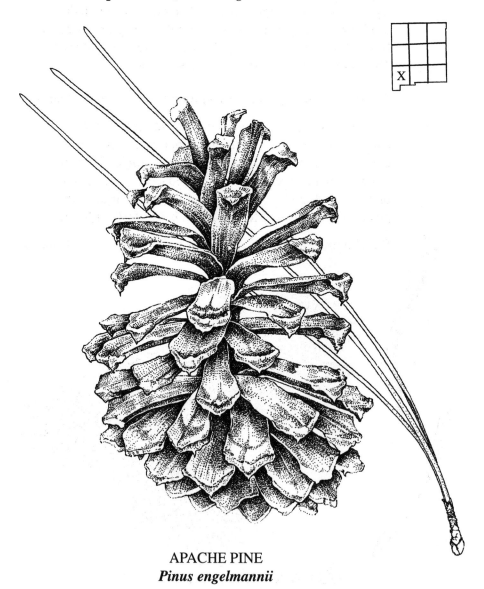

APACHE PINE
*Pinus engelmannii*

19. Needles mostly 4-sided; branchlets roughened by persistent leaf bases; leaves deciduous when specimens are dry ............................ 20.

19. Needles flattened or 2-sided; branchlets not roughened by persistent leaf bases; leaves not deciduous when specimens are dry ..... 21.

    20. Needles rigid, sharp to the touch, almost spine-tipped; cones more than 6.0 cm in length; needles often with a bluish color, giving the tree a bluish caste; large attractive tree often reaching 30.0 m in height; abundant in the foothills and montane over the mountainous portions of New Mexico at 7,200 to 10,500 ft. (2,200 to 3,200 m). This is the State Tree of Colorado and Utah.

        **Colorado Blue Spruce**, *Picea pungens* Engelmann   Pinaceae

    20. Needles somewhat flexible, not very sharp to the touch and not spine-tipped; cones less than 6.0 cm long; bluish color not as obvious; large tree that may reach 40.0 m at maturity, but at tree line it may be reduced in size taking on various shapes; occurring chiefly over the mountainous portions of New Mexico above 8,500 ft. (2,600 m).

        **Engelmann Spruce,** *Picea engelmannii* Parry     Pinaceae

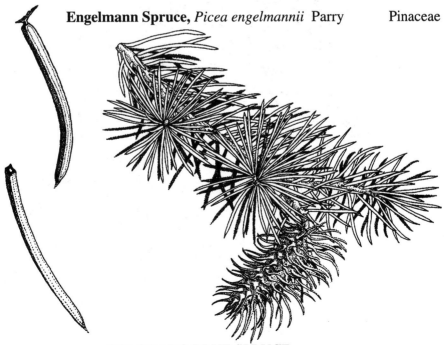

COLORADO BLUE SPRUCE
*Picea pungens*

**COLORADO BLUE SPRUCE**
*Picea pungens*

**ENGELMANN SPRUCE**
*Picea engelmannii*

**COLORADO BLUE SPRUCE**
*Picea pungens*

21.    Needles slightly petioled or stalked, the petioles somewhat twisted; leaf scars elliptic to oval, occasionally extending down the stem below the point of attachment; cones pendulous; the scales persistent with long exserted 3 pointed bracts; an attractive large tree sometimes reaching more than 40.0 m; relatively abundant in the foothills and montane of New Mexico from 6,500 ft. (1,980 m) to almost tree line.

**Douglas Fir**, *Pseudotsuga menziesii* (Mirbel) Franco        Pinaceae

DOUGLAS FIR
*Pseudotsuga menziesii*

21.    Needles sessile; leaf scars orbicular, not extending down the stem below the point of attachment; cones erect, the scales shorter than the bracts or deciduous, lacking long exserted bracts ...................... 22.

22.     Needles averaging 3.0 cm or more in length; resin ducts in the needles near the epidermis or surface; cones grayish-green, 7.0 to 12.0 cm long; bracts of the cone scales with short triangular tips; an attractive tree at maturity reaching 30.0 m; frequently occurring at lower elevations in the mountains from 7,000 to 9,000 ft. (2,130 to 2,770 m).

**White Fir**, *Abies concolor* (Gordon & Glendower) Lindley     Pinaceae

WHITE FIR
*Abies concolor*

22.     Needles averaging 2.5 cm or less in length; resin ducts in needles near the center and inside the epidermis; cones dark purple to dark bluish green, 5.0 to 10.0 cm long; bracts of the cone scales with long awl-shaped tips; range identical to *A. concolor*; trees occurring only at higher elevations in the mountains from 8,500 to 12,000 ft. (2,600 to 3,660 m).

**Subalpine Fir**, *Abies lasiocarpa* (Hooker) Nuttall     Pinaceae

## EPHEDRACEAE

Joint-fir, Mormon-tea or popotillo are common names by which you may have come to recognize these woody shrubs. Scattered throughout New Mexico six or possibly seven dioecious species, all in the single family Ephedraceae and a single genus *Ephedra*, can be identified by their skeleton-like or broom-like appearance. They range in height from less than 0.5 to 4.0 m, and occur on dry prairies and well drained sandy and rocky soils. The genus has been recognized for its medicinal value throughout history. The alkaloid ephedrine, contained in the roots and stems, is known to dilate the bronchi, stimulate respiration and prevent bronchial asthma and hay fever. In collecting the Ephedraceae, one should attempt to collect the female plants with mature seed cones.

1.      Leaves and bracts whorled, 3 at a node; cones sessile ........................ 2.

1.      Leaves and bracts opposite, 2 at a node; cones sessile or on pe-
        duncles ................................................................................................ 3.

  2.      Leaves 8.0 to 13.0 mm in length, averaging 9.0 mm or
          more, persistent with sharp points, shredding with age;
          terminal buds spinose and persistent; seeds smooth; scat-
          tered throughout the southern one-third of New Mexico
          at 4,000 to 6,000 ft. (1,220 to 1,830 m) in elevation. This
          is the largest joint-fir in the State reaching 4.0 m in height.

          **Big Joint-fir,** *Ephedra trifurca* Torrey          Ephedraceae

  2.      Leaves 3.0 to 6.0 mm in length, averaging less than 5.0
          mm, shredding to deciduous with age and becoming re-
          curved; terminal buds disintegrating early and not sharply
          spinose; seeds roughened by cross ridges; common
          throughout the central portion of New Mexico, but to be
          expected statewide at 3,300 to 5,600 ft. (1,010 to 1,710
          m).

          **Torrey Joint-fir,** *Ephedra torreyana* Watson        Ephedraceae

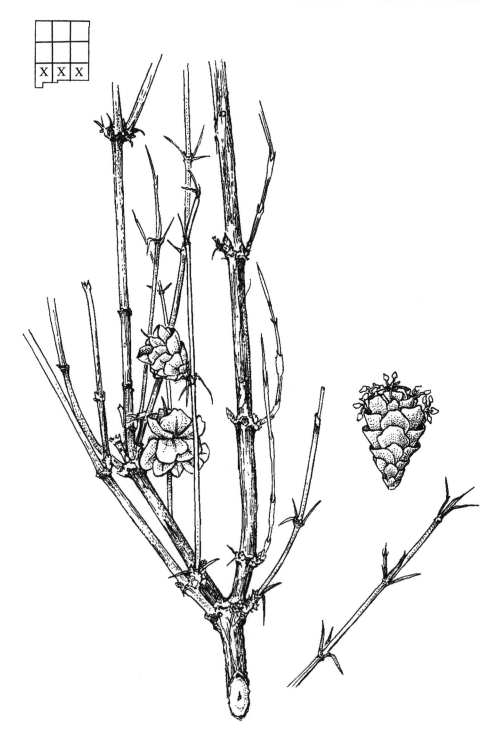

BIG JOINT-FIR
*Ephedra trifurca*

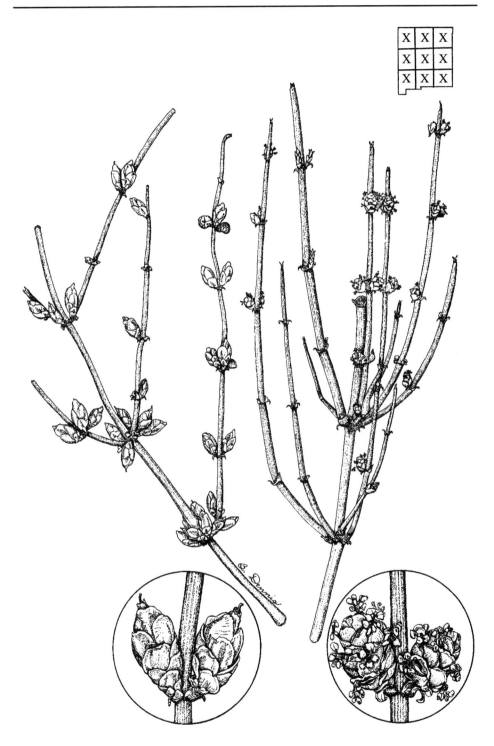

TORREY JOINT-FIR
*Ephedra torreyana*

3.    Twigs viscid, bright green becoming yellow-green with age; bark
      dark red to brown; mature seed cones on peduncles 10.0 to 25.0
      mm in length; ridges between longitudinal grooves on the stem
      have well developed papillae; seeds brown, smooth and paired in
      each cone; occurring in dry, rocky, sandy and flat areas over the
      northwest quarter of the State at 4,500 to 6,000 ft. (1,370 to 1,830
      m). This species has been reported over a larger portion of New
      Mexico, but herbarium records do not support these data.

**Sticky Joint-fir**, *Ephedra viridis* var. *viscida* L. Benson
          Syn. *E. cutleri* Peebles                    Ephedraceae

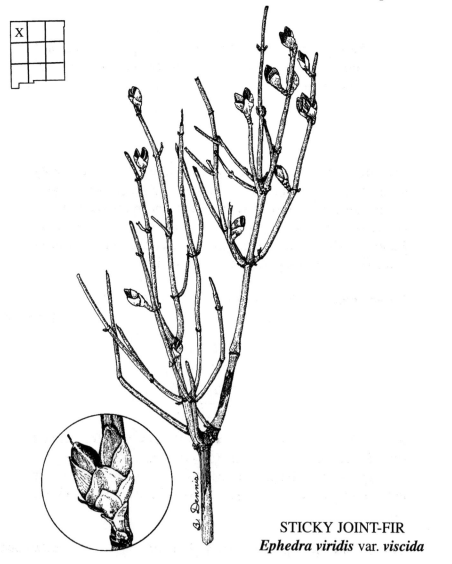

STICKY JOINT-FIR
*Ephedra viridis* var. *viscida*

3.  Twigs not viscid; ranging in color from bright to dull green; bark gray, but appearing slightly reddish brown in *E. coryi*; seed cones sessile or on peduncles of less than 20.0 mm in length ........................ 4.

    4.  Seeds 2 per cone; leaf bases forming a black collar; green stem ridges between the longitudinal grooves sparsely papillate ............................................................................... 5.

    4.  Seeds 1 per cone; leaf bases becoming gray with age and shredding; green stem ridges between the longitudinal grooves poorly developed or absent, not papillate .................. 6.

5.  Bark gray in color; seed cones obovoid, sessile or on short, scaly peduncles, 6.0 to 8.0 mm in length; stems bright green to yellow-green with age; occurring on dry, sandy and rocky slopes in the northwest corner of New Mexico at 4,000 to 7,300 ft. (1,220 to 2,230 m). (Closely related in appearance and habit to the **Sticky Joint-fir**, however the twigs are not viscid.)

    **Green Joint-fir**, *Ephedra viridis* var. *viridis* (Coville)
    L. Benson                                              Ephedraceae

5.  Bark dark red to brown in color; seed cones globose, on short smooth peduncles, 10.0 to 12.0 mm in length; stems green becoming yellow with age; expected to occur on dry sandy dunes in the southeast quarter of New Mexico below 5,000 ft. (1,520 m).

    **Cory's Joint-fir**, *Ephedra coryi* E. L. Reed              Ephedraceae

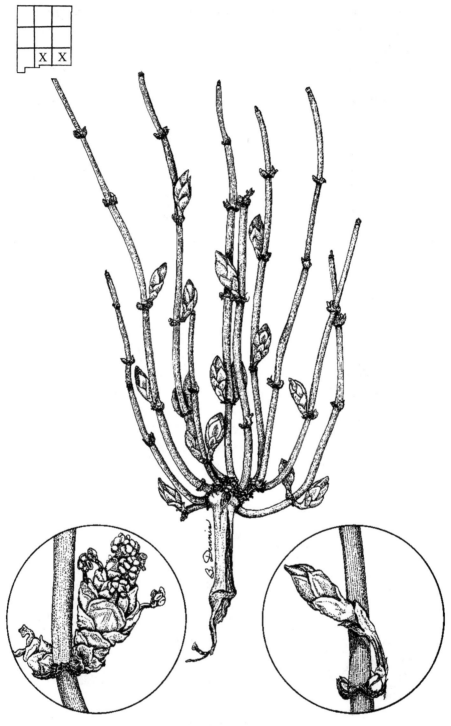

CORY'S JOINT-FIR
*Ephedra coryi*

6.    Stems roughened and scabrous to the touch, pale to dark green
      becoming yellow with age; seed cones sessile or on short, scaly
      peduncles; seeds solitary; infrequent over the southern part of
      New Mexico at 3,800 to 4,200 ft. (1,160 to 1,280 m) in elevation.

**Rough Joint-fir**,  *Ephedra aspera* Engelmann          Ephedraceae

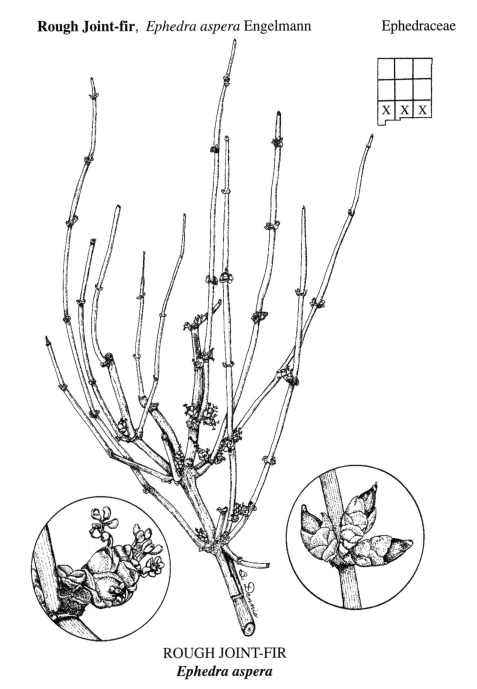

ROUGH JOINT-FIR
*Ephedra aspera*

6.   Stems smooth to the touch and glaucous, green to yellow-green; seed cones sessile or nearly so; seeds solitary or rarely 2; confined to the southeastern corner of New Mexico at 3,200 to 4,500 ft. (980 to 1,370 m) in elevation. If this species occurs in New Mexico it is extremely rare and probably restricted to isolated areas in dry, sandy or gravelly soils on the plains.

**Clapweed** or **Popote**, *Ephedra antisyphilitica* Berlandier

Ephedraceae

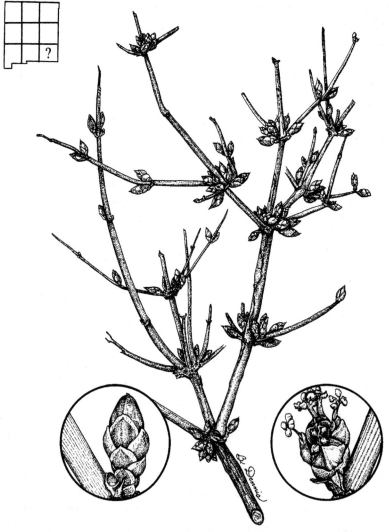

CLAPWEED or POPOTE
*Ephedra antisyphilitica*

## WOODY MONOCOTS

For the beginner the terminology used in separating the monocot plants from the dicot plants may seem confusing, and quite often textbook definitions are not too helpful. However, the confusion can soon be eliminated by taking a short field trip into the arid regions and deserts of southern New Mexico. With fewer than 15 species included in four genera, the woody monocots soon become easy to identify by common and scientific names. They form a unique group of organisms currently placed in one family, the Agavaceae, that have important similarities in both ecology and evolution. Please keep in mind that we are here just becoming familiar with several species of prominent woody monocots.

There are over 55,000 described monocots on planet Earth, most of which are herbaceous species. The grass family, Poaceae, contains roughly 8,000 species and literally feeds the world, ie. wheat, rice, corn, etc. No one knows exactly how many monocots there are in New Mexico, but one could estimate 800 species.

Plant scientists continue the important debate concerning the evolutionary relationship of the Class Monocotyledoneae (monocots) to the Class Dicotyledoneae (dicots) within the Division Anthophyta (flowering plants). We certainly cannot solve this fascinating problem in this book. However, we can learn a few field characteristics that will help us distinguish these two large Classes in the field and, at the same time better appreciate their distinctive geography and evolution.

In working your way through the Preliminary Key you had to distinguish the differences between leaves with parallel veins, and leaves with a single midvein and smaller lateral veins running to the margin. All of the species included in KEY III have parallel veins. If flowers and fruits are not present parallel veins will be the most obvious characteristic to separate these species from the dicots. However, if flowers are present the fact that the flower parts will be in threes or multiples of three in monocots, rather than in fours or fives as in dicots, makes your task easy. Also, mature fruit with three chambers and three carpels will be characteristic of the Monocotyledoneae. Finally, the easier approach is to first browse the illustrations in the book, especially KEY III, so that you can start to sight identify this impressive group of statuesque plants we call the woody monocots.

## WOODY MONOCOTS

1. Leaves firm or rigid and fibrous, not succulent, thin in cross-section, usually less than 6.0 mm in thickness, the base of the leaf expanded in width only slightly; ovary of the flowers superior and hypogynous ............................................................... 2.

1. Leaves soft, somewhat fleshy and succulent, thick in cross-section, usually more than 6.0 mm in thickness, the base of the leaf expanded in width; ovary of the flowers inferior and epigynous....... 13.

  2. Leaf margins with conspicuous and prominent curved or hooked prickles or teeth, leaf rigid, the base of the leaf forming a shallow cup or spoon; the stem short, mostly subterranean with the leaves appearing as a ball at soil level; plants dioecious; flowers unisexual; fruit a capsule, one celled and winged; seeds three angled; staminate flowers in dense flexible spikes ....................................... 3.

  2. Leaf margins lacking conspicuous and prominent curved or hooked prickles, sometimes with fine teeth or fibrous; leaf not rigid, the base of the leaf flat and not forming a shallow spoon; plants with perfect flowers ........................... 4.

3. Teeth on leaf margins curved forward or upward, 1.5 to 3.0 mm long; leaves green, 3.0 to 4.0 cm wide; fruit obcordate, 4.0 to 8.0 mm wide; seed 4.0 mm in length. Widely scattered and common in the southcentral and southwestern parts of New Mexico at 3,500 to 6,000 ft. (1,070 to 1,830 m) in elevation. This species and the following species flower throughout the summer.

**Wheeler Sotol,** *Dasylirion wheeleri* S. Watson    Agavaceae

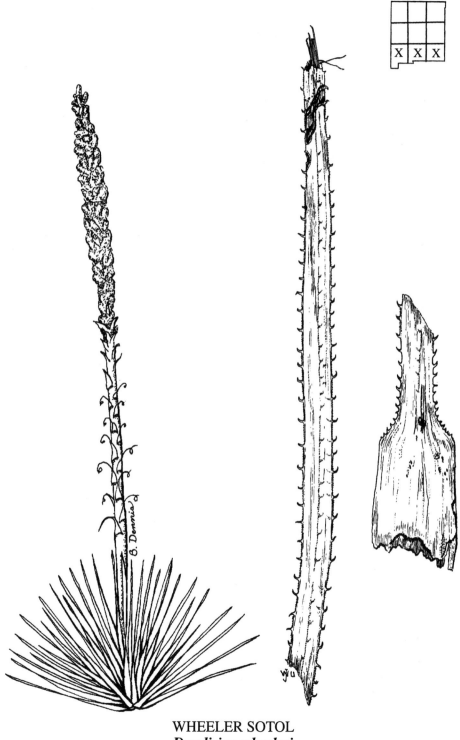

WHEELER SOTOL
*Dasylirion wheeleri*

3.      Teeth on leaf margins curved downward or straight, 3.0 to 4.0
        mm long; leaves somewhat glaucous, 2.0 to 2.5 cm wide; fruit
        elliptic, 3.0 to 5.0 mm wide; seed less than 3.5 mm in length.
        Scattered but less common over the southern part of New Mexico
        at 3,500 to 4,500 ft. (1,070 to 1,370 m) in elevation, this species
        flowers throughout the summer months.

**Desert Candle** or **Smooth Sotol**, *Dasylirion leiophyllum*

Engelmann                    Agavaceae

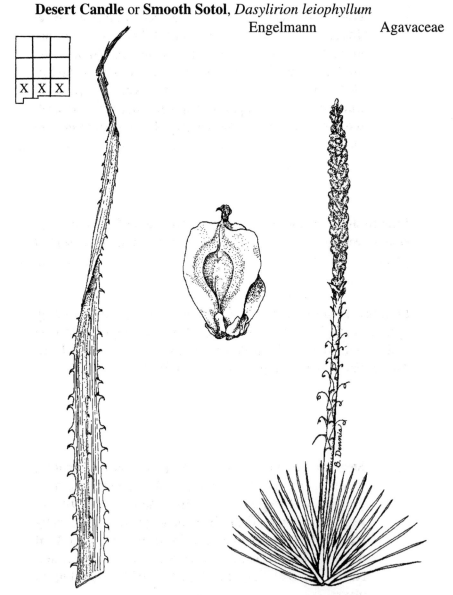

DESERT CANDLE or SMOOTH SOTOL
*Dasylirion leiophyllum*

4.  Leaves rigid, daggerlike and spine-tipped; flowers larger, more than 2.0 cm in length, in loose racemes or panicles, complete and bisexual; sepals and petals more than 10.0 mm in length, each with several veins; fruit with 3 carpels and many flat seeds. **Yucca**, genus *Yucca* ........................ 5.

4.  Leaves firm but not rigid, flexible, grasslike and not spine-tipped; flowers smaller, less than 1.0 cm in length, numerous in dense racemes or panicles, incomplete and unisexual, but also occasionally bisexual; sepals and petals less than 5.0 mm in length, each with a single vein; fruit with 3 carpels, appearing inflated, but with 3 or fewer seeds in each carpel, the seeds globose. **Beargrass**, genus *Nolina* .......................................................................... 12.

5.  Fruit fleshy or spongy, indehiscent, pendulous or falling at maturity; leaves averaging less than 20.0 mm in width at the widest point ................................................................................................. 6.

5.  Fruit dry or papery, dehiscent at maturity, commonly remaining upright through the fall and winter; leaves averaging less than 20.0 mm in width at the widest point, except for the **Harriman Yucca** which may average slightly over 20.0 mm in width ................ 8.

6.  Stems absent, or less than 25.0 cm in height at maturity; leaves arising from the base forming clumps; leaf margins producing coarse fibers; fruit more than 12.0 cm in length; pistil more than 4.5 cm in length; perianth usually 6.0 to 10.0 cm in length and linear. Flowering in April through May this species is widely scattered throughout New Mexico at 3,500 to 7,500 ft. (1,070 to 2,300 m) in elevation.

**Banana Yucca**, *Yucca baccata* Torrey                    Agavaceae

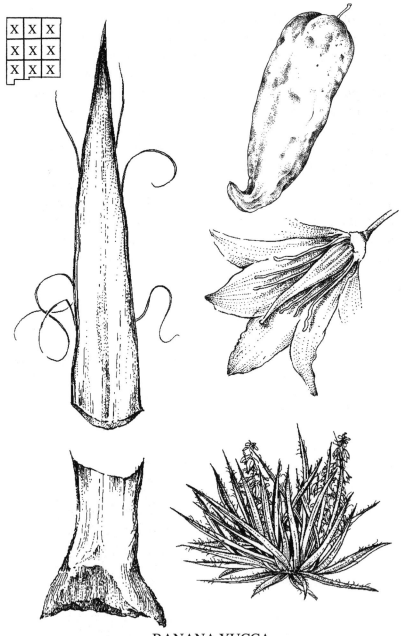

BANANA YUCCA
*Yucca baccata*

6.     Stems 1.0 m or more in height at maturity; leaves abundant at the apex; fruit less than 12.0 cm in length; pistil less than 4.5 cm in length; perianth 3.0 to 8.0 cm in length and elliptic or oblanceolate; species confined to the southern portion of the State ........................................................... 7.

7. Margins of the leaves not separating into fibers, or when old, producing only a few fine, usually brown fibers; leaves flattened in cross-section, somewhat flexible and bluish-green, the apical spine less than 5.0 mm in length; branches of the inflorescence densely pubescent; stems commonly reaching 3.0 to 5.0 m in height; confined to rocky canyons in the southwest corner of New Mexico at 3,700 to 5,000 ft. (1,130 to 1,520 m) in elevation. Flowering in this species is determined by available moisture, commonly occurring from April through August. *Yucca* species contain large quantities of saponins that are steroid derivatives. Research with *Yucca schottii* Engelmann has shown that the saponin-containing fraction of the leaves has anti-inflammatory properties and may be useful in treating arthritis and other joint inflammations.

**Mountain Yucca**, *Yucca schottii* Engelmann      Agavaceae

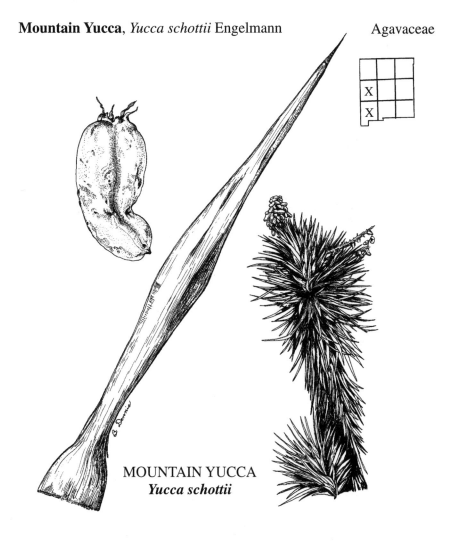

MOUNTAIN YUCCA
*Yucca schottii*

7.  Margins of the leaves separating into fibers, these coarse and gray; leaves curved in cross-section, rigid and yellow-green, the apical spine more than 5.0 mm in length; branches of the inflorescence glabrous or only slightly pubescent; stems seldom reaching 3.5 m in height; confined to dry mesas and plains in southcentral and southeastern portions of New Mexico at 3,500 to 5,000 ft. (1,060 to 1,520 m) in elevation. Flowering usually occurs in the spring, April through June.

**Torrey Yucca**, *Yucca torreyi* Shafer                    Agavaceae

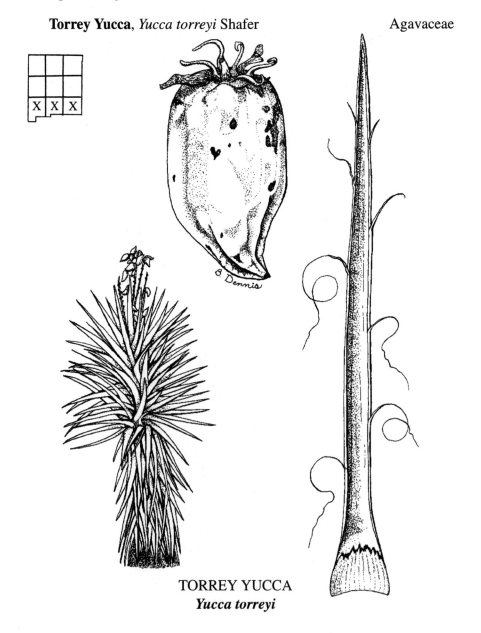

TORREY YUCCA
*Yucca torreyi*

8.    Trunk of mature plants 1.0 to 4.0, seldom 5.0 m in height, arborescent and usually branching; inflorescence a spreading panicle extending well above the foliage; leaves forming a large cluster at the apex; perianth white, seldom appearing slightly green, and 3.0 to 4.0 cm in length; commonly occurring over the central and southern two-thirds of New Mexico at 3,500 to 6,000 ft. (1,070 to 1,830 m) in elevation. This plant produces the official New Mexico State Flower, with flowers occurring in May through July.

**Soapweed** or **Palmilla**, *Yucca elata* (Engelmann)

Engelmann                    Agavaceae

SOAPWEED or PALMILLA
*Yucca elata*

8.     Trunk not developing above the ground level and not branching; inflorescence a raceme or only slightly branched; leaves spreading from the base; species more northern throughout the State ................................................. 9.

9.     Style swollen at the base, 3.0 mm or more in width and ovoid, pale green in color; flowers 3.0 to 4.0 cm in length; leaves seldom more than 1.0 cm in width and somewhat flexible; fruit dry, dehiscent and usually averaging less than 3.5 cm in length; common east of the Continental Divide and over the northern two-thirds of New Mexico at 4,000 to 7,500 ft. (1,220 to 2,290 m) in elevation. Flowering occurs in the spring and early summer. In addition to using the root of the yucca species as a soap substitute, Native Americans soaked their hair in a root solution of *Yucca glauca* to kill head lice and stimulate hair growth. The saponins contained in the roots and leaves contain steroid properties useful in reducing inflammation and swelling due to sprains.

**Great Plains Yucca**, *Yucca glauca* Nuttall                    Agavaceae

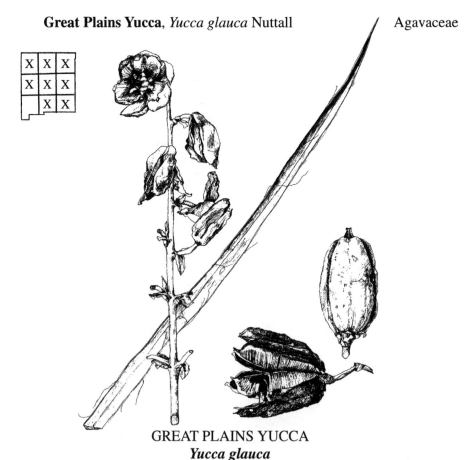

GREAT PLAINS YUCCA
*Yucca glauca*

9.   Style not or only slightly swollen at the base, not exceeding 3.0 mm in width and oblong-cylindric; flowers averaging more than 4.0 cm in length ........................................................................... 10.

   10.   Leaves averaging more than 1.0 cm in width, sometimes reaching 2.5 cm in width, usually stiff; style dark green in color; fruit dry, dehiscent and 3.7 to 5.0 cm in length, usually averaging more than 4.0 cm in length and deeply constricted. This species, confined to the northwest corner of New Mexico at 5,000 to 7,000 ft. (1,520 to 2,130 m) in elevation, commonly flowers in May and June.

   **Harriman Yucca**, *Yucca harrimaniae* Trelease    Agavaceae

   10.   Leaves averaging less than 1.0 cm in width, usually averaging 3.0 to 8.0 mm in width; style white to pale green ........ 11.

11.   Fruits erect and spreading, 3.0 to 4.3 cm in length and usually constricted; scape and inflorescence extending well above the leaves; the plant reaching nearly 2.0 m in height; the leaves linear and flexible, 1.5 to 4.5 dm in length and 4.0 to 8.0 mm in width, the margins white to light green, fibers developing with age; the plants acaulescent, usually 1.6 m or more in total height at maturity. This species, which flowers in May and June, is infrequent in sandy soils in northwestern New Mexico at 5,000 to 7,000 ft. (1,520 to 2,130 m) in elevation.

   **Narrow-leaf Yucca**, *Yucca angustissima* Engelmann *ex* Trelease
   Agavaceae

11.   Fruits pendulous, 4.0 to 7.0 cm in length and seldom constricted; inflorescence low and commonly not reaching the height of the leaves; the leaves linear and flexible, 2.0 to 6.0 dm in length and 3.0 to 8.0 mm in width, the margins white and fibrous; the plants acaulescent, usually 1.0 m or less in total height at maturity. This species, which flowers in May and June, is infrequent in dry rocky soils in the northern part of New Mexico at 4,500 to 7,500 ft. (1,370 to 2,300 m) in elevation.

   **Bailey Yucca**, *Yucca baileyi* Wooton & Standley    Agavaceae

12. Mature leaves averaging 3.0 to 6.0 mm in width, the margins smooth to the touch; capsule not growing as rapidly as the seed, thus the seed extruded at maturity; seeds averaging approximately 3.0 mm in diameter; more widespread throughout New Mexico than earlier thought, frequent over dry, rocky hills and south-facing slopes at 4,000 to 6,500 ft. (1,220 to 1,980 m) in elevation. This species flowers during May and June.

**Texas Beargrass** or **Sacahuista**, *Nolina texana* S.Watson
Agavaceae

12. Mature leaves averaging 6.0 to 12.0 mm in width, the margins serrulate and rough to the touch; capsule growing with the seed, thus the seed enclosed in the capsule at maturity; seeds averaging approximately 2.5 mm in diameter. Widespread in gravelly and sandy soils, on well-drained slopes from woodlands to deserts throughout New Mexico, this species becomes more common in the southern two-thirds of the State at 3,500 to 7,500 ft. (1,070 to 2,300 m) in elevation.

**Sacahuista** or **Beargrass,** *Nolina microcarpa* S. Watson
Agavaceae

13. Leaves Yucca-like in appearance, with thread-like fibers along the margins and occasionally a few spines at the base, the mature leaves usually curved and gradually tapering from the base, less than 1.2 cm in width at the middle of the leaf and approximately 2.5 cm in width at the base, with a total length seldom over 4.0 dm; flower stalk 2.0 to 3.0 m in length at maturity; flowers yellow, 3.0 to 5.0 cm in length; capsule 10.0 to 12.0 mm in length. Confined to dry, rocky slopes in desert grasslands and oak woodlands in the extreme southwest corner of New Mexico at 4,000 to 7,000 ft. (1,220 to 2,130 m) in elevation, this species may flower over a wide range of the growing season.

**Schott's Agave** or **Amole,** *Agave schottii* Engelmann
Agavaceae

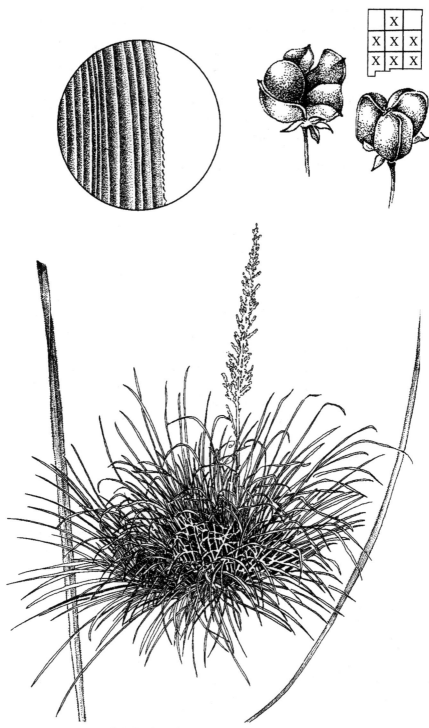

SACAHUISTA or BEARGRASS
*Nolina microcarpa*

13.    Leaves fleshy and not Yucca-like, with spines along the margins and no thread-like fibers, more than 3.0 cm in width at the middle of the leaf from an expanded base of more than 4.0 cm; species found over a much larger range in New Mexico ............................. 14.

14.    Plants low, close to the ground, often growing in large spreading colonies or mats; the leaves not more than 5.0 dm in length and 2.0 to 3.0 cm in width, commonly falcate in appearance; flower stalks unbranched and in tight spike-like panicles; flowers less than 3.8 cm in length and open or shallow, usually in groups of 2 to 4 along the stalk; basal cluster of leaves less than 20 in number, yellow-green in color; confined to dry mesas, hills and plains in southcentral and southeastern New Mexico at 3,500 to 5,000 ft. (1,070 to 1,520 m) in elevation, this species usually flowers from May through June.

**Lechuguilla**, *Agave lechuguilla* Torrey          Agavaceae

14.    Plants large in general appearance, young plants usually some distance from the parent if present, and not in large continuous mats; the leaves usually more than 4.0 dm in length and more than 3.0 cm in width, not appearing falcate; flower stalks branched and occurring in loose, open panicles; flowers more than 4.5 cm in length and forming a deep tube, usually in groups of 4 or more and widely spread along the stalk; the basal cluster of leaves more than 20 in number ................................................................. 15.

15.    Leaves of mature plants more than 6 times as long as wide, usually 4.0 dm or more in length and less than 7.0 cm in width, bright green in color; stamens inserted near the middle of the floral tube; fruit 4.0 to 6.5 cm in length; plants in flower reaching 7.0 m in height; scattered over dry, rocky slopes in the desert grasslands and mountains in the southern and southwestern part of New Mexico at 4,500 to 6,500 ft. (1,370 to 1,980 m) in elevation. It flowers through the summer months.

**Palmer Agave, Century Plant** or **Mescal**, *Agave palmeri*
                                    Engelmann     Agavaceae

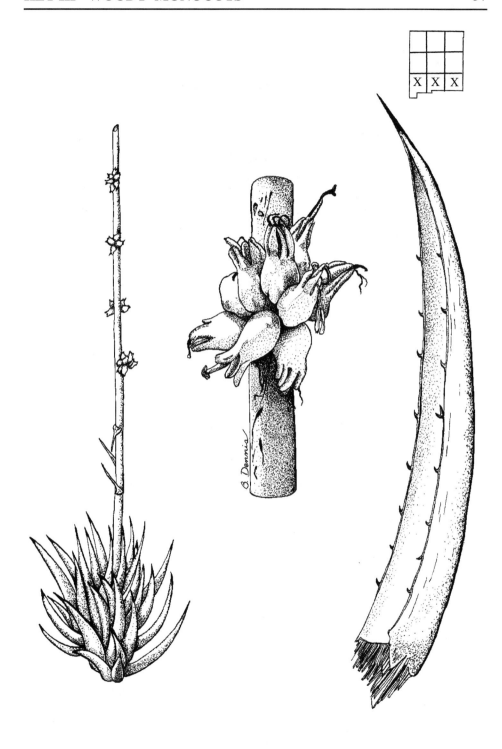

LECHUGUILLA
*Agave lechuguilla*

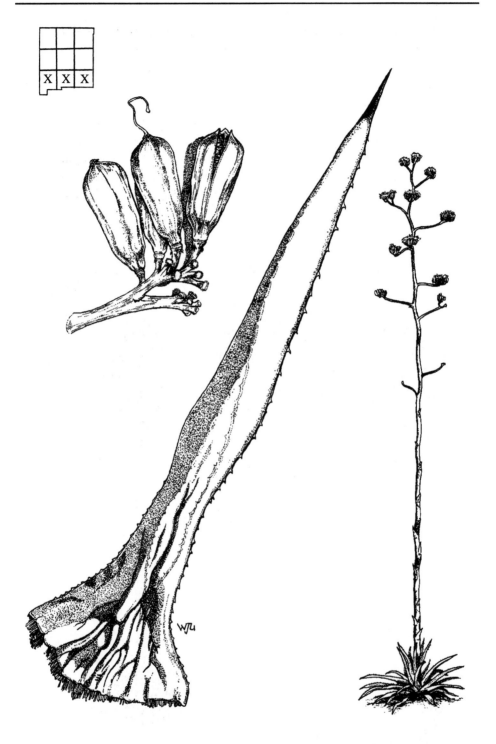

PALMER AGAVE, CENTURY PLANT or MESCAL
*Agave palmeri*

15.   Leaves of mature plants less than 5 times as long as wide, usually less than 3.5 dm in length and more than 7.0 cm in width, blue-green or gray-green in color; stamens inserted near the top of the floral tube ................................................................................. 16.

16.   Leaves many in basal rosettes, 3.0 to 4.0 dm in length and 7.0 to 10.0 cm in width, gray-green in color; panicles 3.5 to 4.5 m in height; capsules 3.5 to 4.0 cm in length; frequent on south-facing slopes in the southern and south-western counties of New Mexico at 4,000 to 6,500 ft. (1,220 to 1,980 m) in elevation, this species flowers in June through August.

**Parry Agave** or **Mescal**, *Agave parryi* Engelmann

Agavaceae

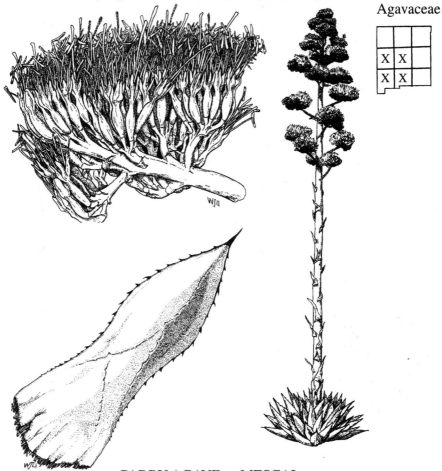

PARRY AGAVE or MESCAL
*Agave parryi*

16.      Leaves few in basal rosettes, 1.5 to 3.0 dm in length and 5.0 to 8.0 cm in width, light green to blue-green in color; panicles 2.5 to 3.5 m in height; capsules 2.5 to 3.5 cm in length; infrequent to rare in southern to southcentral and southeastern New Mexico at 4,500 to 6,500 ft. (1,370 to 1,980 m) in elevation. This species may be a subspecies of the **Parry Agave** and not a distinct species in New Mexico. Gentry (1982) considers it a distinct species and limits the distribution of **New Mexico Agave** to east of the Rio Grande.

**New Mexico Agave,** *Agave neomexicana* Wooton & Standley

Agavaceae

For Further Study:

There is another possible species of *Agave* that is poorly defined in southeastern New Mexico and may be the result of hybridization between *Agave lechuguilla* and *Agave neomexicana*. This is the so called **Slimfooted Agave,** *Agave gracilipes* Trelease. The flowers are smaller and the leaves are smaller and narrower than *A. neomexicana*. The growth habit can sometimes resemble *A. lechuguilla*. Our limited observations would indicate this taxon is extremely difficult to describe and needs additional study. See Burgess (1979).

## THE CACTI

Probably the quickest and easiest approach to teaching how limited water and water conservation are tied to the survival of practically all living organisms, including humankind, is to study the cacti. These very specialized xerophytic succulents are well adapted to reduced moisture and are abundant in the deserts and semideserts of the Southwest. This large and diverse family, the Cactaceae, with over 1,500 species is widely scattered throughout South, Central and North America with several species occurring well into Canada. But the survival of most species is ultimately associated with limited water and arid conditions.

The family Cactaceae is characterized by succulent herbs with a few species upright and woody. The stems are often ribbed, and commonly tuberculate and jointed. The leaves are generally reduced to spines, these arising from pads or cushions called areoles with these areoles often covered with clusters of barbed hairs called glochids. Many people think it is easy to distinguish the cacti by their stems, but some members of the family Euphorbiaceae, which is not closely related, have ribbed stems and may be confused with the Cactaceae. However, the cacti flowers are distinctive and once recognized, seldom confused. The showy and attractive, solitary flowers are bisexual, with many sepals, petals and bracts, all spirally arranged. The single pistil is characterized by several to many carpels and an inferior ovary. The fruit is a berry that is often spiny with numerous seeds.

There are more than 70 species of cacti in New Mexico, but because this publication is limited to woody plants, and more particularly to trees and shrubs, only 12 larger species of cacti are here included. This coverage does not do justice to the beauty and diversity of this unique and highly specialized family. At the same time, becoming familiar with the larger and more obvious species (those over 60.0 cm in height at maturity) may challenge the student to take a more serious look at the many species of herbaceous cacti that are native to New Mexico. **A note of caution**. With the exception of a few of the most common species, many of the cacti are threatened by humankind and overgrazing. Every effort should be made to protect them. We encourage you to enjoy the diversity of the cacti in their native ecosystems, rather than attempting to transplant them to your personal property.

## THE WOODY CACTI

1. Plant ovoid or globose, becoming barrel shaped to columnar with age, producing a massive, single, unbranched stem; the single large stem may reach 4.0 to 7.0 ft. in height, and 1.0 to 2.0 ft. in diameter; ribs range in number from 20 to 30 per stem without well developed tubercles; spines 4 per areole, forming a cross, the lower or central spine flattened and hooked; areoles lacking glochids; flowers orange to yellow in color; fruit becoming yellow at maturity. This attractive species is infrequent on rocky slopes in the southwest corner of New Mexico at 4,000 to 5,000 ft. (1,220 to 1,520 m) in elevation. If thoughtless individuals continue to dig and destroy this attractive species it may soon be eliminated from the New Mexico flora.

**Barrel Cactus**, *Ferocactus wislizeni* (Engelmann) Britton & Rose
Cactaceae

BARREL CACTUS
*Ferocactus wislizeni*

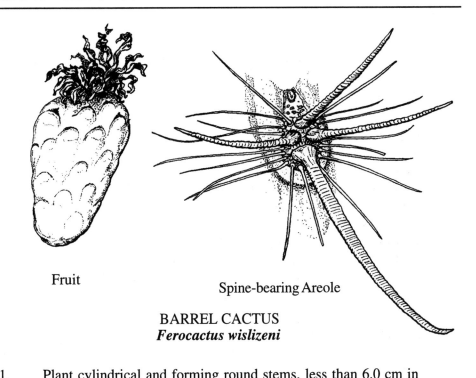

Fruit                          Spine-bearing Areole

BARREL CACTUS
*Ferocactus wislizeni*

1.    Plant cylindrical and forming round stems, less than 6.0 cm in
      diameter, or forming flattened orbicular pads with branching,
      segmented stems; stems often with several branches from the base
      and spreading; spines variable in arrangement from an areole,
      the areole producing many glochids ...................................................... 2.

      2.    Stem joints fleshy, spiny and cylindrical, not forming pads;
            the adult plant arborescent. **Chollas**, subgenus
            Cylindropuntia ...................................................................... 3.

      2.    Stem joints fleshy, usually (but not always) spiny and flat-
            tened, forming orbicular to obovate pads; the adult plant,
            although sometimes branching from a single trunk, ap-
            pearing as a series of pads, one attached to the top of the
            other.   **Prickly Pears**, subgenus Opuntia ............................... 8.

3.    Stems slender, less than 12.0 mm in diameter at maturity; spines
      4 or fewer per areole ........................................................................... 4.

3.    Stems larger, more than 15.0 mm in diameter at maturity; spines
      4 or more per areole ........................................................................... 5.

4.  Stems smooth or with tubercles only slightly obvious;
    joints less than 6.0 mm in diameter; flowers more than
    8.0 mm in width, petals yellow to green to tan; mature
    fruit red, less than 12.0 mm in length. Common on the
    mesas, plains and in adjacent valleys in the eastern and
    southern portion of New Mexico at 3,000 to 5,000 ft. (910
    to 1,520 m) in elevation, the **Pencil Cactus** flowers in
    May and June.

**Pencil** or **Christmas Cactus**, *Opuntia leptocaulis*

DeCandolle                    Cactaceae

PENCIL or CHRISTMAS CACTUS
*Opuntia leptocaulis*

4.    Stems with pronounced, raised tubercles; joints 6.0 to 12.0 mm in diameter; flowers less than 8.0 mm in width, petals dark red to purple; mature fruit red, more than 15.0 mm in length. Infrequent in rocky soils in the eastern and southern portion of New Mexico at 3,000 to 5,000 ft. (910 to 1,520 m) in elevation, this species commonly flowers in May or June.

**Candle** or **Klein's Cholla**, *Opuntia kleiniae* DeCandolle

Cactaceae

CANDLE or KLEIN'S CHOLLA
*Opuntia kleiniae*

5. Mature plants seldom exceeding 70.0 cm in height, often forming low mats or bushes; spines 4 to 9 per areole, with young spines forming a conspicuous sheath; flowers pale to bright yellow in color, less than 5.0 mm in width; fruit yellow and strongly tuberculate; uncommon in grasslands on the plains and in valleys. This species, found in the western half and northwest corner of New Mexico at 4,500 to 6,700 ft. (1,370 to 2,040 m) in elevation, flowers from June to October.

**Whipple's Cholla,** *Opuntia whipplei* Engelmann & Bigelow

Cactaceae

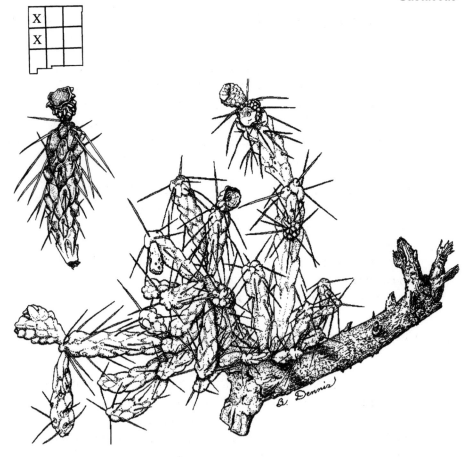

WHIPPLE'S CHOLLA
*Opuntia whipplei*

5. Mature plants commonly 80.0 cm or more in height, often reaching 1.0 m or more; spines usually 6 or more per areole; flowers pink or lavender, tending to purple ....................................................... 6.

6.  Mature terminal branches short and globose to 12.0 cm in length; readily detaching and freely falling as a form of vegetative reproduction, these branches 3.0 to 6.0 cm in diameter; sheaths on the spines straw colored; fruit persistent and forming chains, not or only slightly tuberculate and lacking spines; flower perianth pink or occasionally white with lavender streaks. This species is considered rare and native by some authorities, but we have only observed it under cultivation in the southwest corner of New Mexico below 4,000 ft. (1,220 m) in elevation.

**Jumping Cholla,** *Opuntia fulgida* Engelmann        Cactaceae

6.  Mature terminal branches elongated to more than 12.0 cm, firmly attached, these same branches less than 3.0 cm in diameter; sheaths on the spines reddish pink or light brown; fruit yellow, spineless, not forming chains and strongly tuberculate ................................................................. 7.

7.  Tubercles on the stems less than 2.0 cm in length, appearing ovoid to rounded, with 5 rows visible from one side of the stem; spines normally 10 to 20 per areole, less than 15.0 mm in length, averaging 9.0 to 11.0 mm; sheaths on the spines deciduous; flower petals dark lavender to purple. At maturity this species is a large robust shrub, confined to the southwest quarter of New Mexico at 4,000 to 6,700 ft. (1,220 to 2,040 m) in elevation.

**Cane Cholla,** *Opuntia spinosior* (Engelmann) Toumey        Cactaceae

7.  Tubercles more than 2.0 cm in length, appearing long and narrow, with 3 or 4 rows usually visible from one side of the stem; spines normally 10 to 20 per areole, and more than 15.0 mm in length, averaging 18.0 mm or more; sheaths on the spines persistent throughout the growing season; flower petals red to pink to purple. This is the most common arborescent cactus in New Mexico, growing in sandy and gravelly soils at 3,600 to 6,200 ft. (1,100 to 1,900 m) in elevation.

**Candelabra Cholla,** *Opuntia imbricata* (Haworth) DeCandolle
Cactaceae

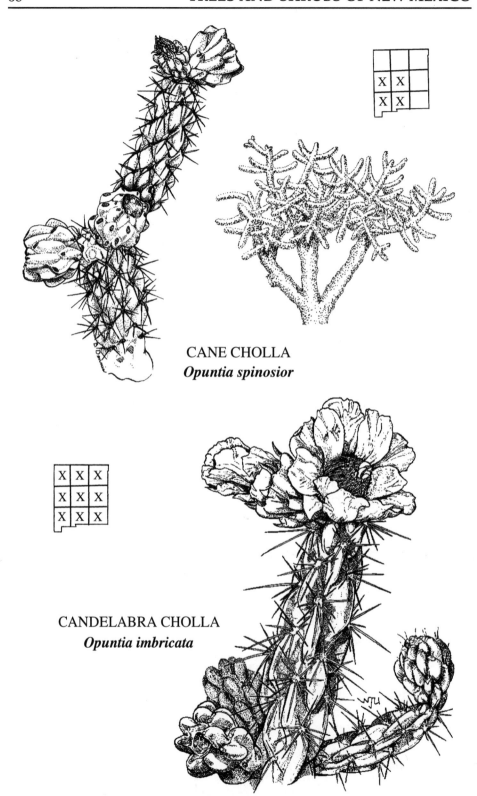

CANE CHOLLA
*Opuntia spinosior*

CANDELABRA CHOLLA
*Opuntia imbricata*

8.      Stem pads or joints strongly tinged with lavender or reddish purple; spines absent or 1 or 2, seldom 3, in the upper areoles; spines exserted in length when present, reach-
ing 4.0 to 18.0 cm in length ...................................................... 9.

8.      Stem pads or joints green during the growing season and
most of the year, occasionally slightly tinged with lavender during the coldest months; spines present, 1 or more
produced in practically all areoles; spines usually less than
8.0 cm in length ................................................................. 10.

9.      Spines long and needle-like, 8.0 to 18.0 cm in length, elliptic to
nearly circular in cross-section, with 1 to 2 per areole, located in
the upper areoles of the joint; joints red to purple to lavender
with dark brown to black spines, spines seldom yellow; flower
petals pale yellow, sometimes red at the base. Growing in sand,
gravel and rocky soils in a wide range of habitats in southwestern
New Mexico at 3,500 to 5,500 ft. (1,070 to 1,680 m) in elevation.
Flowering occurs in April and May.

**Purple Prickly Pear**, *Opuntia martiniana* (L. Benson) Parfitt
Syns. *O. macrocentra* var. *martiniana* L. Benson
*O. violacea* Engelmann                     Cactaceae

9.      Spines absent or few, sometimes only 2 to 4 along the upper
margin of the joint, commonly only 1 spine per areole; joints
orbicular, 15.0 to 20.0 cm in length and red to purple; the spines
light reddish-brown to pink, measuring 4.0 to 7.0 cm in length.
Infrequent in sandy and gravelly soils in the southern two tiers of
counties, at 3,000 to 5,000 ft. (910 to 1,520 m) in elevation. Mature plants may reach more than 1.5 m in height and appear tree-
like with a short trunk. Flowering occurs in April through May.

**Santa-rita Prickly Pear**, *Opuntia santa-rita* (Griffiths & Hare)
Rose
Syns. *Opuntia violacea* var. *santa-rita* L. Benson
Cactaceae

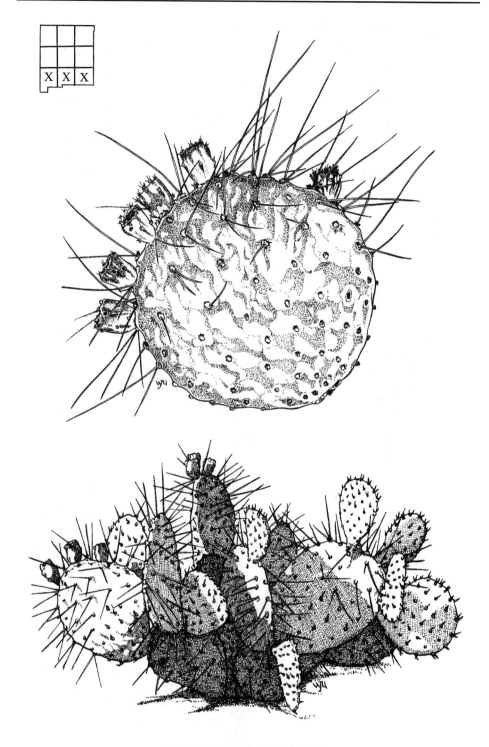

**PURPLE PRICKLY PEAR**
*Opuntia martiniana*

10. Mature plants growing from a single, definite trunk, often reaching 1.0 to 2.0 m in height; spines practically all deflexed, either yellow, translucent or becoming brown to reddish with age; perianth of the flower light yellow with a red tinge; fruit gray to green or only tinged with purple and lacking spines. This relatively rare species is confined to rocky soils in the deserts of the southwestern corner of New Mexico at 3,000 to 4,500 ft. (910 to 1,370 m) in elevation. Flowering occurs in April through June.

**Pancake Prickly Pear,** *Opuntia chlorotica* Engelmann & Bigelow    Cactaceae

PANCAKE PRICKLY PEAR
*Opuntia chlorotica*

10.      Mature plant sprawling from one or more prostrate, upright pads or tending to produce a weak trunk with age, seldom reaching more than 1.5 m in height; spines spreading in several directions over the joint, never all deflexed, and of several colors; fruit ranging from purple to red at maturity .......................................................................... 11.

11.     Spines all yellow or straw colored when young, occasionally red at the base and turning dark gray with age; mature terminal stems obovate to orbicular, green in color; mature plants ranging in height from 1.0 to 2.5 m; growth habit tending toward a single trunk with age, but usually several angled rather than round as in a tree; a relatively rare species confined to the southern half of New Mexico at 3,500 to 6,000 ft. (1,070 to 1,830 m) in elevation. The commonly cultivated **Cow's Tongue Prickly Pear** is often considered to be a variety of this species.

**Texas** or **Cow's Tongue Prickly Pear**, *Opuntia engelmannii* var.
*lindheimeri* (Engelmann)
Parfitt & Pinkava
Syns. *O. lindheimeri* Engelmann
Cactaceae

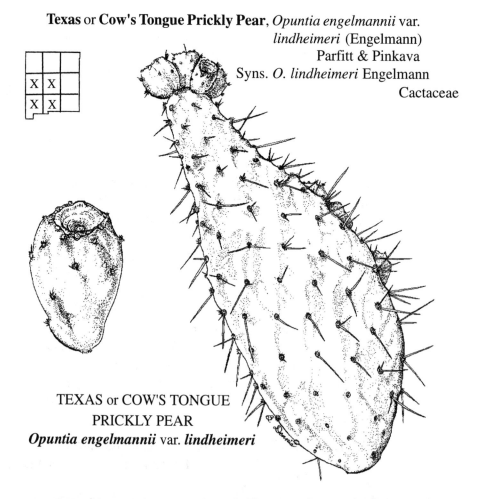

TEXAS or COW'S TONGUE
PRICKLY PEAR
*Opuntia engelmannii* var. *lindheimeri*

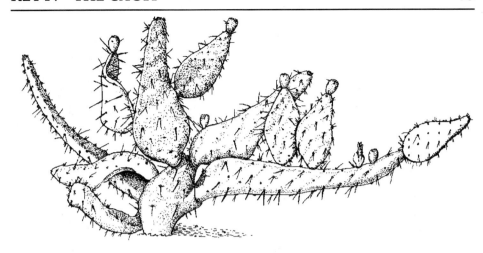

TEXAS or COW'S TONGUE
PRICKLY PEAR
*Opuntia engelmannii* var. *lindheimeri*

11.    Spines never all yellow or straw colored, ranging from white to
       gray or to reddish brown in color; mature stems tending toward
       blue-green; the height seldom more than 2.0 m in New Mexico;
       the growth habit remaining prostrate and spreading or becoming
       tree-like ....................................................................................... 12.

    12.    Mature spines brown to brownish-red or dark yellow-red,
           with the tip often light colored, 2.5 to 8.0 cm in length,
           with larger spines flattened at the base, broader than thick
           in cross-section, usually 3 or more per areole, with the
           spines pointing in all directions and with one single lower
           spine longer than the others; joints broadly obovate to
           ovate, 2.5 to 10.0 cm in length; fruit wine-colored or dark
           purple; stems sprawling to prostrate. Growing in large
           clumps to 1.0 m in height, in sand, gravel and rocky soils,
           this diverse species of several geographical varieties is
           widespread throughout New Mexico at 3,500 to 7,500 ft.
           (1,070 to 2,290 m) in elevation. The fruit, called *tunas* in
           Spanish, of *O. phaeacantha* and the previously described
           *O. santa-rita* are commonly collected and processed for
           juices from which jellies and syrups are made. Tender
           new pads of **Prickly Pear** cacti, called *nopalitos* in Span-
           ish, are eaten as a vegetable.

       **Purple-fruited Prickly Pear**, *Opuntia phaeacantha*
                                     Engelmann            Cactaceae

PURPLE-FRUITED PRICKLY PEAR
*Opuntia phaeacantha*

12. Mature stems all white or pale gray with age and reddish-brown at the very base, 2.5 to 5.0 cm in length, commonly 1 to 4 spines per areole, with the spines pointing in all directions, the lower spine not obviously longer than the others in a single areole; joints orbicular to elliptic, 20.0 to 40.0 cm in length; fruit obovoid, purple, 5.5 to 8.0 cm in length. This large robust species, to 2.0 m in height, occurs in sandy soils on the plains, on geologic benches, in arroyos, and in both deserts and grasslands at 3,000 to 5,000 ft. (914 to 1,524 m) in elevation. It is scattered throughout the central and southwestern portions of New Mexico, with flowering occurring in May and June.

**Engelmann Prickly Pear**, *Opuntia engelmannii* Salm-Dyck
Syns. *O. phaeacantha* var. *discata*
(Griffiths) L. Benson & Walkington
Cactaceae

ENGELMANN PRICKLY PEAR
*Opuntia engelmannii*

## MISTLETOES

We could probably have omitted this family of parasitic plants from the publication and few people would have noticed. Even though their biologic classification defines them as perennials and woody shrubs, and the serious field biologists are aware of the ecologic, evolutionary and economic importance, they are often overlooked in the literature for the layperson. The mistletoes are here included because we consider them to be one of the most fascinating groups of plants in the world and students of botany will want to learn more about their relationships to selected woody plants of the Southwest.

On any field trip in the Southwest you can always bet on an observant student calling the attention of the class to a yellow-green, to green, to sometimes red growth protruding upright or hanging down from the branches of a woody tree or shrub. When students learn that this is a flowering plant that truly belongs with the woody members of the Anthophyta, many questions follow and some explaining is in order.

The mistletoes of the Southwest are today usually placed in the family Viscaceae, however, some authorities have retained them in the Loranthaceae which better reflects their worldwide distribution. Of the approximately 1,300 described species the vast majority are tropical with relatively few extending into the temperate regions. Fewer than a dozen species occur in New Mexico. These are confined to two genera, *Arceuthobium*, the dwarf mistletoes, and *Phoradendron*, the large mistletoes. These two genera are distinguished in the first dichotomy of Key V.

The reproduction, host specificity, geography, evolution, economics and cultural value make this an important group of plants for teaching biology. In this key we have relied heavily on host specificity, which based on the author's field experience is often not reliable and leads one to recognize the need for additional study. We must point out that without the work of the late Frank G. Hawksworth and Delbert Wiens, authors, and Sharon Harris, illustrator, this key would not have been possible. Although we can only introduce the interested student to the mistletoes in this publication, once the mistletoes are recognized in the field they will be easier to study in the laboratory.

## MISTLETOES

1.  Mature stems usually less than 20.0 cm in length, several angled in cross-section when young, straw colored, yellow-green or green, becoming brown to reddish purple with age; leaves reduced to scales or absent, less than 1.0 mm in length; berries green to purple, compressed and explosive; anthers 1-celled; perianth of pistillate flowers 2-lobed; parasitic on several members of the Pinaceae, but not on *Juniperus* (Cupressaceae); growth habit appearing weak, resembling perennial herbs. **Dwarf Mistletoes**, genus *Arceuthobium* .................................................. 2.

1.  Mature stems usually more than 20.0 cm in length, terete, green to yellow-green or gray-green, seldom becoming orange or reddish purple with age; leaves usually foliaceous, blade 0.5 to 6.5 cm in length, leaves reduced to scales in 2 species; berries white to pink, globose and not explosive; anthers 2-celled; perianth of pistillate flowers 3-lobed; parasitic on deciduous trees and shrubs and on Junipers, *Juniperus*; growth habit appearing strong, shrublike and woody. **Mistletoes**, genus *Phoradendron* ............................. 7.

    2.  Parasites commonly confined to the **Pines**, *Pinus* ................... 3.

    2.  Parasites commonly confined to the **Spruces**, *Picea,* and the **Douglas Fir**, *Pseudotsuga* ................................................ 6.

3.  Parasites commonly occurring on the **Piñon Pine** or the **Mexican White Pine**, confined to the soft pines in the subgenus Haploxylon ................................................................................ 4.

3.  Parasites commonly occurring on the **Chihuahua Pine**, **Ponderosa Pine** or the **Apache Pine**, confined to the hard or yellow pines in the subgenus Diploxylon ......................................................... 5.

4. Parasite commonly confined to southern and southwestern New Mexico on **Southwestern White Pine**, *Pinus strobiformis*. This host specific species commonly flowers in September and is limited in elevation to 8,000 to 10,000 ft. (2,440 to 3,050 m).

**White Pine Dwarf Mistletoe** or **Apache Dwarf Mistletoe,** *Arceuthobium apachecum* Hawksworth & Wiens

Viscaceae

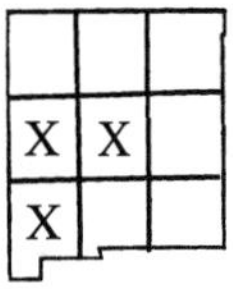

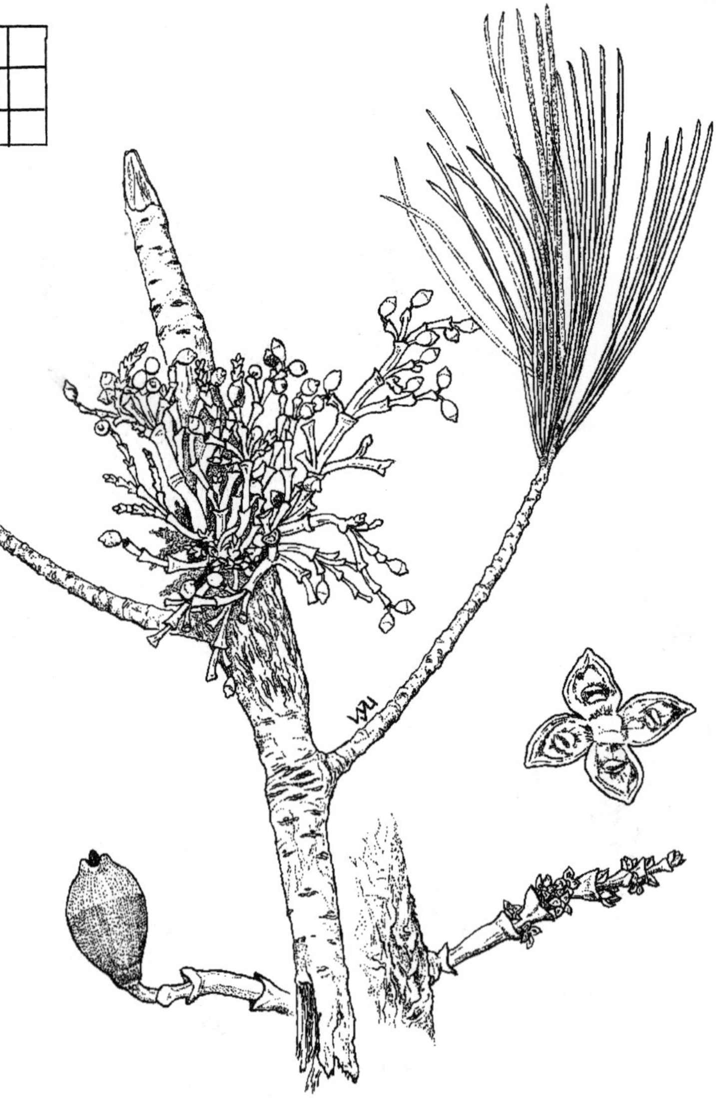

WHITE PINE DWARF MISTLETOE or
APACHE DWARF MISTLETOE
*Arceuthobium apachecum*

4. Parasite commonly confined to **Piñon Pine**, *Pinus edulis*, with the possibility of occurring on **Mexican Piñon Pine**, *Pinus cembroides* in the very southern portions of New Mexico. This species, which flowers in the late summer and fall, is widely scattered over the range of the **Piñon Pine** at 4,700 to 7,500 ft. (1,430 to 2,290 m) in elevation.

**Piñon Pine Dwarf Mistletoe**, *Arceuthobium divaricatum*
Engelmann                    Viscaceae

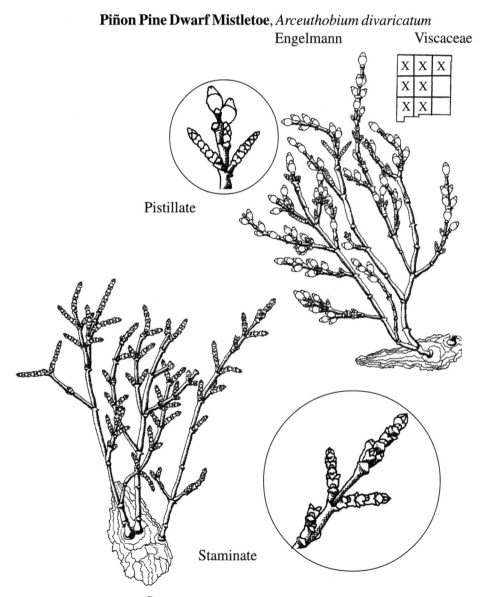

Pistillate

Staminate

PIÑON PINE DWARF MISTLETOE
*Arceuthobium divaricatum*

5.    Parasite commonly confined to the southwestern quarter of New
      Mexico on the **Chihuahua Pine**, *Pinus leiophylla* var. *chihua-*
      *huana*. However, it has been reported to occur on **Ponderosa**
      **Pine**, *Pinus ponderosa*, in northern Mexico. Like practically all
      of these host specific species, **Chihuahua Pine** is the key ingre-
      dient for the distribution of this species at 5,000 to 7,500 ft. (1,520
      to 2,290 m) in elevation.

**Chihuahua Pine Dwarf Mistletoe**, *Arceuthobium gillii*
                                        Hawksworth & Wiens    Viscaceae

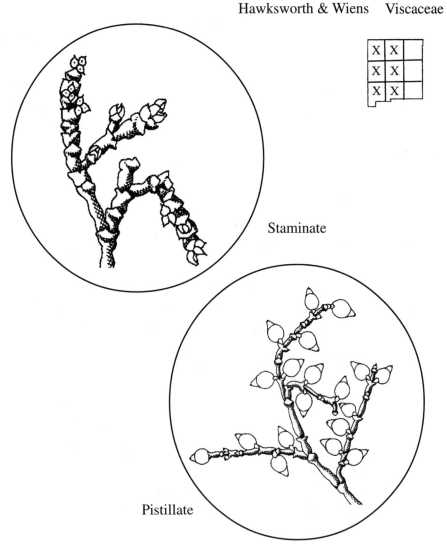

Staminate

Pistillate

CHIHUAHUA PINE DWARF MISTLETOE
*Arceuthobium gillii*

5.    Parasite commonly confined to **Ponderosa Pine**, *Pinus ponde-rosa* var. *scopulorum*, the **Arizona Yellow Pine**, *Pinus ponde-rosa* var. *arizonica* and the **Apache Pine**, *Pinus engelmannii*. Flowering relatively early in April, May and June, this species can be found over the western two-thirds of New Mexico at 6,500 to 9,200 ft. (1,980 to 2,800 m) in elevation. The authors are especially interested in locating this mistletoe on **Apache Pine** in New Mexico as described in the literature.

**Southwestern Dwarf Mistletoe,** *Arceuthobium vaginatum*
ssp. *cryptopodum* Hawksworth & Wiens

Viscaceae

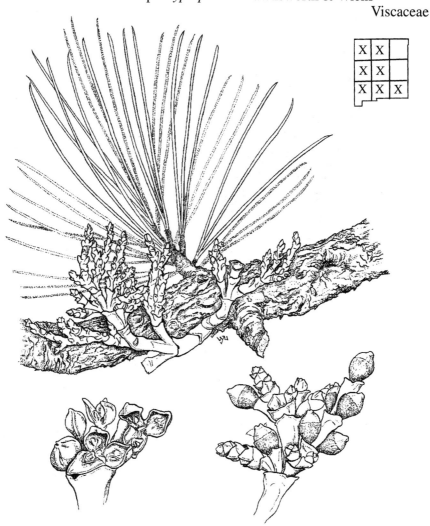

SOUTHWESTERN DWARF MISTLETOE
*Arceuthobium vaginatum* **ssp.** *cryptopodum*

6.    Parasite commonly confined to the **Douglas Fir**, *Pseudot-suga menziesii* in New Mexico, however it has been known to spread to the **White Fir**, *Abies concolor*, and the **Colorado Blue Spruce**, *Picea pungens,* in areas where **Douglas Fir** trees have been heavily infested. Flowering in March and April, this species is confined to higher elevations in montane coniferous forests at 6,500 to 10,000 ft. (1,980 to 3,050 m) in elevation.

**Douglas Fir Dwarf Mistletoe**, *Arceuthobium douglasii*
Engelmann          Viscaceae

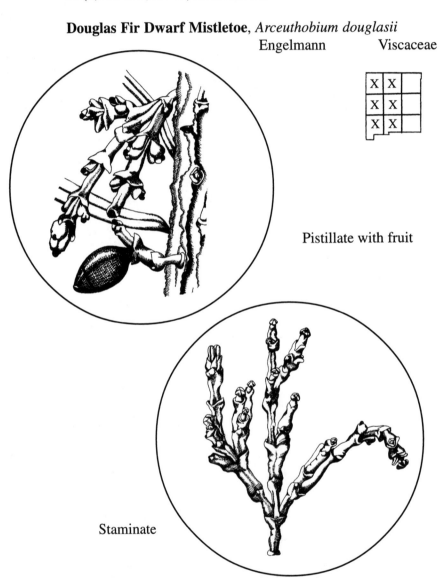

Pistillate with fruit

Staminate

DOUGLAS FIR DWARF MISTLETOE
*Arceuthobium douglasii*

6.  Parasite commonly confined to **Colorado Blue Spruce**, *Picea pungens*, and the **Engelmann Spruce**, *Picea engelmannii,* over a relatively small range in west-central New Mexico and east-central Arizona. Flowering in the fall, August through October, this species is infrequent above 8,000 ft. (2,440 m) in elevation.

**Blue Spruce Dwarf Mistletoe,** *Arceuthobium microcarpum* (Engelmann) Hawksworth & Wiens
Viscaceae

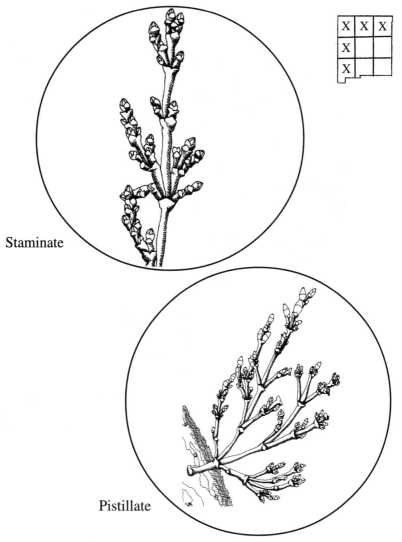

Staminate

Pistillate

BLUE SPRUCE DWARF MISTLETOE
*Arceuthobium microcarpum*

7.     Leaves reduced to triangular scales or scale-like bracts, less than 2.0 mm in length ............................................................................. 8.

7.     Leaves foliaceous, with well-developed and obvious blades, more than 10.0 mm in length ........................................................................ 9.

8.     Parasite commonly confined to Junipers, *Juniperus,* rarely reported to parasitize short-needled pines; stems glabrous, crowded on relatively stout branches and rigid, the internodes 0.6 to 1.6 cm in length; scale-like leaves strongly connate at the base; berries commonly white to pink. Flowering from July to September, this common species is found throughout New Mexico at 5,000 to 7,000 ft. (1,520 to 2,130 m) in elevation.

**Juniper Mistletoe**, *Phoradendron juniperinum*
Engelmann        Viscaceae

JUNIPER MISTLETOE
*Phoradendron juniperinum*

8.     Parasite commonly confined to woody legumes including Mesquites, *Prosopsis*, and **Catclaw Acacia**, especially *Acacia greggii*, and several species of the Buckthorn family, Rhamnaceae, including the genus *Condalia*. It has also been reported to parasitize **Creosote Bush**, *Larrea tridentata*. Stems somewhat loose and thin, not crowded and relatively weak, the internodes 1.3 to 2.8 cm in length; scale-like leaves slightly connate at the base; berries commonly red. This large bush-like species can form extremely large shrubs in the Sonoran desert trees of southern Arizona, extending into Baja California. There is some question as to its occurrence in New Mexico, but based on size alone it would be difficult not to recognize this species.

**California Mistletoe**, *Phoradendron californicum* Nuttall
Viscaceae

9.     Mature leaves linear to narrowly spatulate, less than 5.0 mm in width. The following two species are somewhat confused in the literature and are difficult to separate in the field. They both occur on the Junipers, *Juniperus*, their ranges overlap and the presence or absence of stellate-pubescence becomes the distinguishing characteristic ............................................................................. 10.

9.     Mature leaves ovate to obovate to suborbicular, more than 8.0 mm in width ............................................................................. 11.

10.     Plants stellate-pubescent; parasitic on Junipers, *Juniperus*; anthesis in the male plants occurring from December through February; the fruit white tinged with pink, 3.0 mm in diameter. This species, flowering through the winter months, has only been collected and reported from Hidalgo and Luna Counties in the southwestern corner of New Mexico.

**Juniper Mistletoe**, *Phoradendron capitellatum* Torrey
*ex* Trelease
Syns. *P. bolleanum* ssp. *capitellatum* (Torrey)
Kearney & Peebles
Viscaceae

10.     Plants glabrous to slightly hispid; parasitic on Junipers, *Juniperus*; anthesis in the male plants occurring in May through September; the fruit white, 4.0 mm in diameter. This species, flowering in late summer and early fall, is confined to southern New Mexico at 4,500 to 7,500 ft. (1,370 to 2,300 m) in elevation.

**Narrow-leaf** or **Boll American Mistletoe**, *Phoradendron bolleanum* (Seemann) Eichler
Viscaceae

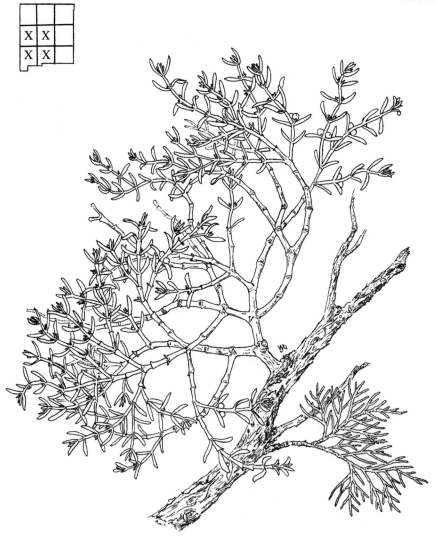

NARROW-LEAF or BOLL AMERICAN MISTLETOE
*Phoradendron bolleanum*

11.    Principal hosts are the Oaks, *Quercus*; mature leaves petiolate, 13.0 to 32.0 mm in length and 10.0 to 20.0 mm in width; new growth of stems densely stellate, internodes 15.0 to 40.0 mm in length; fruit white to pink, 3.0 mm in diameter and somewhat pubescent. Flowering from July through September, this species is common over the southern portion of the State at 4,000 to 8,000 ft. (1,220 to 2,440 m) in elevation.

**Green Mistletoe** or **Cory Mistletoe**, *Phoradendron villosum*
ssp. *coryae* (Trelease) Wiens
Syns. *P. coryae* Trelease
*P. havardianum* Trelease
Viscaceae

GREEN MISTLETOE or CORY MISTLETOE
*Phoradendron villosum* **ssp.** *coryae*

11.    Principal hosts include the Cottonwoods, *Populus*, the Willows, *Salix*, the native Sycamore, *Platanus* and the Ashes, *Fraxinus*; mature leaves 30.0 to 50.0 mm in length and 18.0 to 32.0 mm in width; new growth of stems pubescent to glabrous but not densely stellate, internodes 25.0 to 60.0 mm in length; fruit white, 4.0 to 6.0 mm in diameter and glabrous.

**Yellow Mistletoe**, *Phoradendron macrophyllum* (Engelmann)
Cockerell

Syns. *P. flavescens* Nuttall
*P. tomentosum* (DeCandolle) A. Gray
*P. tomentosum* ssp. *macrophyllum*
(Engelmann) Wiens        Viscaceae

YELLOW MISTLETOE
*Phoradendron macrophyllum*

## OPPOSITE OR WHORLED, SIMPLE, BROAD LEAVES

1.    Leaves palmately lobed, fruit a samara, occasionally some leaves compound .................................................................................. 2.

1.    Leaves not lobed, or if lobed the lobes finely linear and obscure, the fruit variable .......................................................................... 5.

    2.    Mature leaves less than 7.5 cm in width; these native species occurring more commonly in undisturbed or protected areas in national forests and parks .......................................... 3.

    2.    Mature leaves more than 7.5 cm in width; these introduced and cultivated species are planted in lawns or gardens, require additional water and commonly escape cultivation .......................................................................... 4.

3.    Margins of leaves or leaflets, if some leaves compound, finely serrated and the teeth acute, the sinuses V-shaped; young twigs red or yellow in color; flowering in May and June, the stalk of the inflorescence more than 3.0 cm in length; mature samaras average 2.5 to 3.0 cm in length. This woodland shrub or small tree is relatively common throughout New Mexico at 7,000 to 9,500 ft. (2,130 to 2,900 m) in elevation. (Please see Key VII, couplet 24, pg. 183.)

**Rocky Mountain Maple**, *Acer glabrum* Torrey        Aceraceae

3.    Margins of the leaves, which are never compound, are never finely serrated, and the teeth are obtuse, with three or five distinguishable palmate lobes, the sinuses rounded; young twigs gray to dark brown in color; flowering in April through early June, the stalk of the inflorescence is less than 3.0 cm in length or nearly sessile; mature samaras average 2.0 cm in length. Confined to moist canyons over the southern half of the State, this attractive large shrub or tree occurs at 5,500 to 7,500 ft. (1,680 to 2,300 m) in elevation.

**Bigtooth Maple**, *Acer grandidentatum* Nuttall        Aceraceae

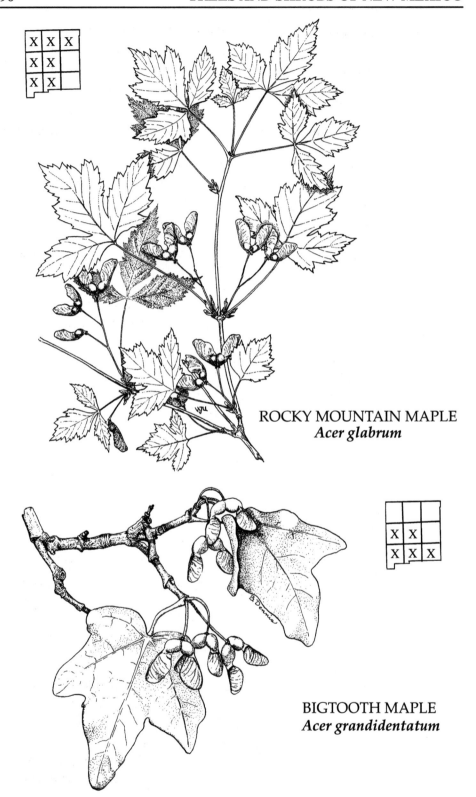

ROCKY MOUNTAIN MAPLE
*Acer glabrum*

BIGTOOTH MAPLE
*Acer grandidentatum*

4.    Spaces (sinuses) between the main lobes deeply V-shaped forming a definite angle; leaves 5 lobed, silvery white beneath; samaras fall before the leaves are mature; widely introduced and escaping cultivation throughout New Mexico.

**Silver Maple**, *Acer saccharinum* L.            Aceraceae

4.    Spaces (sinuses) between the main lobes deeply U-shaped, rounded and not forming a sharp angle; leaves 5 lobed, but commonly light green, not silvery white beneath; widely introduced throughout New Mexico.

**Sugar Maple**, *Acer saccharum* Marshall            Aceraceae

SILVER MAPLE
*Acer saccharinum*

SUGAR MAPLE
*Acer saccharum*

5.      Stems forming vines or creeping and prostrate, spreading over
        the soil from a taproot, rhizome or runner, often forming mats........... 6.


5.      Stems erect, appearing separate; shrubs or trees, usually over 20.0
        cm in height at maturity .................................................................. 12.

        6.      Leaves averaging less than 1.2 cm in width ........................... 7.

        6.      Leaves averaging more than 1.2 cm in width ....................... 10.

7.      Leaves averaging more than 3.0 cm in length, broadly oblan-
        ceolate to nearly obovate or spatulate, appearing whorled along
        the stem, the margins serrate to crenate; the height of the plant
        seldom reaches 25.0 cm; the creeping, woody root is the reason
        we include this species; the flower parts are in fives and the fruit
        is a 5 lobed, loculed capsule. This is a frequent species in moun-
        tain forests at 8,500 to 11,500 ft. (2,600 to 3,500 m) in elevation.

**Pipsissewa**, *Chimaphila umbellata* (L.) W. Barton                Pyrolaceae

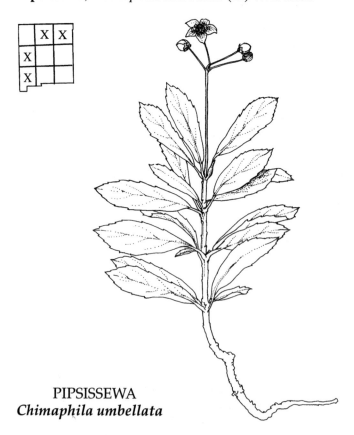

PIPSISSEWA
*Chimaphila umbellata*

7.      Leaves averaging less than 3.0 cm in length, opposite and never appearing whorled ............................................................................ 8.

         8.      Perennial on dry rocky hills and canyons over the southern third of the State at 3,500 to 5,000 ft. (1,070 to 1,520 m) in elevation; woody stems trailing and sometimes climbing and twining, the plant may grow to 25.0 or 30.0 cm in height; the leaves are linear, sessile or with short petioles; the flowers are solitary or in small axillary clusters, yellow to orange or red to brown in color, with parts in fives but sometimes reduced and obscure; the fruit is a dry, two or three winged samara. (Please see couplet 29, page 112 for further description.)

            **Slender Janusia**, *Janusia gracilis* A.Gray      Malpighiaceae

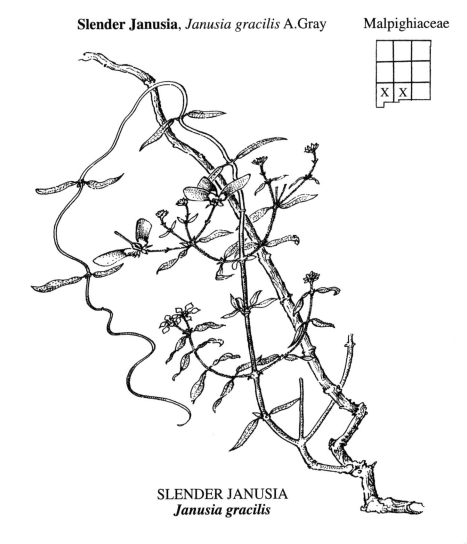

SLENDER JANUSIA
*Janusia gracilis*

8.　　　　Perennials of moist, wooded hillsides over the mountainous areas of the State at 6,500 to 11,000 ft. (1,980 to 3,350 m) in elevation; the somewhat woody stems trailing but not twining, plants remaining low and close to the soil, seldom over 25.0 cm in height ................................................. 9.

9.　　Leaves crenate above the middle, and oval to elliptic to slightly obovate; the younger stems are pubescent forming loose mats; flowers in pairs on erect stalks; these shrubs seldom more than 15.0 cm tall. This slightly woody native species occurs most commonly in the subalpine in spruce-fir forests.

**Twinflower**, *Linnaea borealis* ssp. *longiflora* (Torrey) Hultén

Caprifoliaceae

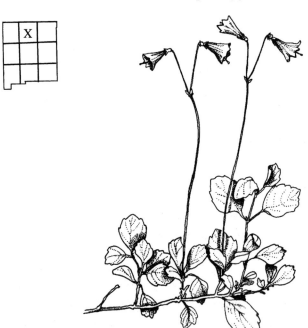

TWINFLOWER
*Linnaea borealis* ssp. *longiflora*

9.　　Leaves serrate above the middle, and elliptic to oblong; the younger stems are glabrous, growing upright or over the soil surface; reddish flowers and fruits are inconspicuous, sessile in the leaf axils. These low, spreading shrubs, that may reach 20.0 cm in height, belong to a relatively rare plant family in the western United States.

**Mountain Lover**, *Paxistima myrsinites* (Pursh) Rafinesque

Celastraceae

MOUNTAIN LOVER
*Paxistima myrsinites*

10.    Stems erect and woody to herbaceous to 20.0 cm in height,
spreading singly from a woody rhizome; the leaves are in
a whorl near the top of the stem and the veins in the leaves
curve from near the base of the apex; the inflorescence is
apical and subtended by 4 or 5 white, petal-like modified
leaves or bracts, with the true flowers at the center; the
fruits form a bright red cluster of drupes at the top of the
plant. This common, northern, circumpolar species is uncommon in New Mexico and is usually found at 8,000 to
11,000 ft. (2,440 to 3,350 m) in elevation in subalpine
forests.

**Bunchberry** or **Dwarf Dogwood**, *Cornus canadensis* L.
Syns. *Chamaepericlymenum canadense*
(L.) Ascherson *ex* Graebner
Cornaceae

BUNCHBERRY or DWARF DOGWOOD
*Cornus canadensis*

10.    Stems trailing or climbing and woody, the bark shredding; the upper pair of opposite leaves connate and perfoliate, lower leaves opposite, but not whorled; the inflorescence is a terminal cluster of several flowers, these may or may not be surrounded by perfoliate leaves or small green bracts; the fruit is a globose berry ...................... 11.

11. Leaves ciliate along the margins, oval to elliptic or oblong, 4.0 to 7.0 cm in length; corolla bright red on the outside and orange on the inner surface, and only slightly bilabiate; the stamens are inserted deeply into the corolla tube; the fruit is a red globose berry. This relatively common species over the western and southcentral portions of the State can be found in the mountains and hill country at 6,000 to 9,000 ft. (1,830 to 2,740 m) in elevation. It normally flowers in June and July.

**Arizona Honeysuckle**, *Lonicera arizonica* Rehder      Caprifoliaceae

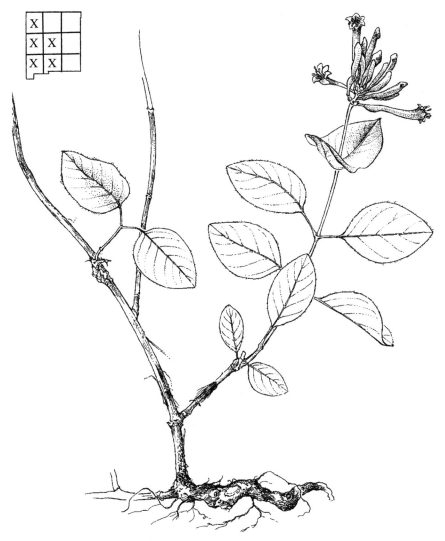

ARIZONA HONEYSUCKLE
*Lonicera arizonica*

11.    Leaves lacking cilia along the margins, orbicular to oval, 2.5 to
       5.0 cm in length; corolla white to cream colored to yellow, and
       deeply bilabiate to almost the length of the corolla; the stamens
       are inserted near the top of the corolla tube; the fruit is a globose
       berry turning black with age. This common species occurs on
       mountain slopes and canyons at 6,000 to 9,000 ft. (1,830 to 2,740
       m) in elevation over the southern third of New Mexico. It flow-
       ers from April to June, depending on available moisture.

**Western White Honeysuckle**, *Lonicera albiflora* Torrey &
A. Gray
Caprifoliaceae

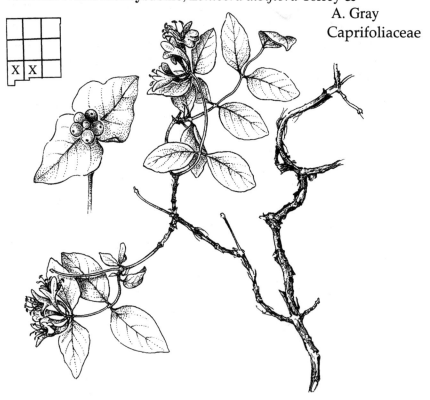

WESTERN WHITE HONEYSUCKLE
*Lonicera albiflora*

(An introduced species, **Japanese Honeysuckle**, *Lonicera japonica* Thunberg, that grows as a twining or trailing vine, is commonly cultivated and escapes cultivation throughout New Mexico. This species would key to this point. If the plant is twin-ing and the strongly bilabiate corolla is white, fading to yellow with age, the plant is probably this species. However, many spe-cies in the genus *Lonicera* are cultivated throughout North America.)

12.   Mature leaves whorled, more than two leaves at each node around the stem, but not fascicled ......................................... 13.

12.   Mature leaves strictly opposite, two leaves at each node, or leaves in fascicles at the opposite nodes .......................... 15.

13.   Mature leaves are commonly more than 15.0 cm in length and 12.0 cm wide and cordate in shape; commonly becoming a relatively large tree to 30.0 m or more in height; the flowers are borne in large terminal panicles, individual flowers are white in color with yellow spots in the throat of the corolla and pale purple spots on the margins; the fruit is a capsule, 2.0 to 4.0 dm in length, containing many seeds, each fringed with numerous hairs. This commonly introduced species is widespread over New Mexico and may be considered naturalized.

**Northern Catalpa** or **Cigar Tree**, *Catalpa speciosa* (Warder) Warder *ex* Engelmann      Bignoniaceae

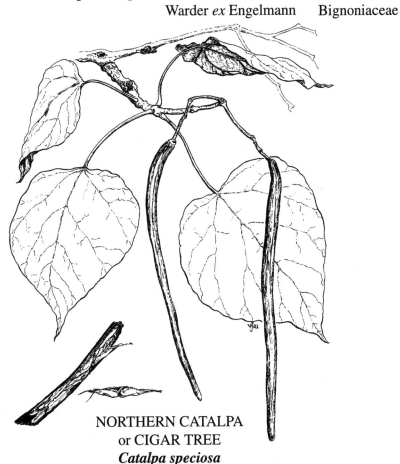

NORTHERN CATALPA
or CIGAR TREE
*Catalpa speciosa*

13.     Mature leaves are commonly less than 10.0 cm in length and 4.0 cm wide, and lanceolate to ovate-lanceolate to ovate-elliptic in shape; commonly shrubs to not more than 1.5 m in height; the flowers are borne in terminal cymes, the corolla is slender or narrowly tubular; the fruit is a globose or subglobose capsule.......... 14.

        14.     Stems woody throughout; the mature leaves lanceolate-oblong, averaging less than 4.0 cm in length and 1.2 cm in width, the leaf surfaces roughly scabrous to hirsutu-lous; the older bark dark gray to white; the corolla red, slender and tubular, 2.0 to 4.0 cm in length. The range for this species appears to be confined to the southwest corner of the State, however it might be expected in canyons at 4,000 to 6,000 ft. (1,220 to 1,830 m) in other locations in the southern tier of counties.

**Scarlet Bouvardia,** *Bouvardia ternifolia* (Cavanilles)
Schlechtendal                    Rubiaceae

SCARLET BOUVARDIA
*Bouvardia ternifolia*

14.    Stems suffrutescent from a woody base; the mature leaves ovate to elliptic to lanceolate-ovate, averaging more than 4.0 cm in length and 2.4 cm in width, the leaf surfaces glabrous to hirtellous below; older bark pale tan to light brown; the corolla red, sometimes white to pink, narrowly tubular, 2.0 to 3.5 cm in length. The range for this species is more restricted to southwestern New Mexico at 4,000 to 9,000 ft. (1,220 to 2,740 m). (Some authorities consider this to be a subspecies of the previous species. Please see description and illustration, page 100.)

**Smooth Bouvardia,** *Bouvardia glaberrima* Engelmann
Rubiaceae

15.    Mature leaves averaging less than 1.0 cm in width ........................... 16.

15.    Mature leaves averaging more than 1.0 cm in width ........................ 52.

16.    Mature leaves averaging less than 4.0 cm in length ....... 17.

16.    Mature leaves averaging more than 4.0 cm in length ........... 48.

17.    Leaves in fascicles, bundles or clusters of two or more leaves at each bud on each side of the stem ..................................................... 18.

17.    Leaves two to the node, one on each side of the stem, not in fascicles, bundles or clusters ............................................................ 24.

18.    Flowers several in head, each cluster of flowers surrounded or subtended by an involucre of bracts; corolla 5 parted, ovary inferior; fruit an achene. Asteraceae ............... 19.

18.    Flowers solitary or in simple cymes, individual flowers with basic flower parts, lacking an involucre of bracts; corolla 4 or 5 parted or absent; fruit variable ...................... 20.

19.    Subshrubs, 25.0 to 55.0 cm in height, leaves clustered due to the
       development of axillary leaves, linear to spatulate-oblong, and
       glandular-punctate; ray flowers absent, head of only 4 to 6 white
       disk flowers, the involucre is lavender to pink and elongate to 2.0
       or 3.0 cm. This is a frequently occurring species in dry mountain
       canyons at 4,500 to 6,500 ft. (1,370 to 1,980 m) in elevation over
       the southern one-third of New Mexico. It may flower from March
       through October.

**Bigelow Bush**, *Carphochaete bigelovii* A. Gray              Asteraceae

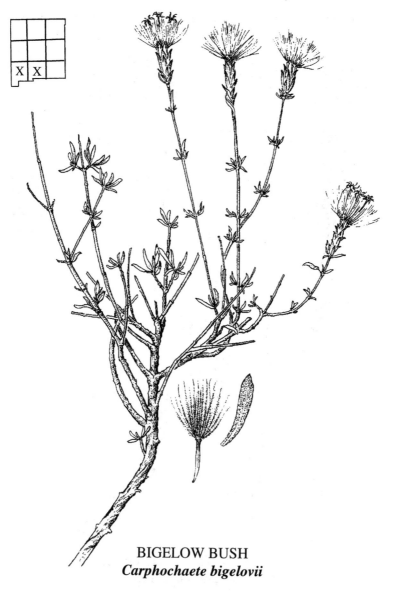

BIGELOW BUSH
*Carphochaete bigelovii*

19.    Subshrubs, 25.0 cm or less in height, leaves clustered and needle-like (thus the specific name "acerose"), and glandular-punctate; ray and disk flowers present and yellow in color, the phyllaries are covered with ill smelling, orange or brown oil glands. The Greek term "dyssodia" refers to the fetid odor given off by the glands. This common species is widely scattered over New Mexico at 3,500 to 6,000 ft. (1,070 to 1,830 m) in elevation on dry and sometimes overgrazed, rocky slopes and mesas. It flowers over most of the growing season.

**Prickleaf Dogweed**, *Thymophylla acerosa* (DeCandolle) Strother
Syns. *Dyssodia acerosa* DeCandolle

Asteraceae

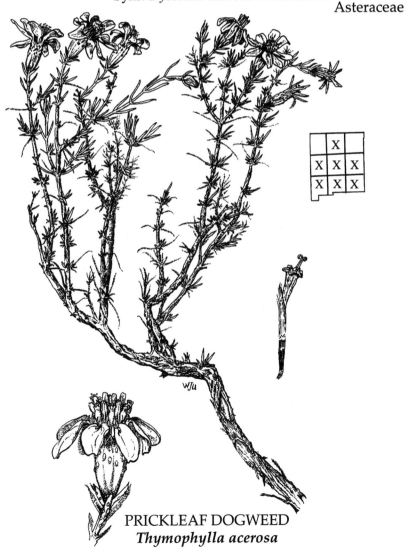

PRICKLEAF DOGWEED
*Thymophylla acerosa*

20.    Flowers solitary; corolla absent; calyx short but with 4
       lobes; stamens numbering 20 to 40 and surrounding a tube
       or sheath that encloses the superior ovary; the fruit a small
       achene measuring less than 1.0 cm; the leaves are linear
       to slightly oblanceolate, entire, and crowded into fascicles;
       the branching is diffuse with the twigs often becoming
       spinescent. Several authors describe this species as rare
       in New Mexico, occurring at 4,000 to 5,500 ft. (1,220 to
       1,680 m) in elevation in the northwest corner of the State.
       No herbarium specimens were found, nor was this spe-
       cies collected, however it can be expected to occur in New
       Mexico.

**Blackbrush,** *Coleogyne ramosissima* Torrey          Rosaceae

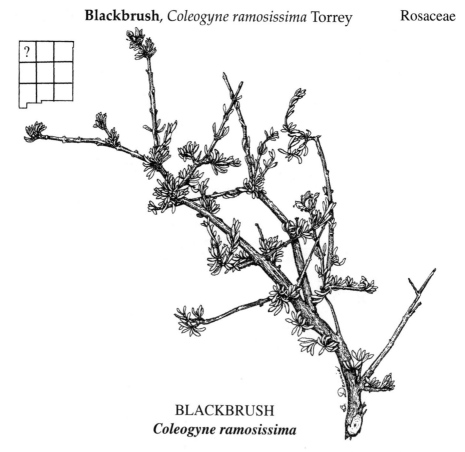

BLACKBRUSH
*Coleogyne ramosissima*

20.    Flowers solitary or in small cymes; the corolla present
       with 4 or 5 petals; the sepals present numbering 4 to 5;
       the ovary variable, but not enclosed by a tube or sheath;
       stamens numbering 10 or less; the fruit a capsule of vari-
       ous shapes, but never an achene ............................................. 21.

21.  Flower parts in fours or multiples of fours, sepals 4 in number and petals 4 in number, stamens 4 or 8 ............................................. 22.

21.  Flower parts in fives or multiples of fives, sepals 5 in number and petals 5 in number, stamens 5 or 10 ......................................... 23.

22.  Widely branched shrub to 2.0 m in height, on rocky slopes in the mountains at 5,500 to 7,500 ft. (1,680 to 2,300 m) in elevation; fruit a capsule, conical to a point, dehiscing into 4 or 5 valves; stamens 8, with 4 cup-shaped, lobed sepals, and 4 clawed, white petals; flowers solitary.

**Cliff Fendlerbush**, *Fendlera rupicola* A.Gray

Hydrangeaceae

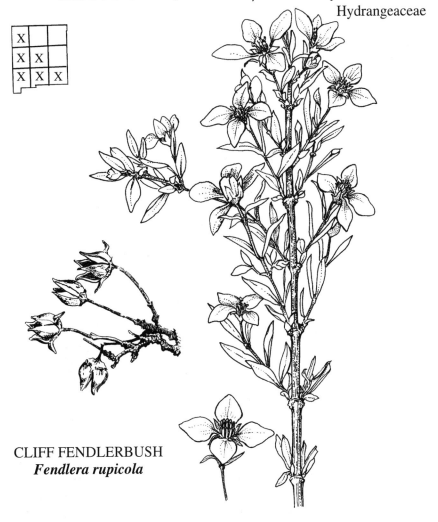

CLIFF FENDLERBUSH
*Fendlera rupicola*

22.    Widely spreading small shrub, 30.0 to 45.0 cm in height,
on dry slopes over central and southern New Mexico at
4,000 to 6,000 ft. (1,220 to 1,830 m) in elevation; fruit a
capsule, forming 2 lobes, each dehiscing, with each lobe
containing 4 or 5 seeds; stamens 4, with 4 small sepals,
and 4 small, white petals with 4 funnelform lobes forming a tubular corolla; the inflorescence a small cyme.

**Fascicled Bluet**, *Hedyotis intricata* Fosberg
Syns. *Houstonia fasciculata* A. Gray      Rubiaceae

23.    Plants of dry, pine covered, mountain slopes and canyons at 5,500
to 8,000 ft. (1,680 to 2,440 m) in elevation, over the southern
half of New Mexico; flowers borne in small compound cymes,
flower parts in fives with 10 stamens, the petals distinct and white;
the fruit is a cylindric capsule with three 1-seeded valves. This
upright shrub may reach 1.0 m or more in height.

**Utah Fendlerella**, *Fendlerella utahensis* (S. Watson) Heller
Hydrangeaceae

UTAH FENDLERELLA
*Fendlerella utahensis*

23.   Plants of strongly alkaline soils at 3,500 to 4,500 ft. (1,070 to 1,370 m) in elevation, with the growing conditions selecting for species; flowers borne solitary or in small clusters of 3 to 7 flowers, flower parts in fives with 5 stamens, occasionally 6, the corolla is small, tubular and white; the fruit is a small linear, 1-celled capsule. This low shrub seldom reaches more than 65.0 cm in height.

**James Frankenia**, *Frankenia jamesii* Torrey *ex* A. Gray

Frankeniaceae

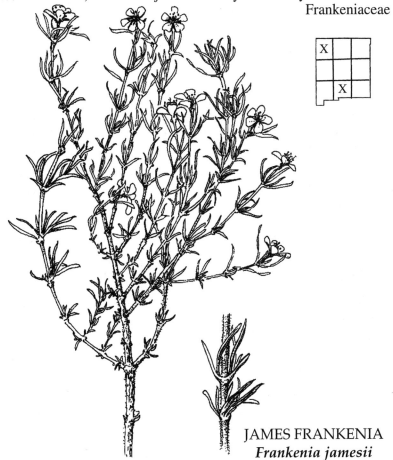

JAMES FRANKENIA
*Frankenia jamesii*

24.   Leaves filiform, linear, awl-shaped to linear-spatulate or slightly lanceolate; usually averaging less than 0.5 cm in width; sessile or with a minute petiole .......... 25.

24.   Leaves broader, lanceolate, elliptic, oblanceolate, hastate, deltoid, ovate or obovate; usually averaging from 0.5 to 1.0 cm in width .................................................. 35.

25.    Flowers several in heads, each cluster of flowers surrounded or subtended by an involucre of bracts; flowers perfect, corolla 5 parted, ovary inferior; fruit an achene. Asteraceae ......................... 26.

25.    Flowers in panicles, racemes, cymes, corymbs or solitary, individual flowers with basic parts, but lacking an involucre of bracts; flowers perfect or imperfect in *Sarcobatus vermiculatus* where the plants may be monoecious or dioecious, corolla 4 or 5 parted, the ovary superior; fruits variable ....................................................... 28.

26.    Stems woody, growing from a taproot, forming low shrubs, 10.0 to 16.0 cm in height; heads solitary and terminal on separate branches; ray flowers present and white, 4 to 6 in number, disk flowers yellow, 8 to 13 in number and turning red with age; leaves are opposite, sessile, linear, with one nerve only at the base, and acerose (needle-like), to 1.0 mm in width. This is a common species over southern New Mexico at 3,500 to 6,000 ft. (1,070 to 1,830 m) in elevation.

**Southern Zinnia**, *Zinnia acerosa* (DeCandolle) A. Gray
Syns. *Z. pumila* A. Gray

Asteraceae

(A closely related, similar, perennial species, not quite as woody from the base, might be identified at this point in the key. This is the **Rocky Mountain Zinnia**, *Zinnia grandiflora* Nuttall. This species is characterized by bright yellow ray flowers and linear, but not acerose, leaves. The leaves have three nerves from the base, these extending up to one-half the length of the leaf. This common species is widely scattered over most of New Mexico, but is not considered a woody plant by most authors.)

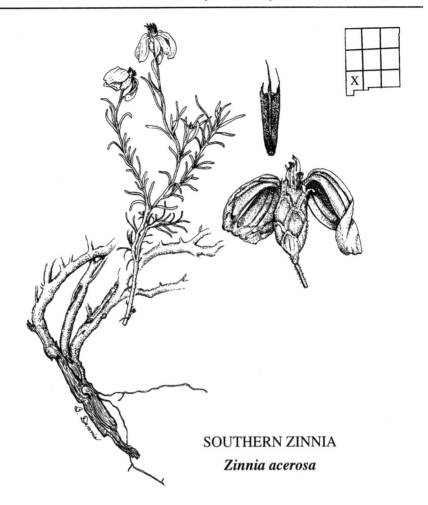

SOUTHERN ZINNIA
*Zinnia acerosa*

26. Stems perennial and suffrutescent, forming taller, glabrous, subshrubs, 20.0 to 60.0 cm in height; heads single, two or several at the ends of the branches; ray flowers absent, disk flowers perfect, numbering more than 15 per head; leaves ranging from alternate to opposite, simple, sessile to subsessile, entire and aromatic, with oil glands along the margin ............................................................. 27.

27. Phyllaries 7 to 9; flowers numbering 40 or more per head, corolla yellow; achenes 3.5 to 5.5 mm in length. This is an infrequent species only in the southern tier of counties at 3,500 to 4,500 ft. (1,070 to 1,370 m) in elevation, with abundance closely associated with limestone and the availability of moisture in arroyos.

**Shrubby Poreleaf,** *Porophyllum scoparium* A. Gray        Asteraceae

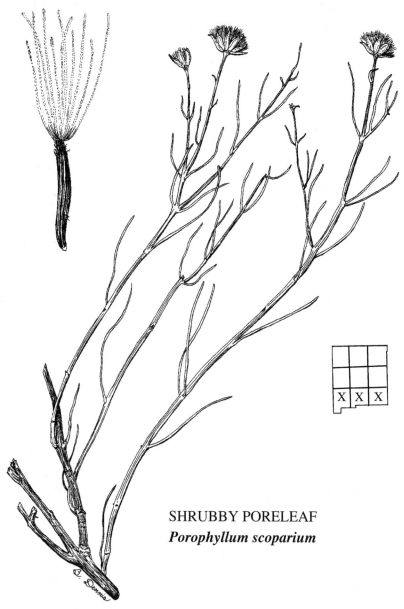

SHRUBBY PORELEAF
*Porophyllum scoparium*

27.    Phyllaries 5; flowers numbering fewer than 30 per head, corolla
       white to purplish with purple streaks; achenes 5.6 to 10.2
       mm in length. Although this species appeared to be lim-
       ited to the very southwestern corner of New Mexico at
       below 4,000 ft. (1,220 m), it has now been collected in
       the Franklin Mountains. Adequate rainfall is critical.

**Slender Poreleaf**, *Porophyllum gracile* Bentham                Asteraceae

28. Flowers imperfect, perianth lacking, with male and female flowers on separate plants (dioecious) or occasionally male and female flowers on the same plant (monoecious), not brightly colored, the staminate flowers develop into a spike, while the pistillate flowers are sessile, solitary or are borne in pairs; the fruit is a green to tan or somewhat reddish winged achene; the mature plant may reach more than 2.0 m in height and commonly reaches 1.0 m, with some rigid branches becoming spinescent; the mature leaves are 1.5 to 4.0 cm in length, somewhat fleshy, sessile, linear and entire. This is a widely scattered species of alkaline soils throughout New Mexico and the Southwest, occurring at 5,000 to 6,500 ft. (1,520 to 1,980 m) in elevation. (Please see Key VIII, couplet 51, page 232 for further description.)

**Greasewood**, *Sarcobatus vermiculatus* (Hooker) Torrey
Chenopodiaceae

GREASEWOOD
*Sarcobatus vermiculatus*

28.　　Flowers perfect, perianth present (although sometimes reduced), perfect and complete flowers occur on a single plant, often with showy white, red, pink, lavender, blue, purple or yellow petals; the fruits are samaras, nutlets or capsules; these shrubs seldom reach more than 60.0 cm in height ............................................................................. 29.

29.　Fruit a dry cluster of 2 or 3 winged samaras; flowers yellow to yellow orange, solitary or in axillary clusters of two, normally with sepals and petals in fives, the ovaries and styles are in threes; the inflorescence a cyme or corymb, the leaves are linear, 1.0 to 3.0 cm in length, and entire to slightly petioled, with 2 or 3 rather obscure tooth-like glands at the base of each leaf. Since this species may grow as a slender, twining and climbing vine or erect shrub it is described earlier in this key. (Please see couplet 8, page 93 for further description and illustration.)

**Slender Janusia**, *Janusia gracilis* A. Gray　　　　Malpighiaceae

29.　Fruit a capsule or nutlet, the nutlets may be borne in a bladder; flowers never yellow, ranging from white to blue, purple, lavender, pink, red; the inflorescence a raceme or a panicle; plants upright and never vine-like. ................................................................ 30.

30.　　Mature fruit a stalked capsule, 10.0 to 22.0 mm in length, the stipe as long or longer than the body; mature leaves filiform to narrowly linear and entire to 4.0 cm in length, the surface glabrous to puberulent; the flowers are borne in axillary pairs or loose panicles, the calyx is 5 lobed, short, but not ribbed, the corolla is tubular, with 4 unequal lobes to 1.0 cm in length and light blue to light purple in color. This slender, weak, perennial shrub is uncommon over the southern and southwestern portion of New Mexico at 3,500 to 5,000 ft. (1,070 to 1,520 m) in elevation. It occurs in sandy alluvial soils and among gravel and rocks often in overgrazed and disturbed soils. This suffrutescent species is considered herbaceous by several authors and could have been omitted from this publication. (Please see couplet 49. page 131 for further description.)

**Heath Carlowrightia**, *Carlowrightia linearifolia*
(Torrey) A. Gray　　　Acanthaceae

HEATH CARLOWRIGHTIA
*Carlowrightia linearifolia*

30.     Mature fruit a nutlet or a capsule, if a capsule, septicidal
        or with 4 valves, and not stalked; flowers in axillary spikes
        or loose to open panicles, the flower parts in fours or fives;
        the leaves are filiform to linear to somewhat lanceolate,
        2.0 to 4.0 cm in length, but never petioled ........................... 31.

31.    Stems typically square in cross section; the ovary distinctly di-
       vided into 4 lobes, with the commonly divided style arising deep
       in the center of the 4 lobes; fruit a nutlet. Lamiaceae ........................ 32.

31.    Stems typically round in cross section; the ovary 2-celled or 2-
       locular and many seeded at maturity; flowers with four fertile
       stamens and one staminode; fruit a septicidal capsule
       Scrophulariaceae, genus *Penstemon* ..................................................... 33.

32.    Calyx with many teeth, but never inflated or bladder-like
       when the plant is in fruit; stamens 2; mature leaves linear
       to oblong or slightly lanceolate and entire to 2.5 cm in
       length, the surface white tomentose; the flowers are ar-
       ranged in axillary spikes, the calyx with more than 12
       ribs, the corolla is bilabiate, pink to lavender in color, and
       it extends well beyond the calyx; the fruits are three to
       four, smooth, oblong nutlets formed in each locule of the
       flower. This robust shrub is uncommon, but locally abun-
       dant in gypsum and sandy soils at 3,600 to 5,500 ft. (1,100
       to 1,680 m) in elevation. Local alkaline soils appear to
       restrict its distribution.

       **Hoary Rosemarymint**, *Poliomintha incana* (Torrey)
                                                      A. Gray
                                                      Lamiaceae

       (Another introduced species of **Rosemary** is cultivated
       in lawns and gardens over the southern part of New
       Mexico. In some areas of the state this is *Poliomintha
       glabrescens* A. Gray, however there are no doubt other
       related introduced species.)

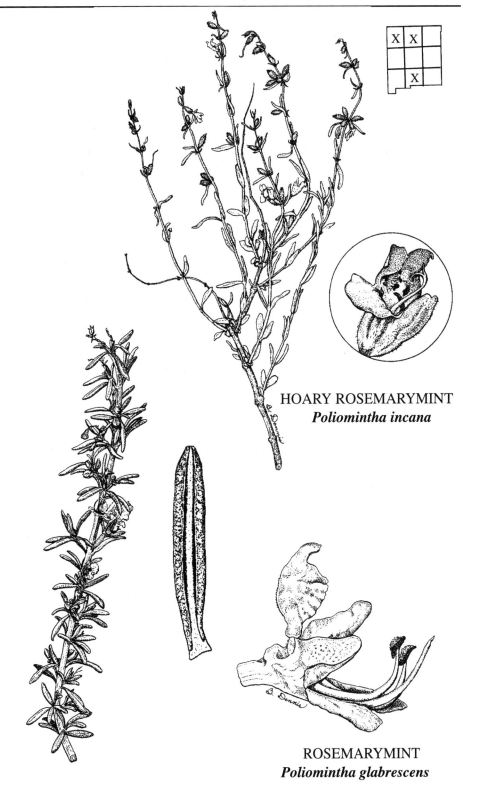

**HOARY ROSEMARYMINT**
*Poliomintha incana*

**ROSEMARYMINT**
*Poliomintha glabrescens*

32.   Calyx 2-lipped, inflated and bladderlike when the plant is in fruit; stamens 4; mature leaves are oblong to elliptic or lanceolate and entire to 3.0 cm in length, the surface is glabrous; flowers are borne in terminal racemes, the corolla is blue to purple with a white floral tube. This rare shrub of southern counties may reach 1.5 m in height. It is usually confined to foothills and arroyos in southern deserts at 3,000 to 3,500 ft. (910 to 1,070 m) in elevation.

**Bladder Sage** or **Paperbag-bush**, *Salazaria mexicana*
Torrey                Lamiaceae

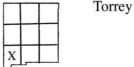

33.   Mature stems less than 30.0 cm in height, with the older stems woody to perennial, decumbent, spreading along the ground and sometimes rooting at the nodes; the corolla dark blue to purple, bilabiate, and to 2.5 cm in length; the flowers in the inflorescence are arranged on one side of the axis; the single staminode in the flower is bearded with bright yellow hairs; leaves are linear, averaging less than 2.5 mm in width. This species is relatively common in ponderosa pine and piñon-juniper forests over the northeastern quarter of New Mexico at 5,000 to 8,000 ft. (1,520 to 2,440 m) in elevation.

**Dwarf Penstemon** or **Crandall's Penstemon**, *Penstemon crandallii* A. Nelson      Scrophulariaceae

33.   Mature stems more than 30.0 cm in height, erect and rarely rooting at the nodes, becoming woody well above the soil level to 15.0 cm or more; the corolla ranging from bright red to scarlet to pink to purple to white, narrowly bilabiate to open, and from 1.5 to 3.3 cm in length ........................................................................... 34.

34.   Petals red to scarlet, strongly bilabiate with the tubular portion narrow, the upper lobes slightly extended; mature stems averaging 30.0 to 40.0 cm in height; inflorescence secund along the axis; staminode bearded with bright yellow hairs. This common species is confined to the mon-

tane coniferous forest in the southwestern corner of New Mexico at 5,500 to 8,000 ft. (1,680 to 2,440 m) in elevation.

**Pine-leaved Penstemon,** *Penstemon pinifolius* Greene

Scrophulariaceae

PINE-LEAVED PENSTEMON
*Penstemon pinifolius*

34. Petals white at the apex of the lobes while the tubular portion is light pink to purple, and the orifice is spreading and open; mature stems averaging 40.0 to 60.0 cm in height; inflorescence branching and the flowers widely spreading; staminode glabrous. This is a common species of the alluvial plains and sandy hills of the Rio Grande Valley and widely scattered throughout the State at 4,000 to 6,000 ft. (1,220 to 1,830 m) in elevation.

**Sand Penstemon**, *Penstemon ambiguus* Torrey

Scrophulariaceae

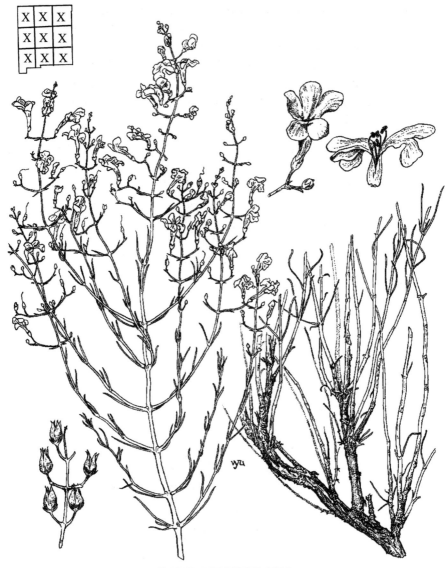

**SAND PENSTEMON**
*Penstemon ambiguus*

35.      Stems square in cross section; fruit a nutlet, 2 to 4 per flower; stamens 2 or 4 per flower; ovary with 1 ovule in each locule, appearing 4 lobed or 4 loculed ............................................................ 36.

35.      Stems round or terete in cross section; fruit a drupe, achene or capsule; stamen number variable; ovary inferior with 1 ovule, or with more than 1 ovule in each locule of a superior ovary and the fruit not separating into one-seeded nutlets ........................................ 38.

36.    Ovary distinctly 4 lobed and 4 loculed, the style arising from deeply in the center of the 4 lobes; corolla purple to bluish-white and zygomorphic; stamens 2; leaf margins entire; plants less than 50.0 cm in height. This woody species is relatively common throughout the southcentral portion of New Mexico at 4,500 to 6,500 ft. (1,370 to 1,980 m) in elevation.

**Canyon Sage**, *Salvia lycioides* A. Gray          Lamiaceae

CANYON SAGE
*Salvia lycioides*

36.    Ovary slightly grooved and 2 loculed, producing 2 nutlets, but not divided; the style arising at the top of the ovary; corolla white, slightly zygomorphic; stamens 4; leaf margins entire and slightly toothed to strongly toothed...... 37.

37.   Leaf blades ovate, 2.0 to 25.0 mm long and 2.0 to 18.0 mm in
      width, with crenate-serrate teeth and densely tomentose and glan-
      dular on the lower surface and glandular-strigose on the upper
      surface. This typical species of the southwest is frequently found
      in rocky canyons and on slopes and arroyo banks over the south-
      ern half of the State at 3,500 to 6,000 ft. (1,070 to 1,830 m) in
      elevation. (Please see couplet 55, page 138 for further descrip-
      tion.)

**High Mass** or **Wright's Lippia**, *Aloysia wrightii* Heller *ex* Abrams
Syns. *Lippia wrightii* A. Gray *ex* Torrey
Verbenaceae

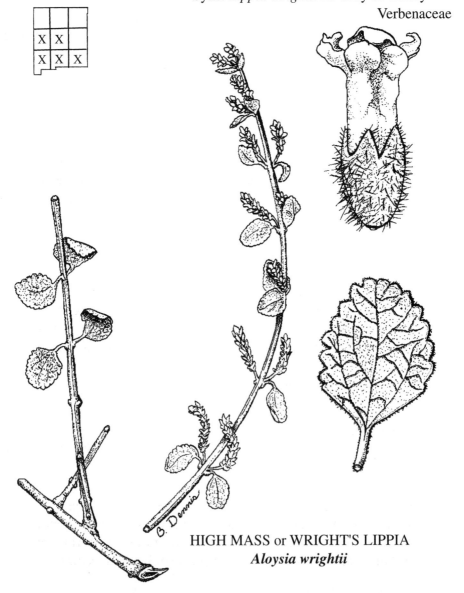

HIGH MASS or WRIGHT'S LIPPIA
*Aloysia wrightii*

37. Leaf blades oblong to elliptic to obovate, 3.0 to 29.0 mm in length and 2.0 to 8.0 mm in width, entire to slightly toothed, slightly pubescent on the upper surface to puberulent on the lower surface. This species, although less common, may be locally abundant and sometimes cultivated. It occurs in the southern third of New Mexico in dry rocky areas and at about the same elevations as the previous species.

**White Bush** or **Palo Amarillo**, *Aloysia gratissima*
(Gillies & Hooker) Troncoso
Syns. *Lippia lycioides* (Chamisseau) Steudel
*Aloysia lycioides* Chamisseau
Verbenaceae

38. Fruit a drupe with one stony seed or berry-like drupe with 2 or 3 seeds; the flowers very small, bluish to green or white, or tubular to 1.2 cm in length and white to pink ......... 39.

38. Fruit an achene or capsule or a pod-like capsule; the flowers small and in heads or borne separately, then showy and conspicuous, ranging in color from red to orange, or lavender to blue, or to yellow or white ................................. 41.

39. Corolla tubular, 10.0 to 13.0 mm in length, salverform, and pink to reddish-white in color; flowers solitary or in pairs, occasionally in several flowered racemes, quite fragrant; the fruit white, ellipsoid, and 8.0 to 10.0 mm in length. This low spreading shrub with drooping branches and shredding bark is relatively uncommon over the central and southern portions of New Mexico. It occurs at 5,000 to 8,000 ft. (1,520 to 2,440 m) in elevation, in dry, rocky foothills and canyons.

**Desert Snowberry**, *Symphoricarpos longiflorus* A. Gray
Caprifoliaceae

39. Corolla never tubular or salverform, may be absent, or if present white in color; inflorescences more elaborate in terminal panicles or lateral clusters, or separate in greenish to yellowish flowers lacking a corolla; fruit dark red to purple or black at maturity ......... 40.

DESERT SNOWBERRY
*Symphoricarpos longiflorus*

40.    Flowers small and inconspicuous, appearing before the
       leaves, borne in axillary, few flowered, clusters, or soli-
       tary at the nodes, and ranging from unisexual to perfect
       but never complete, the corolla absent and the sepals much
       reduced, the parts usually in fours but occasionally in fives;
       the fruit is a purple to black, ellipsoid drupe. This com-
       mon species is sometimes separated into two species based
       on habitat and growth habit. It is here retained as a single
       species, widely scattered over the State in dry to moist
       areas at 4,000 to 7,000 ft. (1,220 to 2,130 m) in elevation.
       (Please see couplet 57, page 138.)

**New Mexican Forestiera** or **New Mexico Olive**,
                *Forestiera pubescens* var. *pubescens* Nuttall
            Syns. *F. neomexicana* A. Gray                    Oleaceae

NEW MEXICO FORESTIERA or NEW MEXICO OLIVE
*Forestiera pubescens* var. *pubescens*

40.　Flowers perhaps small but not inconspicuous, appearing with the leaves, borne in terminal panicles, white in color, with 5 sepals and petals and complete; the fruit a black drupe with 3 stones. Our only collections of this rare, low growing shrub are from Guadalupe Canyon in Hidalgo County, growing in alluvial soil on the steep banks of an intermittent stream at 5,400 ft.(1,650 m) in elevation.

**Wright's Sageretia**, *Sageretia wrightii* S. Watson
Rhamnaceae

41.    Fruit an achene; inflorescence a head of 15 to 20 disk flowers, the heads solitary or in weak panicles; the individual flowers whitish but not showy; the mature leaves on the lower stem triangular, deltoid or hastate, toothed at the base, with some leaves reaching slightly more than 1.0 cm in width, but less than 1.8 cm in length. This sprawling, Chihuahuan Desert shrub might reach 1.0 m in height. It is rare in New Mexico appearing to be confined to the southwestern corner of the State. Our single collection is from the Tres Hermanas Mountains in Luna County at 4,700 ft. (1,430 m) in elevation.

**Coulter's Brickellia,** *Brickellia coulteri* A. Gray        Asteraceae

COULTER'S BRICKELLIA
*Brickellia coulteri*

41. Fruit a capsule with several locules or pod-like; inflorescence a terminal cyme, corymb, panicle, or in tight clusters in the axils of the leaves, but never in true heads; leaves variable but not triangular or hastate ............................................................................ 42.

    42. Flowers in dense, sessile or slightly stalked clusters in the axils of the upper leaves or terminal cymes, individual flowers small, less than 5.0 mm in length and crowded; corolla cream-colored to white or light blue; leaf margins crenate to crenate-dentate to entire or with a few teeth.......... 43.

    42. Flowers borne towards the apex of the stems or axillary, solitary or in few flowered panicles, cymes or corymbs and larger, more than 10.0 mm in length; corolla showy, red-orange, lavender, blue, yellow or white; leaf margins entire ............................................................................... 44.

43. Flower parts in fours and multiples of fours, and the flowers in dense, tomentose, ball-like clusters in the axils of the tomentose leaves; leaves averaging 1.5 to 3.0 cm in length, the margin crenate to dentate-crenate; the fruit is an oblong, pod-like capsule dehiscing at the apex. This rare, but highly aromatic shrub, to 3.0 m in height is described from the southeast corner of New Mexico, on dry, south-facing slopes at 3,000 to 6,000 ft. (910 to 1,830 m) in elevation.

    **Escobilla Butterfly Bush,** *Buddleja scordioides* Kunth
                                       Buddlejaceae or Loganiaceae

43. Flower parts in fives and multiples of fives, the flowers terminal or in axillary clusters, if axillary the inflorescence not ball-like and only minutely hairy; the leathery leaves, on rigid branches, average less than 1.5 cm in length, the margins are entire to only slightly toothed; the fruit is a 3-lobed capsule that has been identified as a drupe by some authors. This frequent shrub, to 2.0 m, occurs over the southern portion of the State, in dry mountains and canyons at 4,500 to 7,000 ft. (1,370 to 2,130 m) in elevation.

    **Desert Ceanothus** or **Desert Buckthorn**, *Ceanothus greggii*
                                                  A. Gray
                                                 Rhamnaceae

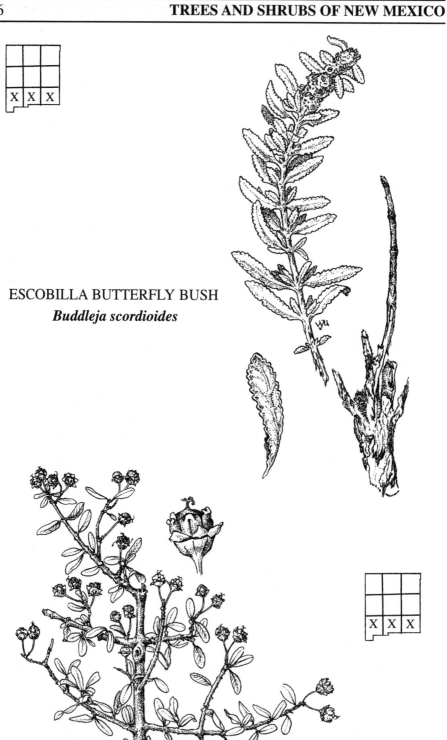

ESCOBILLA BUTTERFLY BUSH
*Buddleja scordioides*

DESERT CEANOTHUS or
DESERT BUCKTHORN
*Ceanothus greggii*

44. Flowers yellow; fruit a distinctly 2-lobed capsule; the oblong to oblanceolate or lanceolate leaves may be both opposite and alternate on a single plant, the alternate leaves above and the opposite leaves below; appearing as suffrutescent herbs from a woody base and only becoming slightly woody with age ................................................. 45.

44. Flowers white, red-orange, blue or lavender; fruit a capsule, but not distinctly 2-lobed, if 2-celled this will be obscure externally; the ovate to elliptical to oblanceolate or lanceolate leaves decidedly opposite; generally woody or sub-shrubs that become woody throughout or woody over the lower portion of the plant at maturity ..................... 46.

45. Corolla campanulate to rotate, the tube less than 1.0 cm in length, the lobes of the petals spreading from near the middle of the corolla tube; the leaves are usually alternate above and opposite below. The scabrous condition referred to in the specific name cannot be counted on in the several varieties described in the literature. This common species is widely scattered over New Mexico on dry rocky mesas, desert habitats and oak woodlands at 3,000 to 7,000 ft. (910 to 2,130 m) in elevation. (Please see couplet 211, Key VIII, page 396, for further description.)

**Rough Menodora**, *Menodora scabra* A. Gray          Oleaceae

45. Corolla salverform, the tube more than 2.0 cm in length, the lobes of the petals spreading only at the apex of the floral tube; the leaves are usually opposite throughout. This rare or only locally abundant species appears to be confined to dry hillsides in southeastern New Mexico at 4,500 to 6,500 ft. (1,370 to 1,980 m) in elevation.

**Showy Menodora**, *Menodora longiflora* A. Gray          Oleaceae

46. Petals white to an occasional off-white pink, separate, arising from a floral cup or hypanthium; stamens many; the bark shredding in mature shrubs; the leaf shape ovate, elliptic, oblong to oval; the plant reaching a height of 1.5 m. This common species occurs in rocky, well-drained

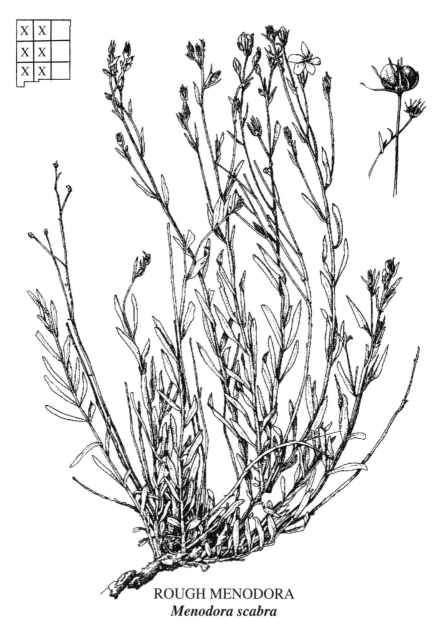

ROUGH MENODORA
*Menodora scabra*

soils throughout the State at 7,000 to 9,500 ft. (2,130 to 2,900 m) in elevation. This species and several closely related varieties are commonly cultivated. The genus *Philadelphus* is confusing in the western states and needs serious taxonomic work.

**Little Leaf Mockorange**, *Philadelphus microphyllus*
A. Gray                    Hydrangeaceae

LITTLE LEAF MOCKORANGE
*Philadelphus microphyllus*

46.     Petals showy red to purple-red or orange-red, or lavender
        to light blue or white, fused and forming a tube; floral
        parts not forming a hypanthium; stamens 2 or 4; these
        shrubs with continuous bark; the leaf shape lanceolate,
        ovate-lanceolate, oblanceolate, elliptic or obovate ............... 47.

47.     Flowers solitary and axillary, red to purple-orange to orange, sometimes white; stamens 2; shrub freely branching to 1.0 m in height. This attractive species is limited to dry rocky mesas, canyons and arroyos in the southwest corner of New Mexico at 4,000 to 5,500 ft. (1,220 to 1,680 m) in elevation. (Please see further descriptions at couplets 53 and 71 on pages 136 and 153.)

**Desert Honeysuckle**, *Anisacanthus thurberi* (Torrey)      Acanthaceae

DESERT HONEYSUCKLE
*Anisacanthus thurberi*

47.     Flowers in loose terminal panicles, purple, lavender to light blue or rarely white; stamens 4; shrub low, branches gray to white at maturity, and reaching only 0.5 m in height. Found only in the southeastern corner of New Mexico, this relatively rare shrub occurs at 4,000 to 5,000 ft. (1,220 to 1,520 m) in elevation.

**Parry Ruellia**, *Ruellia parryi* A. Gray                          Acanthaceae

PARRY RUELLIA
*Ruellia parryi*

48.  Mature leaves filiform to narrowly linear, averaging less than 2.0 mm in width; both alternate and opposite leaves may be present on the same plant, with some leaves lobed, and averaging more than 4.0 cm in length............................ 49.

48.  Mature leaves not filiform, but oblong, oblanceolate to more broadly linear, averaging  more than 4.0 mm in width; chiefly opposite or only occasionally alternate leaves present, leaves never lobed, and averaging more than 4.0 cm in length ........................................... 51.

49.  Flowers not in heads, individual flowers borne in axillary pairs or loose panicles on short pedicels; the fruit a stalked capsule, 10.0 to 22.0 mm in length. This slender, weak, perennial shrub is uncommon over southern and southwestern New Mexico at 3,500 to 5,000 ft. (1,070 to 1,520 m) in elevation. (Please see description at couplet 30, page 112 and illustration on page113.)

**Heath Carlowrightia**, *Carlowrightia linearifolia (*Torrey*)*
A. Gray          Acanthaceae

49.    Flowers several in heads, each cluster of flowers surrounded or
       subtended by an involucre of bracts; corolla 5 parted, ovary infe-
       rior; the fruit an achene. Asteraceae ................................................. 50.

    50.    Heads solitary on long naked peduncles; the ray flowers
           numbering 10 to 16 and yellow; the involucral bracts in 3
           series. This common shrub of rocky and often gypsum
           soils, may reach more than 1.0 m in height. It occurs over
           southern and southeastern New Mexico at 3,200 to 6,200
           ft. (980 to 1,890 m) in elevation. (Please see Key VIII,
           couplet 117, page 199 and Key IX, page 459 for further
           description.)

           **Skeletonleaf Goldeneye**, *Viguiera stenoloba* Blake

                                                               Asteraceae

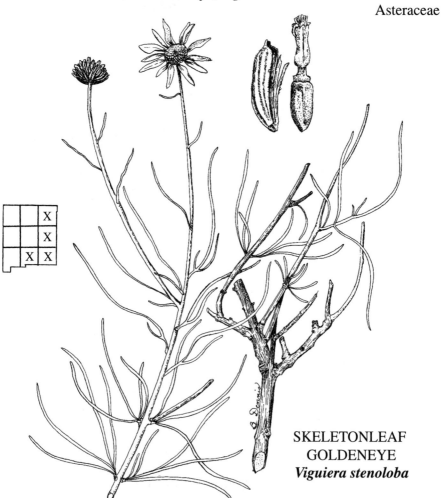

SKELETONLEAF
GOLDENEYE
*Viguiera stenoloba*

50.  Heads borne in dense, narrow or pyramidal panicles and sessile; ray flowers absent, the corolla on the disk flowers white to light pink; the involucral bracts seriate, imbricate and pale green. This low growing, rare shrub appears to be confined to the dry valleys in the southwestern corner of New Mexico at 4,000 to 6,000 ft. (1,220 to 1,830 m) in elevation.

**Scaly Brickellia**, *Brickellia squamulosa* A. Gray   Asteraceae

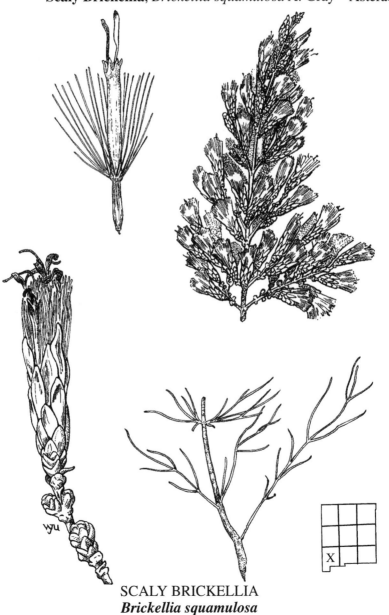

SCALY BRICKELLIA
*Brickellia squamulosa*

51.    Flowers in heads, these numbering 20 to 28 flowers per head,
       these heads in panicles; the narrowly oblong to linear leaves veiny,
       thus the common and specific names; the younger stems gray-
       tomentose, the older stems dark brown and becoming glabrous
       with age, at maturity reaching to 1.0 m in height, the stems woody
       near the base; the fruit is an achene with approximately 10 ribs.
       This rare or only locally abundant species appears to be confined
       to southern and southwestern New Mexico at 4,000 to 5,500 ft.
       (1,220 to 1,680 m) in elevation.

**Veiny Bricklebush**, *Brickellia venosa* (Wooton & Standley)
                                                    B. L. Robinson

                                                        Asteraceae

VEINY BRICKELLIA
*Brickellia venosa*

51.     Flowers not in heads, the individual flowers in short axillary racemes, dioecious, petals lacking, hypanthium well developed, the staminate flowers often clustered on short spurs and the pistillate flowers on stout pedicels; the fruit is a 1-seeded drupe, borne separately or in clusters, becoming bright red at maturity; the opposite leaves are covered with silvery, peltate scales and the lateral veins are indistinct. The twigs are often thorny. This rare species may grow to 6.0 m, becoming a large shrub or small tree. It occurs in valleys, along the banks of streams or on eroded dry hillsides in the northwestern part of New Mexico at 4,500 to 6,000 ft. (1,370 to 1,830 m) in elevation. The tart, red fruit of the **Buffaloberry** was used for food and for medicinal purposes by Native Americans of the northern plains. The Cheyenne collected the fruits after the first freeze, which was thought to sweeten them for eating. The dried, ground berries seem to have therapeutic value in treating amoebic dysentery and malaria. (Please see further description on page 154.)

**Silver Buffaloberry**, *Shepherdia argentea* (Pursh) Nuttall

Elaeagnaceae

SILVER BUFFALOBERRY
*Shepherdia argentea*

52.      Mature leaves averaging less than 4.0 cm in length ............. 53.


52.      Mature leaves averaging more than 4.0 cm in length............ 63.


53.      Fruit a capsule, longitudinally dehiscent, and 2-celled; the flow-
         ers bright red to orange-red, borne solitary and axillary, with 2
         stamens; the showy corolla 3.0 to 5.0 cm in length, bilabiate, 4
         lobed and zygomorphic; the leaves lanceolate to elliptic. This
         attractive species, growing to 2.5 m in height, is limited to dry
         rocky mesas, canyons and arroyos in the southwest corner of New
         Mexico at 4,000 to 5,000 ft. (1,220 to 1,520 m) in elevation.
         (Please see couplet 47, page 130 and couplet 71, page 152 for
         further description and illustration.)

         **Desert Honeysuckle**, *Anisacanthus thurberi* (Torrey) A. Gray
                                                          Acanthaceae


53.      Fruit a drupe or berry, usually 1 or 2 seeded or a nutlet; the flow-
         ers white, yellow, lavender, light green to pink, but never bright
         red or orange; the corolla less than 2.0 cm in length, and ranging
         from actinomorphic to zygomorphic; the leaves variable ................ 54.


         54.      Fruit a nutlet, producing 2 or 4 per flower; flowers per-
                  fect, stamens 2 or 4 per flower; ovary with 1 ovule in
                  each locule appearing 4 lobed or 4 loculed, 1 or 2 ovules
                  sometimes aborted; stems square in cross-section ................ 55.


         54.      Fruit a drupe, berry or sometimes berry-like with 1 or 2
                  seeds; flowers perfect or plants dioecious in *Garrya* and
                  *Forestiera,* stamens variable in number, but usually 4 or
                  more; stems not square in cross-section, the exception
                  again in *Garrya* where the young tips of branches may be
                  square, becoming terete with age ......................................... 56.

55.    Ovary distinctly 4 lobed and 4 loculed, producing 4 nutlets with 1 occasionally aborted, the style arising from deep in the center of the 4 lobes; corolla blue and zygomorphic; stamens 2; leaves 2.0 to 5.5 cm in length, the petiole reaching to 2.0 cm in length, and white canescent on the lower surface and green above. This common shrub may reach more than 1.0 m in height. It is frequently found on dry mesas and hillsides at 3,500 to 7,000 ft. (1,070 to 2,130 m) in elevation over the southern and southeastern portion of New Mexico. The classic traditional use of *Salvia pinguifolia* was to wean infants from breastfeeding. A cool tea made from the plant in flower was drunk and the breasts were also washed with the tea. (Please see couplet 67, page 150 for further description.)

**Blue Sage** or **Shrubby Salvia**, *Salvia pinguifolia* (Fernald) Wooton & Standley

Lamiaceae

BLUE SAGE or
SHRUBBY SALVIA
*Salvia pinguifolia*

55.     Ovary slightly grooved with 2 locules, producing 2 nutlets, the style arising at the top of the ovary; corolla white and only slightly zygomorphic; stamens 4; leaves 0.3 to 1.5 cm in length, the petiole reaching to only 0.5 cm or the leaves sessile, and yellow-green to green on the upper surface and tomentose on the lower surface. This typical species of the southwest may grow to 2.0 m in height, and is frequently found in rocky canyons and on slopes and arroyo banks over the southern half of New Mexico at 3,500 to 6,000 ft. (1,070 to 1,830 m) in elevation. (Please see couplet 37, page 120 for further description and illustration.)

**High Mass** or **Wright's Lippia**, *Aloysia wrightii* Heller *ex* Abrams
Syns. *Lippia wrightii* A. Gray *ex* Torrey
Verbenaceae

56.     Flowers reduced in size, green and obscure, unisexual or bisexual, if bisexual, then one sex reduced, poorly developed and not functional, the corolla absent or much reduced; the mature fruit a drupe, dark in color maturing from purple to black; the inflorescence a small cluster of flowers at the nodes, borne before the leaves are obvious, or pendulous catkins borne in the axils of leathery leaves; bark of older twigs not noticeably peeling ............................ 57.

56.     Flowers perfect on each plant, pink to red, yellow or white, larger in size, and obvious if present, the corolla well developed and tubular or funnelform; the mature fruit a berry-like drupe, light gray, white, pink, orange to yellow or red in color; inflorescence a solitary flower, paired or in small clusters of flowers, sometimes appearing as a small spike or limited raceme; bark on older twigs often peeling ............................................................................ 60.

57.     Flowers borne in axillary, few flowered, clusters or solitary at the nodes usually before the leaves develop; individual flowers ranging from unisexual to perfect, but never complete, the corolla absent and the sepals reduced or absent; the fruit is a purple to black, ellipsoid drupe; the twigs are terete and light gray at maturity. This erect shrub, which may occasionally become a small tree, ranges in height from 1.0 to 3.0 m at maturity. (Please see couplet 40, page 122 and illustration, page 123.)

**New Mexican Forestiera** or **New Mexico Olive**,
*Forestiera pubescens* var. *pubescens* Nuttall
Syns. *F. neomexicana* A. Gray          Oleaceae

57.   Flowers borne on pendulous catkins in the axils of leathery leaves or triangular bracts, at or near the tips of the new branches; the plants evergreen, dioecious; individual flowers small, unisexual; petals 4 or 5 or absent, the sepals 4 or 5 or absent; the fruit is a 1 or 2 seeded berry-like drupe; petioles of opposite leaves connate; the twigs 4-angled, especially when young, often becoming terete and black, dark gray to dark brown with age ............................... 58.

58.   Mature leaves markedly undulate, densely covered with woolly, crinkly hairs, especially the lower surface, elliptic, 3.0 to 6.0 cm in length; the fruit 4.0 to 8.0 mm in diameter and dark blue in color. This species may reach a height of 2.5 m. It appears to be confined to the southeastern corner of New Mexico and Trans-Pecos Texas at 4,500 to 8,000 ft. (1,370 to 2,440 m) in elevation. The genus *Garrya* should be widely collected throughout New Mexico and the Southwest.

**Eggleaf Silktassel**, *Garrya ovata* ssp. *goldmanii*
(Wooton & Standley) Dahling
Garryaceae

58.   Mature leaves not undulate, the margins entire; the plants glabrous to pubescent, the catkins silky pubescent in *Garrya flavescens*. The following two species are more widely scattered over southern New Mexico, but are more common in the southwestern corner and into Arizona ................. 59.

59.   Bracts on the inflorescences leaf-like and not triangular, flowers in the inflorescence loose and open; fruit a globose, glabrous, dark blue drupe; mature leaves averaging less than 5.0 cm in length, the margin often denticulate with a callous appearance, glabrous to slightly pubescent on the lower surface. This evergreen shrub may reach a height of 3.0 m in southern New Mexico. It occurs over dry slopes and in canyons at 4,000 to 7,500 ft. (1,220 to 2,300 m) in elevation. There are reports of small quantities of rubber being extracted from this plant.

**Wright Silktassel**, *Garrya wrightii* Torrey ·            Garryaceae

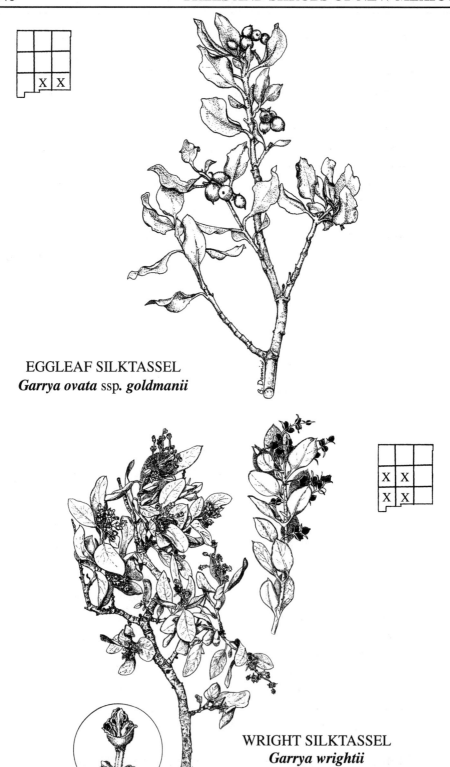

EGGLEAF SILKTASSEL
*Garrya ovata* ssp. *goldmanii*

WRIGHT SILKTASSEL
*Garrya wrightii*

59.  Bracts on the inflorescences triangular and not leaf-like, flowers
     in the inflorescence sessile and dense; fruit an ellipsoid to ovoid,
     densely sericeous, appearing whitish, drupe; mature leaves aver-
     aging more than 5.0 cm in length, the margin entire and not copi-
     ously denticulate, abundantly tomentose on the lower surface.
     Seldom reaching 2.0 m in height, the common name describes
     the silky catkins that droop from the branches. This species is
     limited to canyons and hillsides at 3,500 to 7,000 ft. (1,070 to
     2,130 m) in elevation. The bitter taste of the leaves provides a
     sour, quinine-like flavor.

**Yellow Silktassel** or **Quinine Bush**, *Garrya flavescens* S. Watson

Garryaceae

YELLOW SILKTASSEL
or QUININE BUSH
*Garrya flavescens*

60.  Corolla campanulate, the lobes of the corolla equalling
     or longer than the corolla tube, the corolla 5.0 to 9.0 mm
     in length, the tube not swollen at the base ............................. 61.

60.  Corolla salverform, tubular or funnelform, the lobes of
     the corolla one-third or less the length of the corolla tube,
     the corolla 8.0 to 15.0 mm in length, the tube not swollen
     at the base ........................................................................ 62.

61.  Mature leaves 1.0 to 3.0 cm in length, the petioles 2.0 to 3.0 mm
     in length; the corolla tube 5.0 to 6.0 mm in length and pink in
     color; the style and stamens shorter than or only equalling the
     corolla and not extending beyond the corolla; the fruit white, borne
     solitary or in pairs in the axils of the upper leaves. This is an
     infrequent species, growing to 1.0 m in the foothills, canyons
     and on rocky slopes through central and northern New Mexico at
     5,500 to 7,800 ft. (1,680 to 2,380 m) in elevation.

**White Snowberry,** *Symphoricarpos albus* (L.) S. F. Blake

Caprifoliaceae

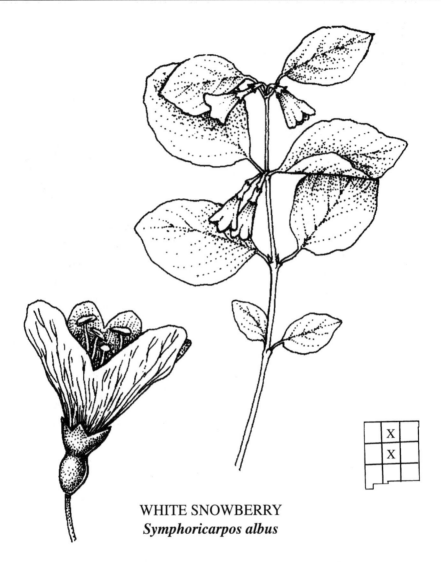

WHITE SNOWBERRY
*Symphoricarpos albus*

61.    Mature leaves 3.0 to 10.0 cm in length, the petioles 3.0 to 10.0 mm in length; the corolla tube 6.0 to 9.0 mm in length and pink to white in color; style and stamens exserted and extending beyond the corolla; fruit greenish-white, usually borne in crowded, spike-like clusters. This is a more common species growing to 1.5 m in height. It occurs over a wide range of habitats, from dry rocky soils on the plains and mesas to wet areas in the valleys at 4,500 to 8,000 ft. (1,370 to 2,440 m) in elevation. (Please see couplet 77, page 155 for further description.)

**Western Snowberry,** *Symphoricarpos occidentalis* Hooker
Caprifoliaceae

WESTERN SNOWBERRY
*Symphoricarpos occidentalis*

62.     Corolla yellow, 2-lipped and slightly zygomorphic, the
        tube slightly swollen at the base; flowers borne in pairs;
        fruit a berry, orange to yellow or red in color. This rare
        shrub, which may grow to 1.5 m in height, appears to be
        confined to dry open woods on the western edge of New
        Mexico at 7,000 to 10,000 ft. (2,130 to 3,050 m) in eleva-
        tion.

**Utah Fly Honeysuckle**, *Lonicera utahensis* S. Watson

Caprifoliaceae

UTAH FLY HONEYSUCKLE
*Lonicera utahensis*

62. Corolla white to pink, radially symmetrical, the tube not swollen at the base; flowers borne separately or in pairs; fruit a berry-like drupe, white in color. This common shrub, which grows to 1.0 m in height, is common over the western and northern parts of New Mexico at 6,000 to 10,000 ft. (1,830 to 3,050 m) in elevation. Two morphologically and geographically extremely close species will key to this point. We probably make a serious mistake in attempting to separate them. A rather weak separation follows.

62 A. Young twigs pubescent, with short hairs, sometimes only puberulent; the corolla densely hairy inside, averaging 9.0 to 11.0 mm in length.

**Roundleaf Snowberry,** *Symphoricarpos rotundifolius*
A. Gray         Caprifoliaceae

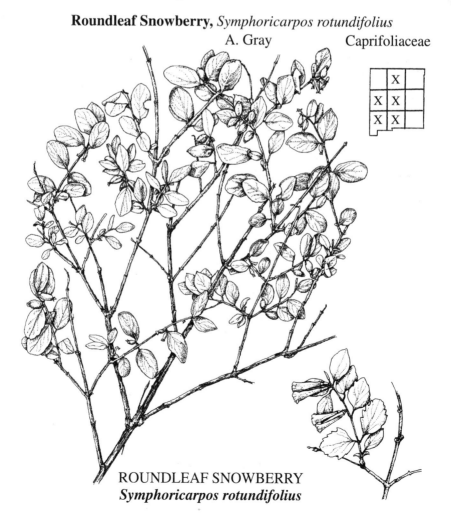

ROUNDLEAF SNOWBERRY
*Symphoricarpos rotundifolius*

62 B.  Young twigs glabrous; the corolla only slightly hairy to glabrous inside, averaging 10.0 to 15.0 mm in length.

**Mountain Snowberry,** *Symphoricarpos oreophilus*
A. Gray                    Caprifoliaceae

63.    Leaf margins mostly serrate, crenate or dentate ................................. 64.

63.    Leaf margins mostly entire, occasionally with only a few leaves slighty undulate or weakly serrate ........................................................ 69.

64.    Flowers several, averaging about 10 per head, each cluster of flowers surrounded or subtended by an involucre of often purple tinged bracts, the heads arranged in a panicle; flowers 5 parted, pale yellow, the ovary inferior; fruit an achene; stems woody at the base, the wood extending up the stems, plants reaching 50.0 cm in height. The range for this uncommon and poorly defined species has not been well established, but it appears to be more common at 5,000 to 7,000 ft. (1,520 to 2,130 m) in elevation in the southern and southwestern part of New Mexico.

**Wooton Brickellia,** *Brickellia lemmonii* var. *wootonii*
(Greene) B. L. Robinson      Asteraceae

64.    Flowers solitary, in small clusters, axillary, in cymes or in spikes, if in heads then not surrounded by an involucre of bracts; corolla parts in 4's or 5's, or multiples of 5's; fruit a capsule, nutlet, drupe or berry-like, but never an achene ................................................................................. 65.

65.    Stems terete in cross-section; fruit a capsule; flowers actinomorphic ........................................................................................... 66.

65.    Stems square or 4-angled in cross-section; fruit a drupe or nutlet; flowers zygomorphic ................................................................. 67.

WOOTON BRICKELLIA
*Brickellia lemmonii* var. *wootonii*

66.    Shrubs with hollow or chambered pith, not continuous between the nodes; flowers yellow, parts in 2's or 4's, the perianth deeply four-lobed; fruit a capsule. Two species are widely cultivated in lawns and gardens throughout New Mexico, *Forsythia viridissima* Lindley with chambered pith and *Forsythia suspensa* (Thunberg) Vahl with hollow pith.

**Forsythia** or **Golden Bell**, *Forsythia* Vahl          Oleaceae

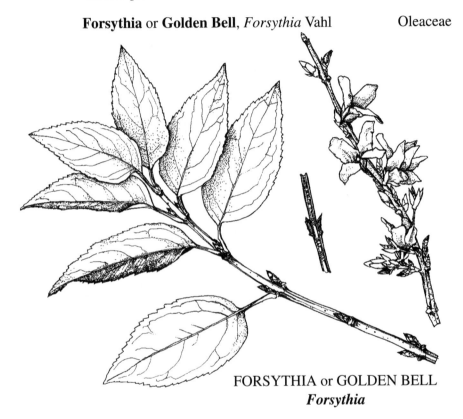

FORSYTHIA or GOLDEN BELL
*Forsythia*

66.    Shrubs with continuous or spongy pith between the nodes, internodes not chambered or hollow, the reddish brown bark peeling; the leaves green above and whitish-tomentose below; the inflorescence is a cyme, appearing white and hairy; flowers with 5 sepals, 5 white petals, averaging 10 stamens and the ovary half inferior; the fruit a capsule. This relatively common shrub may reach 2.0 m in height in the canyons of the mountainous regions of New Mexico at 6,500 to 9,500 ft. (1,980 to 2,900 m) in elevation.

**Waxflower**, *Jamesia americana* Torrey & A. Gray
                                    Hydrangeaceae

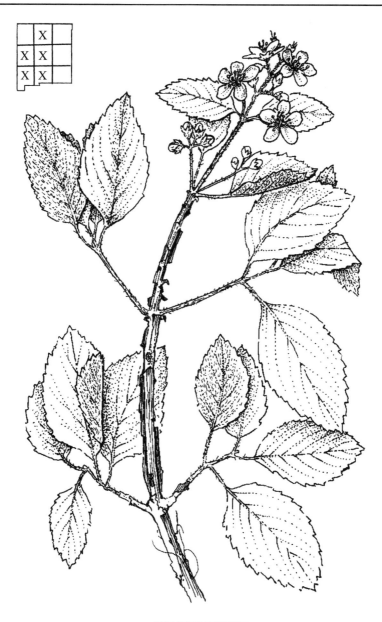

WAXFLOWER
*Jamesia americana*

Several cultivated species of the genus *Viburnum* (also a
common name) may key to this point. This common taxon
of the southeastern quarter of the United States is grown
in lawns and gardens in our area, however it does require
moisture above the level normally received in the Southwest.

67.     Ovary distinctly 4 lobed and 4 loculed, producing 4 nutlets in
        fruit, with 1 occasionally aborted, the style arising from deep in
        the center of the 4 lobes; corolla blue and zygomorphic; stamens
        2; leaves 2.0 to 5.5 cm in length, white canescent on the lower
        surface and green above. This common shrub may reach more
        than 1.0 m in height. It is frequently found on dry mesas and
        hillsides at 3,500 to 7,000 ft. (1,070 to 2,130 m) in elevation over
        the southern and southeastern portion of New Mexico. (Please
        see couplet 55, page 137 for further description and illustration .)

        **Blue Sage** or **Shrubby Salvia**, *Salvia pinguifolia* (Fernald)
                                    Wooton & Standley          Lamiaceae

67.     Ovary slightly grooved with 2 locules, producing 2 nutlets in
        fruit, the style arising at the top of the ovary; corolla ranging in
        color from red to yellow or orange, if white then the center yel-
        low and slightly zygomorphic; stamens 4 and didynamous. Al-
        though the following two members of the Verbenaceae are con-
        sidered native to New Mexico they, and several closely related
        varieties that are common to Mexico, are also commonly culti-
        vated throughout the southern part of the State ................................. 68.

68.     Fruit with a thin, dry, dark exocarp; flowers borne in the
        leaf axils, usually 4 to 6 per node; calyx deeply 2 to 5
        toothed or lobed; corolla tube white or yellow with a yel-
        low center; leaf blades commonly 1.5 to 6.5 cm in length
        and 0.5 to 3.0 cm in width, the margin coarsely crenate.
        This pubescent and aromatic shrub, commonly growing
        to less than 3.0 m, has been reported to grow to 6.0 m in
        height. It is rare in the State, and confined to the southern
        counties at less than 5,500 ft. (1,680 m) in elevation.

        **Red Brush**, *Lippia graveolens* Humboldt, Bonpland,
                                    Kunth                    Verbenaceae

68.    Fruit with a fleshy black to dark blue exocarp, seldom
       becoming dry; flowers borne in dense heads on cylindric
       extensions of the main stem; calyx obscurely toothed or
       lobed; corolla showy, yellow to orange or red; leaf blades
       commonly 3.0 to 5.0 cm in length and 2.0 to 4.0 cm in
       width, the margin coarsely serrate. This rare shrub, which
       may grow to 2.0 m in height, and may or may not be
       armed with prickles, has a pungent scent. It occurs in sandy
       and gravelly soils over the very southern portion of the
       State at less than 6,000 ft. (1,830 m) in elevation.

**Texas Lantana** or **Calico Bush**, *Lantana urticoides* Hayek
Syns. *L. horrida* var. *latibracteata* Moldenke
Verbenaceae

       Another related species may also key to this point. The
       **Desert Lantana**, *Lantana achyranthifolia* Desfontaines
       (Syns. *L. macropoda* Torrey), overlaps the range of the
       previous species and is characterized by pink to lavender
       flowers. However, it is uncommon in New Mexico.

69.    Fruit a samara or capsule; flower color red-orange, red, lavender
       and showy, or small, greenish, then the perianth obscure, parts in
       multiples of 2 or 4; flowers borne singly or in panicles ................... 70.

69.    Fruit a drupe, berry or berry-like drupe; flower color white, pink,
       yellow, lavender or small and greenish, parts in multiples of 4 or
       5; the inflorescence a pendulous catkin, spike, cyme, raceme, or
       in axillary pairs ........................................................................... 72.

70.    Fruit a samara, 15.0 to 25.0 mm in length and completely
       winged, often notched at the base; leaf shape of simple
       leaves orbicular or ovate, the margin entire to slightly
       crenate-sinuate, some leaves may be compound and tri-
       foliate. Normally a shrub to 2.5 m, this species may be-
       come tree-like with age to 6.0 m. It commonly occurs in
       moist canyons and adjacent to streams in the western and
       northwestern counties of New Mexico at 4,400 to 6,000
       ft. (1,340 to1,830 m) in elevation. (Please see Key VII,
       couplet 17, page 175, and pages 182-83 for further de-
       scription and illustration.)

**Singleleaf Ash** or **Colorado Ash**, *Fraxinus anomala*
Torrey *ex* S. Watson
Oleaceae

70.    Fruit a 2-celled capsule; leaf shape either lanceolate to
       oblong or ovate with a cordate or subcordate base; flower
       color red-orange to red or lavender to white ........................ 71.

71.    Leaves lanceolate to oblong or ovate-lanceolate, 1.0 to 6.0 cm in
       length; flowers solitary and axillary, red to red-orange or occa-
       sionally white; stamens 2; freely branching shrub to 1.0 m in
       height. This attractive species is limited to dry rocky mesas, can-
       yons and arroyos in the southwest corner of New Mexico at 4,000
       to 5,500 ft. (1,220 to 1,680 m) in elevation. (Please see couplet
       47, page 130 and couplet 53, page 136 for further descriptions
       and illustration.)

**Desert Honeysuckle**, *Anisacanthus thurberi* (Torrey) A. Gray
Acanthaceae

71.    Leaves ovate with a cordate or subcordate base, 5.0 to 10.0 cm in
       length; flowers in dense panicles, 1.0 to 2.0 dm in length, com-
       monly bright lavender in color, but in some varieties white; sta-
       mens 2, occasionally 4. If not controlled this common Eurasian
       shrub will reach a height of more than 2.0 m. It has been intro-
       duced to lawns and gardens throughout most of North America
       for many years.

**Lilac**, *Syringa vulgaris* L.                                    Oleaceae

LILAC
*Syringa vulgaris*

72.     Plants dioecious, the flowers imperfect, the staminate and pistillate flowers borne on different plants of the same species; flowers often obscure and not obvious; petals often reduced and not showy or absent ................................. 73.

72.     Plants bearing perfect flowers, the stamens and pistils borne in each flower; flowers obvious if in season; petals present and often showy ....................................................... 76.

73.   Inflorescence a spike, often pendulous or forming a catkin; young branchlets 4-angled; petioles of opposite leaves connate at the base; fruit a drupe, purplish-black to black in color ......................... 74.

73.   Inflorescence an axillary raceme of few to several, often paired, flowers; young branchlets terete; petioles of opposite leaves not connate; fruit a berry-like drupe, red or yellow in color .................. 75.

74.    Bracts on the inflorescence leaf-like and not triangular, flowers in the inflorescence loose and open; fruit a globose, glabrous, dark blue drupe; mature leaves averaging 3.0 to 5.0 cm in length. This evergreen shrub may reach a height of 3.0 m in southern New Mexico. (Please see couplet 59, page 139 for further description and illustration, page 140.)

**Wright Silktassel**, *Garrya wrightii* Torrey          Garryaceae

74.    Bracts of the inflorescence triangular and not leaf-like, flowers in the inflorescence sessile and dense; fruit an ellipsoid to ovoid, densely sericeous, whitish drupe; mature leaves averaging 3.0 to 5.0 cm in length. This species seldom reaches 2.0 m in height and appears to be confined to the southeastern corner of New Mexico. (Please see couplet 59, page 141 for further description and illustration.)

**Yellow Silktassel** or **Quinine Bush**, *Garrya flavescens*
S. Watson     Garryaceae

75.  Leaves silvery on both surfaces, narrowly elliptic to oblong, 2.0 to 6.0 cm in length and 0.6 to 1.4 cm in width; twigs often becoming spiny; berries silvery in color. This uncommon shrub may reach to 6.0 m in New Mexico, becoming almost a small tree. It occurs along drainage ditches and streams at 4,500 to 6,000 ft. (1,370 to 1,830 m) in elevation in the northwestern counties. (Please see couplet 51, page 135 for further description and illustration .)

**Silverberry** or **Silver Buffaloberry,** *Shepherdia argentea*
(Pursh) Nuttall     Elaeagnaceae

75.  Leaves green on the upper surface and rusty, scurfy and scaly below, oval to ovate and elliptic, 1.75 to 6.0 cm in length and 1.0 to 2.5 cm in width; twigs never or rarely becoming spiny; berries red or orange-red in color. This infrequent shrub seldom reaches 2.0 m in height over northcentral New Mexico. It occurs in moist areas along streams and on damp, rocky slopes in pine forests at 8,000 to 9,800 ft. (2,440 to 3,000 m) in elevation.

**Buffaloberry,** *Shepherdia canadensis* (L.) Nuttall          Elaeagnaceae

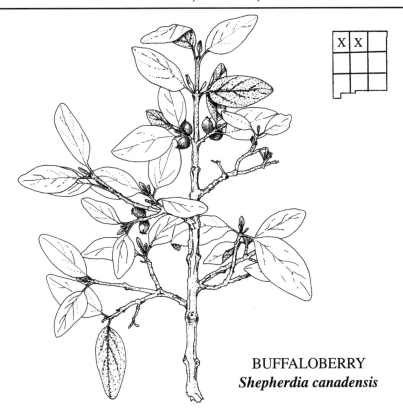

BUFFALOBERRY
*Shepherdia canadensis*

76.    Bark of older branches and some younger stems loose,
       peeling in long shreddy pieces; flowers mostly 5-merous,
       occasionally 4-merous; corolla lavender, yellow or white
       to pink in color; fruit a berry-like drupe or berry ................. 77.

76.    Bark of older branches and most younger stems firm and
       smooth, not peeling or shredding; flowers 4-merous; co-
       rolla white or cream colored; fruit a drupe ........................... 79.

77.  Corolla regular, radially symmetrical, pink to white in color, tube
     6.0 to 9.0 mm in length; stamens exserted and extending beyond
     the corolla; fruit greenish-white, usually borne in crowded, spike-
     like clusters; leaves 3.0 to 10.0 cm in length. This is a more com-
     mon species growing to 1.5 m in height. It occurs over a wide
     range of habitats, from dry rocky soils on the plains and mesas to
     wet areas in the valleys at 4,500 to 8,000 ft. (1,370 to 2,440 m) in
     elevation. (Please see couplet 61, page 142 for further descrip-
     tion and illustration, page 143.)

**Western Snowberry,** *Symphoricarpos occidentalis* Hooker
                                                    Caprifoliaceae

77.      Corolla somewhat irregular, two-lipped, or bilaterally symmetrical, yellow in the native species, and in some cultivated species lavender, white or pink in color; fruit black, purplish-black, red or red-orange in color or not developing in some cultivated species ............................................................................................. 78.

     78.      Fruit black or purplish-black and often shiny; corolla yellow, sometimes tinged with red, corolla lobes half as long as the tube; flowers on long peduncles, to 15.0 mm or more in length, borne singly or in 2's or 3's in the axils of the leaves; mature leaves 5.0 to 15.0 cm in length. This native shrub to 2.0 m in height is sometimes cultivated. It is frequently found at 7,500 to 10,500 ft. (2,300 to 3,200 m) in elevation, in moist, calcareous soils in the mountainous regions of New Mexico.

**Bush Honeysuckle** or **Inkberry**, *Lonicera involucrata*
Banks *ex* Sprengel      Caprifoliaceae

BUSH HONEYSUCKLE
or INKBERRY
***Lonicera involucrata***

78.    Fruit red, orange-red or sometimes aborted or poorly developed; corolla white, pink or lavender, sometimes fading to yellow, the lobes equal to or as long as the corolla tube; flowers in sessile pairs or on short peduncles, averaging less than 15.0 mm in length; leaves averaging less than 6.0 cm in length; shrubs reaching 3.0 m. Several introduced and cultivated species of **Honeysuckle** may key to this point. These include *Lonicera morrowii* A. Gray, with white flowers that fade to yellow, and *Lonicera tatarica* L., with a white to pink corolla. These two species often escape cultivation.

**Honeysuckle,** *Lonicera* L.                    Caprifoliaceae

Another commonly cultivated member of the Caprifoliaceae might key to this point. The genus *Abelia*, an introduced Asian genus, can commonly be found in lawns and gardens throughout the Southwest. The tubular or bell-shaped flowers are white tinged with pink or lavender, and borne in panicles or weak umbels, with only the sepals remaining after the petals fall; the fruit is often poorly developed. The most common species, *A.* x *grandiflora* (André) Rehder may grow to 3.0 m and become a hedge.

79.    Leaves with lateral veins running parallel with the margins to near the apex of the leaf; twigs dark red to dark reddish-brown; fruit a white drupe at maturity; flowers borne in flat-topped open cymes, white to yellowish in color; flowers 4-merous, stamens 4. This frequent shrub, which may reach to 2.0 m in height, is found near streams and wet areas, from the foothills to the subalpine at 5,500 to 9,000 ft. (1,680 to 2,740 m) in elevation. A native species, it is often transplanted to lawns and gardens.

**Red-osier** or **Dogwood,** *Cornus sericea* L.
                    Syns. *C. stolonifera* (Michaux)
                        *Swida stolonifera* (Michaux) Rydberg
                                        Cornaceae

RED-OSIER or DOGWOOD
*Cornus sericea*

79.   Leaves with lateral veins ending near the margin and not running
      to the apex; twigs cream colored to brown or gray; fruit a black
      drupe at maturity; flowers borne in small panicles at the apex of
      the twigs or on short lateral branches, white to cream-colored;
      flowers 4-merous, stamens 2. This commonly introduced Euro-
      pean species has been planted as hedge rows for more than a
      century throughout North America. One seldom sees the flowers
      in highly trimmed lawns. In the Southwest this species requires
      considerable additional water, and even then it has a limited life
      expectancy.

**Privet**, *Ligustrum vulgare* L.                                    Oleaceae

## OPPOSITE, COMPOUND, BROAD LEAVES

1.      Stems climbing, twining, trailing or if erect then plant usually less than 50.0 cm in height ................................................................. 2.


1.      Stems erect, not climbing, twining or trailing, trees or shrubs over 50.0 cm in height ............................................................................ 9.


    2.      Fruit a stout, fusiform, leathery capsule, ranging in length from 8.0 to 20.0 cm; leaves once, odd pinnately, compound; stems becoming large and woody with age and climbing by aerial roots; flowers complete, arranged in corymbs, usually 2 to 10 in number and on stout pedicels, the corolla forming a bright orange to red tube, 5.0 to 10.0 cm in length. This attractive introduced vine will climb trellises, walls or trees and attract a wide range of hummingbirds and bats.

       **Trumpet Creeper**, *Campsis radicans* (L.) Seemann
                                  *ex* Bureau
                                Bignoniaceae


    2.      Fruit a globose cluster of often densely pubescent achenes, appearing as a fuzzy ball, the individual mature styles measuring from 1.5 to 7.0 cm in length; leaves pinnately compound and becoming ternately or biternately compound, with the petioles often clasping and twining to support the entire plant; stems ranging from perennial herbs to woody throughout; flowers incomplete, lacking petals, solitary or in clusters, and ranging from open to cup-shaped, the sepals numbering 4 or 5, flowers perfect or imperfect, the plants then dioecious or polygamous. The plants that follow in this section are referred to by such common names as **Virgin's Bower, Sugarbowls** or **Clematis.** A number of scholars disagree over the genus *Clematis.* However, we have elected not to bring this confusion to a book devoted to the layperson. This taxon, with considerable study, will someday appear very different than here described. ........................................................ 3.

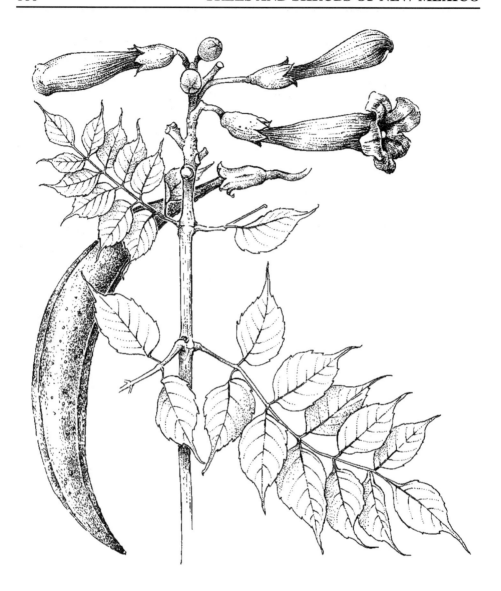

TRUMPET CREEPER
*Campsis radicans*

3.    Sepals white or cream colored and averaging less than 15.0 mm
      in length; flowers unisexual, borne in cymes or weak panicles
      and occasionally solitary ................................................................. 4.

3.    Sepals bright yellow, blue or purple and averaging more than
      15.0 mm in length; flowers perfect, borne solitary or few to a
      cluster ................................................................. 5.

4.    Mature styles in fruit averaging 4.0 to 7.0 cm in length; leaflets averaging 1.2 to 5.0 cm in length, pubescent, somewhat gray in color, the apical leaflet broad, often cleft or parted with pronounced lateral lobes and not strongly attenuate; sepals 10.0 to 12.0 mm in length and villous. Based on field collections this is a more southern ranging species in New Mexico that is thought to hybridize with the following species. Spreading over fence rows along roadsides and thickets, it occurs at 3,500 to 5,500 ft. (1,070 to 1,680 m) in elevation.

**Drummond's Clematis**, *Clematis drummondii* Torrey &

A. Gray     Ranunculaceae

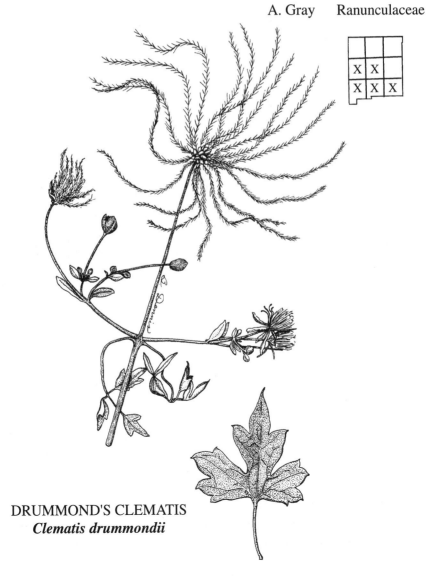

DRUMMOND'S CLEMATIS
*Clematis drummondii*

4. Mature styles in fruit averaging 1.5 to 4.5 cm in length; leaflets averaging 3.5 to 8.0 cm in length, glabrous or only slightly pubescent, tending to dark green, the apical leaflet attenuate or slightly lobed, longer than wide; sepals 8.0 to 11.0 mm in length, somewhat tomentose. Occurring throughout New Mexico, this is a highly variable species. It is thought to hybridize and form, with the previous species, *C. neomexicana* Wooton & Standley. Common in canyons and on roadsides at 4,000 to 8,000 ft. (1,220 to 2,440 m).

**Western Virgin's Bower**, *Clematis ligusticifolia* Nuttall
Syns. *C. neomexicana* Wooton & Standley
Ranunculaceae

WESTERN VIRGIN'S BOWER
*Clematis ligusticifolia*

5.    Sepals yellow, thin, elliptic, and often tinged with red or green, and over 1.5 cm long; leaflets entire, toothed or lobed, the terminal leaflet usually the longest; the bi- or triternately compound leaves green and glabrous on the upper surface and pale green to puberulent below; the plumose styles are 2.0 to 5.0 cm in length. This introduced vine from Asia is herbaceous except for the woody base. It occasionally escapes cultivation. More common in the northern part of New Mexico, it can be found in disturbed areas at 5,500 to 8,000 ft. (1,680 to 2,440 m) in elevation.

**Oriental Clematis**, *Clematis orientalis* L.          Ranunculaceae

ORIENTAL CLEMATIS
*Clematis orientalis*

5.      Sepals blue or purple, occasionally fading to white with age, but
        never tinged with red or green, the margins of the sepals are white
        in several species .............................................................. 6.

    6.      Sepals thin, light blue, glabrous to slightly pubescent,
            becoming opaque with age, averaging more than 3.5 cm
            in length at maturity; flowers usually solitary, stamens
            and sepals often spreading; leaflets ranging in shape from
            entire to toothed or cleft; leaves bi- or triternate to trifoli-
            ate. The habitat is variable for this climbing vine, from
            open to wooded areas and thickets, often found on talus
            slopes at higher elevations, from 6,000 to 10,000 ft. (1,830
            to 3,050 m).

**Rocky Mountain Clematis,** *Clematis columbiana*
(Nuttall) Torrey & A. Gray
Syns. *C. pseudoalpina* (Kuntze) A. Nelson
Ranunculaceae

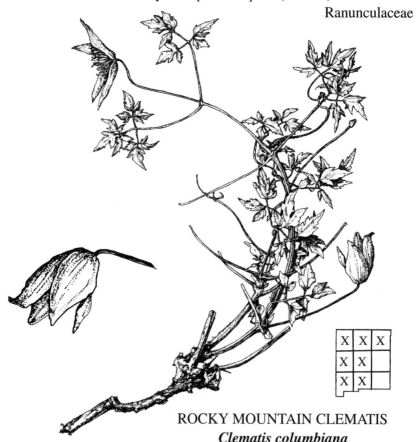

ROCKY MOUNTAIN CLEMATIS
*Clematis columbiana*

6.   Sepals thick, dark blue to purple or dull brown, heavily white pubescent, usually with white margins, averaging less than 3.5 cm in length at maturity; flowers usually solitary, erect, appearing as a bowl with the sepals and stamens spreading only slightly, if at all; leaves pinnately or bipinnately dissected. These species climbing, also commonly trailing or growing upright to 40.0 to 50.0 cm in height ................................................................................. 7.

7.   Veins in the leaflets obviously reticulate and often appearing to have three veins from near the base; the leaflets ovate to elliptic or oval, and at maturity some leaflets distinctly lobed, averaging 5.0 to 6.0 cm in length and 2.5 to 3.5 cm in width; the flowers are borne on extended peduncles and nodding, with the dark purple to brownish red sepals, 20.0 to 25.0 mm in length; the styles in fruit are 2.0 to 3.7 cm in length, glabrous to slightly pubescent. This semi-climbing species occurs infrequently in the southeastern counties of New Mexico and should not be heavily collected. It is a canyon species growing at 4,500 to 8,000 ft. (1,370 to 2,440 m) in elevation.

**Pitcher's Clematis,** *Clematis pitcheri* Torrey & A. Gray
                                                              Ranunculaceae

7.   Veins in the leaflets not obviously reticulate; the leaflets appearing either linear to lanceolate or palmately lobed or divided, with the margins appearing toothed rather than oval .................................. 8.

8.   Leaflets filiform to linear or oblong-lanceolate, averaging 2.0 to 4.5 cm in length and less than 1.0 cm in width; stems not usually twining, but erect, unbranched and suffrutescent; commonly one flower is produced per stem or plant, occasionally two; sepals thick, dark purple, 2.0 to 4.5 cm long and reflexed at the apex. This is a widespread, northern species, more common in the foothills and mountains. Frequent at 6,000 to 8,000 ft. (1,830 to 2,440 m) in elevation. Authors have described several varieties of this species throughout the western states based on leaf length and width, sepal length and growth habit.

**Hairy Leatherflower,** *Clematis hirsutissima* Pursh
                  Syns. *C. palmeri* Rose
                                                              Ranunculaceae

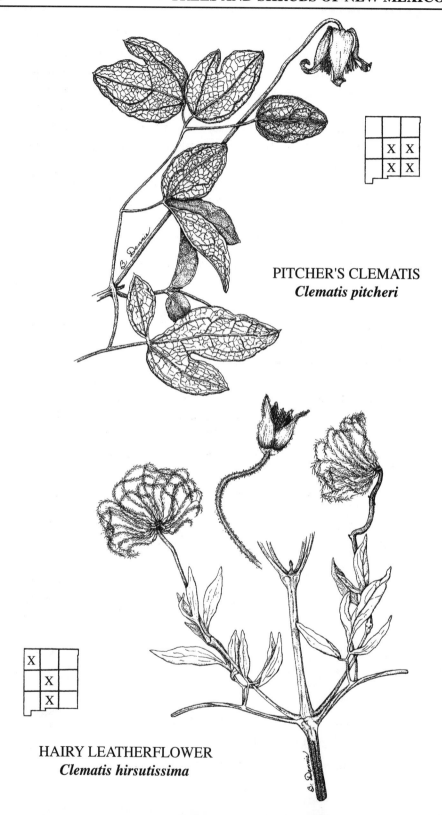

PITCHER'S CLEMATIS
*Clematis pitcheri*

HAIRY LEATHERFLOWER
*Clematis hirsutissima*

8.    Leaflets appearing palmately lobed with 2 to 5 lobes and averaging less than 2.5 cm in length and width, margins often coarsely toothed rather than oval; stems twining, branched and becoming woody with age in the lower stem; one to several nodding flowers per plant, commonly with a single flower at the end of each branch; sepals 1.5 to 2.5 cm in length, thick, dark purple to brownish-purple with white woolly margins; mature styles 3.5 to 5.0 cm in length and plumose. This species is scattered at 5,000 to 7,500 ft. (1,520 to 2,300 m) in elevation over the southwestern quarter of New Mexico. Some authorities have described *C. bigelovii* as a subspecies of *C. hirsutissima*.

**Palmer Leatherflower,** *Clematis bigelovii* Torrey
Ranunculaceae

9.    Leaves bifoliate compound, with only two small leaflets, each measuring less than 1.0 cm in length; flowers solitary and perfect, petals 5 and yellow, sepals 5, yellowish and deciduous, stamens 10, carpels 1 seeded; fruit an indehiscent, globose, white, villous capsule often developing along with continuous flowering. This common shrub, usually measuring 1.0 to 1.5 m in height, sometimes reaching 3.0 m, is strongly scented, and is used by Native Americans of the Southwest in tea, tincture or salve to slow the rate of bacterial growth. **Chaparral** is the most common name for *Larrea tridentata* when referred to as a medicinal plant. It occurs on well drained soils and on the dry mesas south of Albuquerque through the central and southern portions of the State at 3,000 to 5,500 ft. (910 to 1,680 m) in elevation.

**Creosote Bush** or **Hediondilla,** *Larrea tridentata* (Sessé & Moçiño *ex* DeCandolle) Coville
Zygophyllaceae

9.    Leaves pinnately or palmately compound or trifoliate, the three or more leaflets per leaf measuring 2.0 cm or more in length .......... 10.

10.    Leaves pinnately compound ................................................... 11.

10.    Leaves palmately compound or trifoliate ............................. 21.

CREOSOTE BUSH or HEDIONDILLA
*Larrea tridentata*

11. Flowers bright yellow, funnelform and campanulate, 3.0 to 6.0 cm in length; inflorescence a panicle or raceme of 5 to 18 flowers; fruit a long flattened, leathery capsule, 9.0 to 15.0 cm in length; leaves 10.0 to 20.0 cm in length, with 5 to 11 leaflets; leaflets elliptic to lanceolate or linear, the apex acuminate, the base attenuate and often asymmetrical, the margins sharply serrate, 4.0 to 9.0 cm in length and 0.7 to 1.6 cm in width. These large shrubs, to 2.0 m in height, occur on dry hills and slopes in well drained soils and in full sun over the very southern part of New Mexico at 3,500 to 5,000 ft. (1,070 to 1,520 m) in elevation. This species is widely distributed over Mexico and Central America and used medicinally as a treatment for adult-onset, insulin-resistant diabetes. A standard infusion of the dried leaves and flowers is thought to stimulate liver glycogenesis - return by the liver of excessive glucose, and has virtually no toxicity as with prescription drugs.

**Yellow Trumpet** or **Tronadora**, *Tecoma stans* (L.) Jussieu *ex* Kunth      Bignoniaceae

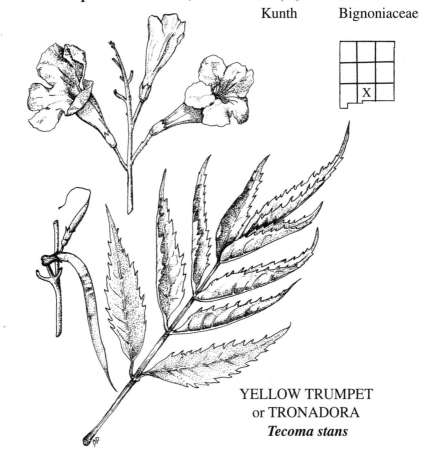

YELLOW TRUMPET
or TRONADORA
*Tecoma stans*

11.     Flowers small and inconspicuous, white, cream colored or green, less than 1.0 cm in length or absent, inflorescence a cyme, reduced panicle or drooping raceme; fruit a drupe or a samara, never a capsule; leaves variable in size; plants ranging from small to large trees ................................................................................. 12.

    12.     Fruit a berry-like drupe; inflorescence a compound cyme; flowers perfect, the corolla white or cream colored; pith in younger twigs often large, comprising most of the stem; large, raised, corky lenticels can often be seen in the bark ..... 13.

    12.     Fruit a samara; inflorescence a panicle or drooping raceme; flowers small, polygamous or unisexual, corolla none or poorly developed; pith in younger twigs usually small, comprising less than 25 percent of the stem; when present lenticels less obvious and seldom raised ................... 15.

13.     Inflorescence pyramidal in shape, the central axis of flowers extending well above the lateral flower and fruit branches; pith of the older twigs dark orange or brown; flowers small and white to pale yellow in color; fruit ranging in color from red to black at maturity; leaves with 5 to 7 leaflets, the leaflets 5.0 to 15.0 cm in length; plants becoming large shrubs, from 2.0 to 3.0 m in height at maturity. This species, including several varieties, is more common along streams at higher elevations in the northern, central and western portions of New Mexico at 7,000 to 12,000 ft. (2,130 to 3,660 m).

**Rocky Mountain Elder,** *Sambucus racemosa* var. *microbotrys*
(Rydberg) Kearney & Peebles
Syns. *S. melanocarpa* A. Gray
*S. racemosa* L.
*S. pubens* Michaux                    Caprifoliaceae

13.     Inflorescence flat-topped in shape and spreading, the central axis of flowers not extending above the lateral flower and fruit branches, but shorter than the marginal flower or fruit branches; pith of the older twigs white to cream colored ................... 14.

ROCKY MOUNTAIN ELDER
*Sambucus racemosa* var. *microbotrys*

14.    Leaflets averaging 2.5 to 9.0 cm long, elliptic to narrowly
       oblong or ovate, occasionally obovate, but short acumi-
       nate to the tip; leaves persistent, usually 3 to 5, rarely 7
       leaflets per leaf; flat-topped cyme averaging 10 or less
       cm in width. This species often develops into a large shrub
       or even into a small tree reaching 8.0 or 9.0 m. It occurs
       frequently along stream margins over the southern part
       of New Mexico at 4,000 to 5,500 ft. (1,220 to 1,520 m).

       **Mexican Elder** or **Flor Sauco**, *Sambucus mexicana*
                                    K. Presl *ex* DeCandolle
                                              Caprifoliaceae

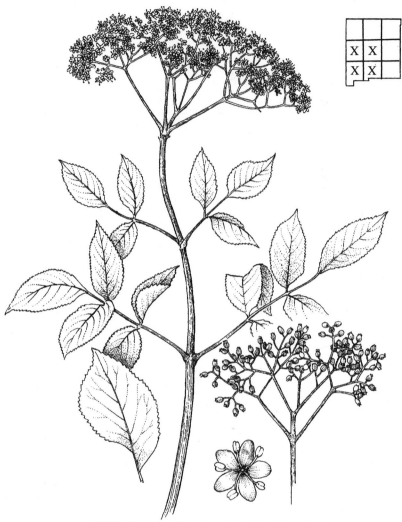

MEXICAN ELDER or FLOR SAUCO
*Sambucus mexicana*

14.     Leaflets averaging 9.0 to 15.0 cm long, narrow to oblong lanceolate and long attenuate; leaves deciduous, usually 5 to 9 leaflets per leaf; flat-topped cyme averaging 16.0 cm or more in width. This species remains a shrub or small tree to 4.0 or 5.0 m. It is abundant along streams at 7,000 to 9,000 ft. (2,130 to 2,740 m) in elevation throughout the central and southern portion of New Mexico.

**New Mexico Elder**, *Sambucus cerulea* Rafinesque
                Syns. *S. neomexicana* Wooton
                           Caprifoliaceae

NEW MEXICO ELDER
*Sambucus cerulea*

15.    Fruit a paired samara; lateral buds light green or tan; twigs often glaucous; leaflets 3 to 5, seldom 7 in number and coarsely serrate above the middle; plant dioecious; inflorescence an extended drooping raceme. This adventive, weedy species is often a shrub but may become a large tree to 20.0 m in height with age. It is widely distributed over New Mexico at 5,200 to 7,500 ft. (1,600 to 2,300 m) in elevation. (Please see couplet 24, page 184 for further description.)

**Box Elder** or **Fresno de Guajuco**, *Acer negundo* L.        Aceraceae

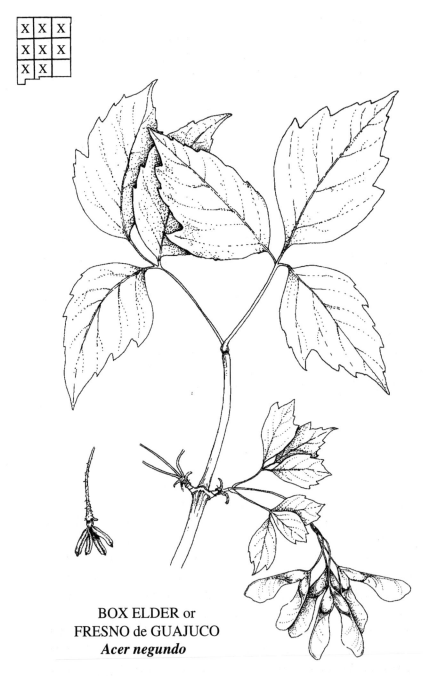

BOX ELDER or
FRESNO de GUAJUCO
*Acer negundo*

15.    Fruit a solitary samara; lateral buds often brown or black; twigs
       seldom glaucous; leaflets 3 to 9 in number, entire to serrate; plants
       dioecious or flowers polygamous; inflorescence a panicle. This
       widely dispersed genus, *Fraxinus*, includes mostly native spe-
       cies ranging from shrubs to large trees ................................ 16.

16.    Twigs strongly four-sided with protruding phellem or cork
       at the corners; wings of the samaras continuing to the base
       of the elliptic or ovate fruit, the fruit thin and compressed
       with the seed central; leaves ranging from simple to com-
       pound or trifoliate ................................................................. 17.

16.    Twigs terete and rounded at the corners, lacking the pro-
       truding cork at the corners; wings of the samaras not or
       seldom continuing to the base of the obovate to ovate fruit,
       the fruit not compressed, the seed basal; leaves never
       simple, but compound with 3 to 7 leaflets ............................ 18.

17.  Leaves simple or compound and trifoliate, the simple leaf or ter-
     minal leaflet orbicular or ovate; the margins of the leaflets entire
     to crenate-serrulate; mature samaras 18.0 to 25.0 mm in length,
     often notched at the apex; usually a shrub or small tree to 6.0 m
     at maturity. This common species occurs in moist canyons and
     adjacent to streams in the western and northwestern portions of
     New Mexico at 4,400 to 6,000 ft. (1,340 to 1,830 m) in elevation.
     (Please see couplet 70, Key VI, page 152, and further descrip-
     tion and illustration, couplet 23, page183.)

**Singleleaf Ash** or **Colorado Ash,** *Fraxinus anomala*
                                        Torrey *ex* S. Watson
                                                          Oleaceae

17.  Leaves never simple, but compound with 3 to 7 leaflets; the ter-
     minal leaflet lanceolate to elliptic; the margins of the leaflets of-
     ten entire over the lower half while the upper half serrulate; ma-
     ture samaras 22.0 to 30.0 mm in length, occasionally notched at
     the apex. This small tree to 8.0 m in height at maturity was col-
     lected only one time on the Catwalk National Trail, adjacent to
     and above the upper falls, in Catron County, at 5,200 ft. (1,600
     m) in elevation. Some authorities consider this species to be a
     variety of the previous species, but the general morphology and
     growth habit fail to support this common relationship. These two
     species should be further studied.

**Lowell Ash,** *Fraxinus lowellii* Sargent
         Syns. *F. anomala* var. *lowellii* (Sargent) Little          Oleaceae

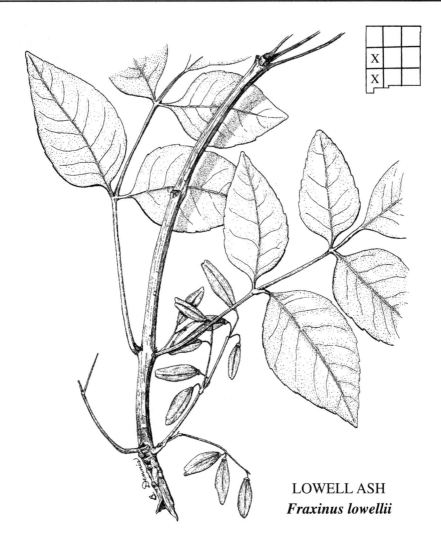

LOWELL ASH
*Fraxinus lowellii*

18. Mature leaves 2.0 to 6.0 cm in length, with the leaflets measuring 1.0 to 2.5 cm in length, usually 3 in number and occasionally 5 to 7, and sessile, the margins entire to crenate or dentate, and the rachis narrowly winged; samaras 1.3 to 2.0 cm in length, and the peduncles less than 0.5 cm in length; the flowers lacking a true corolla. This attractive shrub or small tree often forms a clump and may reach 8.0 m in height. It is uncommon over the central and western portion of New Mexico, on steep rocky slopes, at 4,000 to 6,000 ft. (1,220 to 1,830 m) in elevation.

**Gregg Ash**, *Fraxinus greggii* A. Gray          Oleaceae

GREGG ASH
*Fraxinus greggii*

18.    Mature leaves 7.0 to 16.0 cm in length, with the leaflets measuring 3.0 to 10.0 cm in length, usually 3 to 9 in number and sessile or petiolate, if sessile averaging 3.3 cm or more in length, the rachis never winged; the samara averaging 2.0 cm or more in length; the flowers with or without a corolla ........................................................................ 19.

19.     Flowers producing a true corolla of 4 petals, green to white in
        color, and more than 1.0 cm in length; the new inflorescences are
        produced each spring toward the tip of the branches in the region
        of new growth; the leaves 7.5 to 14.0 cm in length, with the leaf-
        lets measuring 3.5 to 6.5 cm in length, numbering 5 to 7, and the
        margins entire or nearly so; mature samaras are thin and strongly
        compressed, averaging less than 2.5 cm in length. The fragrant
        flowers distinguish this species as do the delicate drooping leaves.
        The range extends over rocky slopes into montane areas in south-
        ern and western New Mexico at elevations from 5,000 to 7,000
        ft. (1,520 to 2,130 m).

**Flowering Ash**, *Fraxinus cuspidata* Torrey                    Oleaceae

FLOWERING ASH
*Fraxinus cuspidata*

19.    Flowers lacking a true corolla, perfect or unisexual, then the plants dioecious, but never complete; the new inflorescences produced each spring in the lateral axils of the leaves produced the previous year; the leaflets of mature leaves averaging 3.5 cm or more in length; mature samaras thick, appearing terete, but not compressed, usually averaging more than 2.5 cm in length .................... 20.

     20.    Leaflets sessile, glabrous to glaucous and papillose on the lower surface, 5 to 9 in number, and 3.0 to 7.0 cm in length; the leaves 8.0 to 15.0 cm in length; the wing of the samara longer than the body. This small tree may reach 6.0 m in height, is extremely rare, or perhaps does not exist in the southwestern portion of New Mexico. We have located only two herbarium sheets that seem to fit this description. It has been reported in canyons near moisture at 3,000 to 6,500 ft. (910 to 1,980 m) in elevation. Considerable field work will be required to demonstrate that this questionable species is established in New Mexico.

     **Chihuahua Ash**, *Fraxinus papillosa* Lingelsheim     Oleaceae

     20.    Leaflets petiolate, finely pubescent to sometimes glabrous on the lower surface but lacking papilla, 3 to 7 in number; and 3.0 to 8.0 cm in length; the leaves 7.5 to 16.0 cm in length; the wings of the samaras are equal to or shorter than the seeds. This medium sized tree may reach 12.0 m or more in height and is the most common native ash in the southern third of New Mexico at elevations from 4,500 to 8,000 ft. (1,370 to 2,440 m).

     **Velvet** or **Arizona Ash**, *Fraxinus velutina* Torrey
         Syns. *F. pennsylvanica* ssp. *velutina* (Torrey) G. N. Miller
            *F. velutina* var. *toumeyi* (Britton) Rehder
                                            Oleaceae

(The **Green Ash**, *Fraxinus pennsylvanica* H. Marshall, has for many years been introduced into New Mexico and commonly escapes cultivation. It has been suggested that it forms hybrids with the **Velvet Ash**. The two species appear to be closely related.)

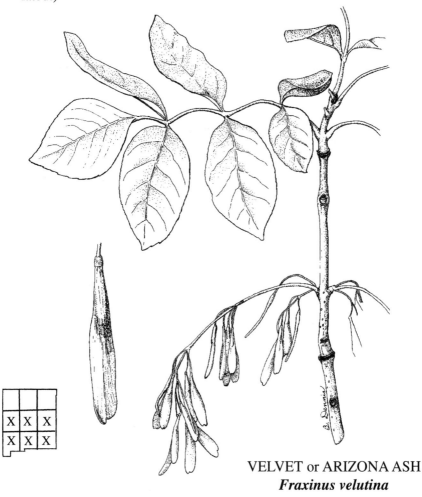

VELVET or ARIZONA ASH
*Fraxinus velutina*

21.     Leaves palmately compound with more than 3 leaflets; leaflets ranging in number from 5 to 13 ........................................................ 22.

21.     Leaves trifoliate or if not strictly trifoliate then ranging from trifoliate to simple or trifoliate to pinnately compound, with mixed combinations of these characters on the same plant. Due to polymorphism the following three species will usually key correctly to other points in the book, depending on the development of the leaves .......................................................................................... 23.

22.　Leaflets elliptic to obovate or oblanceolate, 9.0 to 15.0 cm in length, usually 5 per leaf but occasionally 6 to 7 in number and not stongly aromatic; fruit a globose to subglobose capsule with a rusty-brown spiny hull, 3.0 to 4.5 cm in diameter; inflorescence a terminal panicle of 4 to 10 flowers. This is a widely planted, introduced tree often reaching 15.0 to 25.0 m in height at maturity.

**Horse Chestnut** or **Ohio Buckeye**, *Aesculus glabra* Willdenow
Hippocastanaceae

HORSE CHESTNUT
or OHIO BUCKEYE
*Aesculus glabra*

22.　Leaflets linear, 2.5 to 4.5 cm in length, commonly 5 to 7 in number per leaf but sometimes ranging to 12 or 13 leaflets and strongly aromatic with a citrus odor; fruit a follicle of 2 to 5 divergent carpels on solitary or branched peduncles; flowers solitary or in 2 to 4 flowered axillary cymes. This is an infrequent, but locally common native shrub to 2.0 m in height, occurring at 4,500 to 5,500 ft. (1,370 to 1,680 m) in elevation, on rocky canyon slopes in the southeast corner of New Mexico.

**Mexican Orange**, *Choisya dumosa* (Torrey) A. Gray
Rutaceae

MEXICAN ORANGE
*Choisya dumosa*

23.     Fruit a single samara, not united in pairs, measuring 11.0 to 25.0
        mm in length and completely winged; many leaves commonly
        simple and pinnately veined, however some leaves will often be
        truly trifoliate, the simple leaves and the apical leaflets commonly
        orbicular, oval to ovate, with margins that range from crenate to
        undulate. This infrequent, native shrub or small tree, growing to
        6.0 m in height, is usually found on rocky slopes and often adja-
        cent to streams in the dry northwestern and western counties of
        New Mexico, at elevations ranging from 4,400 to 6,000 ft. (1,340
        to 1,830 m). (Please see descriptions and illustrations, pages 152,
        175.)

**Singleleaf** or **Colorado Ash**, *Fraxinus anomala* Torrey *ex* S. Watson
                                                              Oleaceae

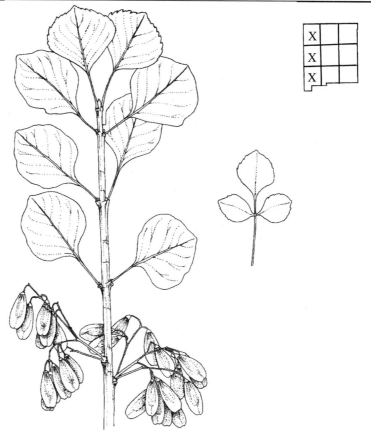

SINGLELEAF or COLORADO ASH
*Fraxinus anomala*

23.    Fruit formed from a double samara, two united samaras forming
       a V-shaped fruit; leaves trifoliate, and then with some leaves ei-
       ther simple and palmately lobed, or pinnately compound with 3
       to 7 leaflets .............................................................................. 24.

       24.    Leaves trifoliate or simple and palmately lobed, averag-
              ing less than 10.0 cm in length, the lower surface lacking
              pubescence along the veins; new stems red to brown in
              color; species monoecious or occasionally dioecious or
              with perfect flowers. This shrub or small tree is common
              along streams and in canyons in the foothills, montane
              and subalpine, from 7,000 to 9,500 ft. (2,130 to 2,900 m)
              in elevation. (Please see couplet 3, page 89, Key VI and
              illustration, page 90.)

       **Rocky Mountain Maple**, *Acer glabrum* Torrey      Aceraceae

24.    Leaves trifoliate or pinnately compound with 3 to 7 leaf-
       lets, averaging more than 12.0 cm in length, the lower
       surface pubescent along the veins; new stems green to
       blue or gray in color and often glaucous; species dioe-
       cious, thus the flowers imperfect. This widespread, much
       cultivated weedy shrub, that may become a relatively large
       cultivated tree to 20.0 m is common throughout the state
       in moist areas, occurring at from 5,200 to 7,500 ft. (1,600
       to 2,300 m) in elevation. (Please see couplet 15, page
       174 for further description.)

**Box-Elder** or **Fresno de Guajuco**, *Acer negundo* L.

Aceraceae

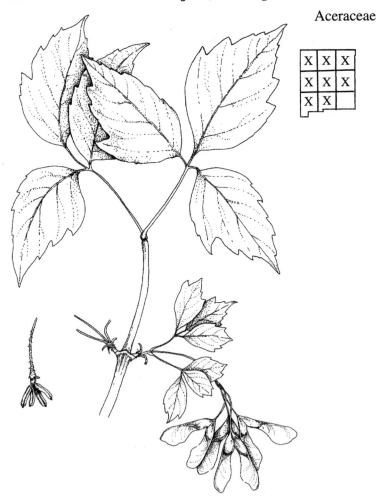

BOX-ELDER or FRESNO de GUAJUCO
*Acer negundo*

## ALTERNATE, SIMPLE, BROAD LEAVES

1.  Leaves lobed or notched at the apex ...................................................... 2.

1.  Leaves not lobed or only slightly notched, in several species leaves
    absent or scale-like ........................................................................... 40.

    2.  Plants with spines or thorns on stems ...................................... 3.

    2.  Plants without spines or thorns on stems ................................. 7.

3.  Spines 1.5 cm or more in length, these are the flowering stems
    that have ceased to produce flowers, glaucous; leaves villous,
    0.5 to 2.0 cm in length including the petioles which are indis-
    tinct, finely divided into 5 to 7, 3-parted lobes; stems white to-
    mentose; inflorescence a head of small yellow-green flowers; fruit
    an achene. These are pungently aromatic, low shrubs to 40.0 cm
    in height. Confined to the northwest corner of New Mexico at
    4,500 to 8,000 ft. (1,370 to 2,440 m) in elevation, this species
    flowers in early spring and occurs on dry slopes and mesas and
    often on alkaline flats.

**Spiny Sagebrush**, *Artemisia spinescens* D. C. Eaton    Asteraceae

SPINY SAGEBRUSH
*Artemisia spinescens*

3.     Spines less than 1.5 cm in length, commonly 1, 2 or 3 at the
       nodes, glossy; leaves glabrous to glandular-pubescent, 1.0 to 10.0
       cm in length, including distinct petioles; stems whitish to dark
       brown, lacking tomentum, but sometimes with several bristles in
       the internodes; inflorescence a raceme or flowers solitary; flow-
       ers perfect with an inferior ovary and a well developed hy-
       panthium; fruit a berry. genus *Ribes* L. .............................................. 4.

       4.     Hypanthium and fruit glandular-bristly, bristly or spiny,
              the glandular-bristles, bristles or spines long and exserted........ 5.

       4.     Hypanthium and fruit glabrous or merely glandular-pu-
              bescent, the glandular-pubescence, when present, com-
              monly short and obscure ......................................................... 6.

5.     Berries red and glandular-pubescent, 6.0 to 10.0 mm in diameter
       at maturity; hypanthium open and saucer-shaped; leaves 15.0 to
       35.0 mm in width, deeply incised; inflorescence of 3 to 7 flow-
       ers; flowers dull pink to red; stems straggly to 75.0 cm in height,
       bearing 1 to 3 spines at the nodes. This northern species, frequent
       at 7,500 to 11,200 ft. (2,290 to 3,410 m) in elevation can be found
       in the southern mountains of New Mexico. It flowers and pro-
       duces fruit throughout the summer months.

**Redfruited Gooseberry** or **Alpine Prickly Gooseberry**,
                                        *Ribes montigenum* McClatchie
                                                      Grossulariaceae

5.     Berries orange to purplish-red at maturity, bristly to spiny, 8.0 to
       15.0 mm in diameter at maturity; hypanthium tubular; inflores-
       cence few flowered; flowers up to 18.0 mm in length; leaves 25.0
       to 40.0 mm in width, not deeply incised; stems to 2.0 m in height,
       bearing 1 to 3 stout spines at the nodes. Occurring at 6,800 to
       11,500 ft. (2,070 to 3,500 m) in elevation, and flowering over the
       summer months, this frequent southern mountain species can be
       readily identified by the spine covered berries.

**Orange Gooseberry,** *Ribes pinetorum* Greene          Grossulariaceae

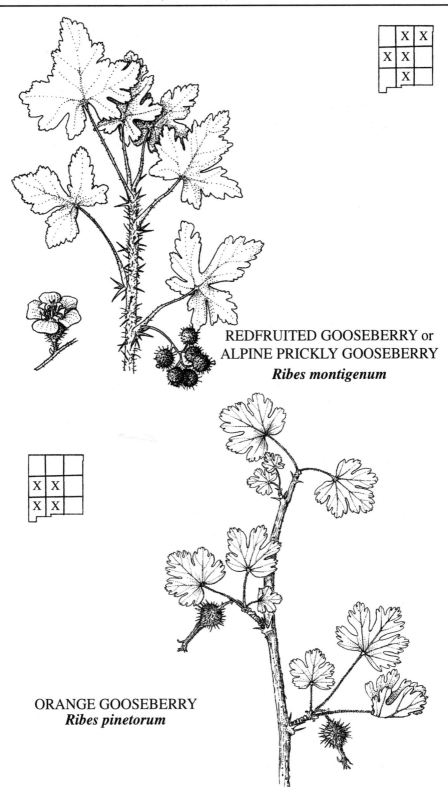

REDFRUITED GOOSEBERRY or
ALPINE PRICKLY GOOSEBERRY
*Ribes montigenum*

ORANGE GOOSEBERRY
*Ribes pinetorum*

6.      Flowers with reflexed sepals, petals pink to white, broader and shorter than the sepals, style pilose-pubescent; leaves 1.5 to 6.0 cm in width, averaging 2.0 cm or more in width at maturity, the petiole equaling or longer than the blade. This common shrub, with smooth whitish bark in younger stems, may have spines present or it may be unarmed. It grows to 1.0 m and is common over the mountainous regions of New Mexico at 5,500 to 11,000 ft. (1,680 to 3,350 m) in elevation. Occurring in moist woods, flowers are produced in April or May.

**Common Gooseberry** or **Whitestem Gooseberry**,

*Ribes inerme* Rydberg      Grossulariaceae

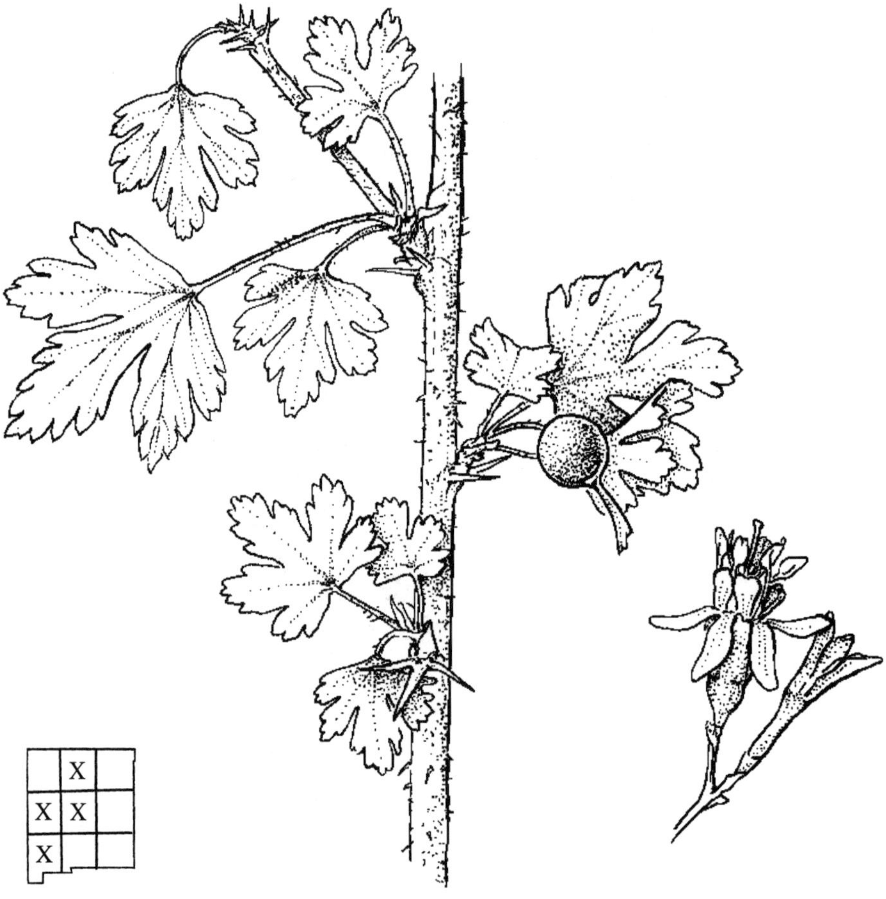

COMMON GOOSEBERRY or
WHITESTEM GOOSEBERRY
*Ribes inerme*

6.     Flowers with erect sepals, petals pink to white, narrow
       and oblong; leaves 0.5 to 2.5 cm in width, averaging less
       than 2.0 cm in width at maturity, the petiole shorter than
       the blade. This  shrub is common to wooded areas and
       canyons. Characterized by gray to brown bark and many
       spines, it may occasionally reach 2.0 m in height at matu-
       rity. It occurs throughout New Mexico at 6,500 to 10,000
       ft. (1,980 to 3,050 m) in elevation and flowers in early
       spring.

**Trumpet Gooseberry** or **Western Gooseberry**,
                    *Ribes leptanthum* A. Gray      Grossulariaceae

TRUMPET GOOSEBERRY
or WESTERN GOOSEBERRY
*Ribes leptanthum*

7.      Stems climbing and twining, forming vines, tendrils commonly
        present; leaves palmately lobed to almost entire and palmately
        veined, and up to 18.0 cm in width; flowers unisexual or perfect,
        commonly polygamous; fruit a berry (grape); the genus *Vitis,* fam-
        ily Vitaceae.  Some authorities have described as many as seven
        species in New Mexico, but our field collections have been lim-
        ited to just 3 or 4 species and these are poorly defined. The spe-
        cies listed below are reported for New Mexico and are found
        labeled as such in the major state herbaria. However, the charac-
        teristics used to distinguish among these species are weak and
        unclear at best. Additional field work and further systematic stud-
        ies are needed before a reliable key can be written. The **Canyon
        Grape** and **Sweet Mountain Grape** appear to be the most com-
        mon.

**Bush Grape**, *Vitis acerifolia* Rafinesque
                Syns. *V. longii* Prince
                        *V. riparia* Michaux                         Vitaceae

**Canyon Grape**, *Vitis arizonica* Engelmann
                Syns. *V. treleasei* Munson *ex* Bailey
                        *V. arizonica* var. *glabra* Munson        Vitaceae

**Frost Grape**, *Vitis vulpina* L.                                Vitaceae

**Sweet Mountain Grape**, *Vitis monticola* Buckley
                Syns. *V. texana* Munson
                                                                   Vitaceae

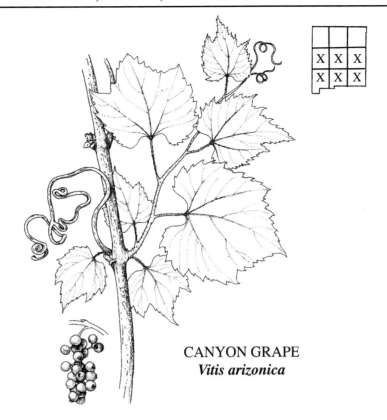

**CANYON GRAPE**
*Vitis arizonica*

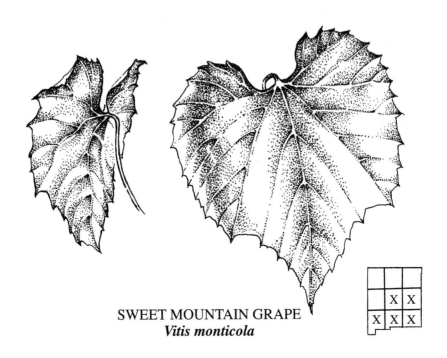

**SWEET MOUNTAIN GRAPE**
*Vitis monticola*

7. Stems forming trees and shrubs, never forming climbing or twining vines, tendrils absent; leaves variously lobed.............................. 8.

  8. Leaves pinnately lobed and with one main vein (midrib) from the base or two or three small lobes at the apex of the leaf ................................................................................. 9.

  8. Leaves palmately lobed and/or with more than one main vein (midrib) from near the base ............................................ 24.

9. Inflorescence is a catkin or the flowers borne solitary, either laterally or at the ends of the branches; fruit is a nut or an acorn subtended only partially by a cup-like involucre, or an achene with an elongated and somewhat exserted style; sepals and petals reduced and inconspicuous or fused only at the base or from a hypanthium and conspicuous ........................................................... 10.

9. Inflorescence is a head of many flowers surrounded by an involucre of bracts; fruit is an achene formed from each of the separate flowers in the head; petals fused forming a tube and the sepals absent or forming a pappus of hair at the top of the inferior ovary. Asteraceae - Aster, Composite or Sunflower Family .............. 15.

  10. Fruit a nut or an acorn, (an acorn is a nut with a subtending cupule); mature leaves 3.0 to 15.0 cm in length; sepals and petals reduced and inconspicuous; plants monoecious, stamens borne in catkins, carpellate flowers borne separately; stamens 4 to several. Fagaceae - Oak Family...... 11.

  10. Fruit is an achene with an elongated and somewhat exserted style; mature leaves 0.5 to 2.0 cm in length; sepals and petals conspicuous; flowers perfect and complete, and borne solitary at the tips of the branches; stamens numerous, usually 20 to 44 in number. Rosaceae - Rose Family...... 13.

11.     Lobes of leaves rounded; native shrub or small tree to 15.0 m in height; leaves 5.0 to 15.0 cm in length with 5 to 9 distinct lobes; acorns 8.0 to 20.0 mm in length, the cupule deeply rounded with ovate scales. This common oak is widely scattered over most of New Mexico at 6,000 to 8,500 ft. (1,830 to 2,590 m) in elevation. Although the leaves are deciduous, new leaves may not develop in extremely dry years, and flowering, as well as fruit formation, may be delayed until adequate moisture is available. (Please see page 302, couplet 123 for further description.)

**Gambel Oak,** *Quercus gambelii* Nuttall                Fagaceae

GAMBEL OAK
*Quercus gambelii*

11.     Lobes of leaves spine-tipped; native or introduced ............... 12.

12.    Native shrub to 1.0 m in height at maturity, commonly forming thickets through underground rhizomes; leaves may be more coarsely toothed than lobed in some clones; acorns 12.0 to 25.0 mm in length and ovoid to oblong in shape. This species appears to be isolated on the sandy plains in the southeastern corner of New Mexico at 3,500 to 4,500 ft. (1,070 to 1,370 m) in elevation. (Please see page 302, couplet 124 for further description.)

**Havard Shin Oak**, *Quercus havardii* Rydberg        Fagaceae

HAVARD SHIN OAK
*Quercus havardii*

12.    Introduced and cultivated tree to 40.0 m in height at maturity; commonly planted in city parks and lawns, especially in northern and cooler areas in New Mexico cities; leaves 10.0 to 15.0 cm in length; acorns less than 2.0 cm in length, depending on irrigation practices, borne solitary or in small clusters.

**Pin Oak,** *Quercus palustris* Münchhausen        Fagaceae

A wide range of introduced species of eastern oaks, with lobed leaves, including both **Black Oaks** (spine-tipped lobes) and **White Oaks** (round-lobed) species, have been introduced in the western states. We include the **Pin Oak**, which is commonly cultivated, to remind those using the key to be aware of those cultivated species.

13.     Pistils 1 or 2 per flower, styles slightly exserted with a stout beak, but not becoming elongate or feather-like in the fruit, petals pale yellow, sepals covered with stalked glands; mature achenes 0.8 to 1.2 cm in length, 3-lobed at the apex, revolute and white-to-mentose beneath. Frequent over northern New Mexico at 4,000 to 9,000 ft. (1,220 to 2,740 m) in elevation, this spreading shrub may reach to nearly 3.0 m in height. With adequate moisture the solitary flowers may be produced over most of the growing season.

**Bitterbush** or **Antelopebush**, *Purshia tridentata* (Pursh)
DeCandolle      Rosaceae

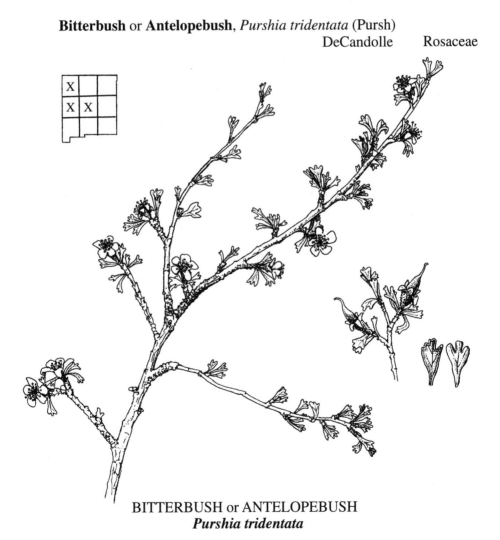

BITTERBUSH or ANTELOPEBUSH
*Purshia tridentata*

13.     Pistils 5 to many per flower, styles strongly exserted and becoming elongate, feather-like and showy in fruit ..................................... 14.

14.    Flowers yellow or cream-colored and terminal, less than
       1.5 cm in diameter, pistils 5 to 10 per flower, stamens
       numerous; achenes 5 to 10 per flower, glabrous with per-
       sistent, silvery and pubescent, tail-like styles 1.5 to 5.0
       cm in length; leaves 0.6 to 1.4 cm in length, pinnately
       lobed with 3 to 9 lobes, revolute, thick, coriaceous and
       glandular-dotted. The **Cliffrose** is more common to the
       western half of the State at 3,000 to 8,000 ft. (910 to 2,440
       m) in elevation. Flowering throughout the spring and sum-
       mer months, this attractive shrub may reach 2.0 m in height
       at maturity.

**Cliffrose**, *Purshia stansburiana* (Torrey) Henrickson
            Syns. *Cowania mexicana* var. *stansburiana*
                                          (Torrey) Jepson
            *C. stansburiana* Torrey                Rosaceae

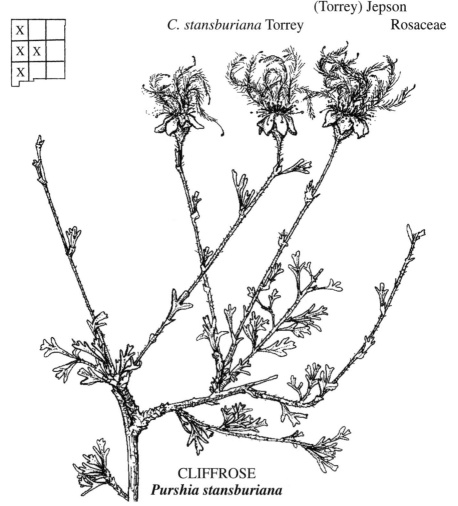

CLIFFROSE
*Purshia stansburiana*

14.  Flowers white and showy, more than 2.0 cm in diameter, pistils 20 or more per flower with long, slender, persistent styles, stamens numerous; achenes formed from each of the many separate pistils, with the exserted, reddish styles reaching 2.5 to 5.0 cm in length; leaves 0.6 to 1.4 cm in length, some fascicled, revolute, with 3 to 7 lobes, and white-tomentose on the lower surface. Occurring over New Mexico and the Southwest on dry, rocky slopes and in arroyos at 4,500 to 7,500 ft. (1,370 to 2,290 m) in elevation, both the large, white flowers and the attractive, red feathery fruit distinguish this plant from the previous species. Flowering throughout the growing season it is possible to find some plants in flower and fruit practically all summer.

**Apache Plume**, *Fallugia paradoxa* (D. Don) Endlicher
*ex* Torrey          Rosaceae

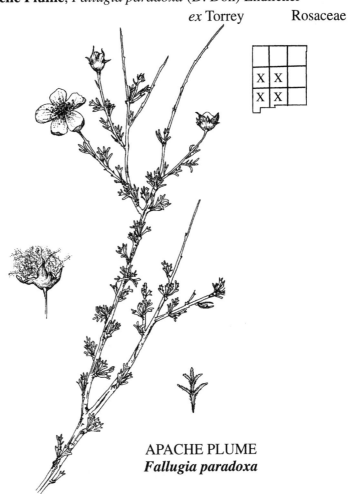

APACHE PLUME
*Fallugia paradoxa*

15.　　Most of the leaves basal to 20.0 cm or less above the soil level, these decumbent or forming woody mats, the taller stems commonly herbaceous becoming somewhat woody with age, and extending separately above the basal cluster of leaves; mature leaves deeply divided or dissected to the midrib, leaf segments linear to somewhat oblong with an aroma of sage; heads of flowers on leafy panicles or racemes. Growing to 50.0 cm in height at maturity and flowering in late summer and fall, this widely scattered species is found in dry soils at 5,500 to 8,000 ft. (1,680 to 2,440 m) in elevation. Often described as a perennial herb from a woody base, this species probably should be omitted from this publication, however it is very common over New Mexico and especially the northern two-thirds of the State. Plains Indians had many medicinal uses for this common sage they called "she sage". *A. frigida* is a source of camphor. The leaves were chewed for heartburn and applied to reduce swelling and nosebleed.

**Pasture Sage** or **Estafiata**, *Artemisia frigida* Willdenow　　　Asteraceae

PASTURE SAGE
or ESTAFIATA
*Artemisia frigida*

15.   Most of the leaves scattered along the erect, woody stems to 25.0 cm or more in height at maturity, plants not forming mats, but freely branching, the branches forming true, upright shrubs ............. 16.

    16.   Mature leaves filiform, linear or thread-like, commonly averaging more than 4.5 cm in length ................................... 17.

    16.   Mature leaves elliptic, rhombic-ovate, spatulate-oblong, truncate, obovate or fasiculate, commonly averaging less than 4.5 cm in length ............................................................... 20.

17.   Heads solitary at the ends of the branches, on long, exserted peduncles, often 5.0 to 10.0 cm above the vegetative portions of the plant, disk 8.0 to 12.0 mm in width, involucre in 2 or 3 series, ray flowers yellow, numbering 10 to 16 and 8 to 14 mm in length; leaves 4.5 to 8.0 cm in length, leaves and leaflets linear to filiform, both alternate and opposite, as well as simple and compound, thus this species will key out several places. Limited in its range to the southern and southeastern portions of New Mexico, at 3,500 to 6,000 ft. (1,070 to 1,830 m) in elevation, this shrub commonly reaches 50.0 to 100.0 cm in height. Flowering throughout the summer months, it is uncommon in rocky soils in the drainage of both the Pecos River and the Rio Grande. (Please see Key VI, page 132 for description and illustration, and Key IX, page 459 for further description.)

**Skeletonleaf Goldeneye**, *Viguiera stenoloba* Blake
Syns. *Heliomeris tenuifolia* A. Gray

Asteraceae

17.   Heads on short peduncles, not exserted, and not extending well above the vegetative portions of the plant, heads arranged racemose or paniculate along the stems or corymbose ........................... 18.

18.     Heads 1.0 to 2.0 mm in diameter, racemose or paniculate,
        3 to 5 flowers per head; pappus absent or weakly present,
        ray flowers yellowish-white and obscure; leaves finely
        filiform, villous-tomentose, and revolute to the point of
        appearing almost terete; herbage silvery-canescent and
        often becoming tan with age. This shrub, often reaching
        0.5 to 1.0 m in height at maturity, is common at 3,500 to
        6,000 ft. (1,070 to 1,830 m) in elevation. It flowers in late
        summer and into the fall, occurring over dry plains and
        hills, in sandy soils. (Please see couplet 85, page 264 and
        couplet 108, page 286 for further descriptions.)

**Sand Sage** or **Threadleaf Sage**, *Artemisia filifolia* Torrey
Syns. *Oligosporus filifolius* (Torrey) W. A. Weber

Asteraceae

SAND SAGE
or THREADLEAF SAGE
*Artemisia filifolia*

18.     Heads 5.0 to 15.0 mm in diameter, corymbose with 14 or fewer heads per corymb, and 8 to many flowers per head; pappus of capillary bristles, ray flowers yellow and attractive; leaves linear, but not finely filiform; herbage glabrous to sparsely pubescent or with tomentum and sometimes becoming purple with age ............................................. 19.

The following two species are only slightly woody at the base with age and have been described as perennial herbs. They are included here because the stems are erect and the growth habit may reach 1.0 m or more in height. Students mistakenly identify them as woody plants, especially in New Mexico where warm winters may allow them to continue growing over several seasons.

19.     Heads cylindric or subcylindric, involucral bracts 8 to 13, the outer ones much reduced and inconspicuous, ray flowers yellow and 4 to 8 in number; leaves both lobed and not lobed, linear to 12.0 cm in length, sessile; plants glabrous or sparsely pubescent, to 70.0 cm in height. Although widespread throughout New Mexico, this plant is more common in northern counties at 6,000 to 9,000 ft. (1,830 to 2,740 m) in elevation. The attractive flowers are produced over much of the growing season. (Please see couplet 86, page 265 for further description.)

**Broom Groundsel**, *Senecio spartioides* Torrey & A. Gray

Asteraceae

19.    Heads campanulate to broadly campanulate, involucral bracts
       numbering 13 to 21, the outer ones conspicuous, ray flowers yel-
       low and 8 to 17 in number; leaves both lobed and not lobed,
       linear to 12.0 cm in length, sessile; plants tomentose to glabrous
       in some varieties, reaching from 80.0 to 130.0 cm in height. This
       common and attractive species is found throughout the State at
       3,000 to 8,000 ft. (910 to 2,440 m) in elevation. Flowering in the
       fall, it occurs in a wide range of habitats, including sandy and
       rocky soils, on the plains, in washes and disturbed areas.

**Douglas Groundsel**, *Senecio flaccidus* var. *douglasii*
                    (DeCandolle) B. L. Turner & T. M. Barkley
              Syns. *S. douglasii* ssp. *longilobus*
                              (Bentham) W. A. Weber
                                             Asteraceae

DOUGLAS GROUNDSEL
*Senecio flaccidus* var. *douglasii*

20.    Mature pinnate leaves with 3 (sometimes 2 to 5) lobes or
       pronounced teeth at the apex ................................................. 21.

20.    Mature pinnate leaves lobed or toothed along the lateral
       margins, but not at the apex .................................................. 22.

21. Heads with both disk (central) and ray (marginal) flowers, ray flowers pistillate and disk flowers perfect and either fertile or sterile; heads numerous in a narrow sometimes spike-like panicle; shrub commonly 30.0 to 50.0 cm in height and silver-canescent; leaves 0.3 to 2.3 cm in length, apex 3-lobed or sometimes 2-lobed, some of the upper leaves entire. Occurring in the central portion of the State at 5,000 to 7,500 ft. (1,520 to 2,290 m) in elevation, it can be found on well-drained slopes in rocky soils. It flowers late in the growing season. This species, like the following one, and several other members of the genus *Artemisia* are not well defined in the literature.

**Bigelow Sagebrush**, *Artemisia bigelovii* A. Gray          Asteraceae

BIGELOW SAGEBRUSH
*Artemisia bigelovii*

21. Disk and ray flowers similar, perfect and fertile; heads many in a definite, rather broad panicle; shrub commonly 3.0 to 4.0 m in height at maturity and silvery-canescent; leaves 0.5 to 5.0 cm in length, apex 3-lobed or sometimes 5-lobed, some of the upper leaves entire. **Big Sagebrush** is one of the most common and widely known shrubs of the Southwest, and in some areas of dry plains and mesas or on rocky slopes it may be practically the only shrub in sight. It is common in the northern and especially in the northwestern portions of New Mexico, but also occurs in the central and some southern areas at 4,500 to 8,500 ft. (1,370 to 2,590 m) in elevation.

**Big Sagebrush** or **Wormwood**, *Artemisia tridentata* Nuttall

Asteraceae

BIG SAGEBRUSH
or WORMWOOD
*Artemisia tridentata*

Another questionable and closely related species, *Artemisia arbuscula* Nuttall, may key to this point. Thought to be confined to the northwestern corner of New Mexico at about the same elevations, it grows to less than 40.0 cm in height, and the leaves are more commonly 5-lobed. We note that up to 9 subspecies of *Artemisia tridentata* are reported in the literature, and the major state herbaria contain large collections of this taxon, yet considerable confusion persists.

22.    Leaves sessile, 2.0 to 5.0 cm in length, oblong and pinnately cleft into 4 to 8 linear lobes, the mid-vein resinous-punctate, with clear glandular hairs; inflorescence cymose; flowers 6 to 15 per head. This shrubby perennial becomes more woody with age, reaching to 70.0 or 80.0 cm in height at maturity. Ranging from San Juan to Grant counties in the western part of the State, it occurs at 5,000 to 6,500 ft. (1,520 to 1,980 m) in elevation. It grows over arid slopes and mesas, flowering from August through October.

**Goldenweed**, *Isocoma tenuisecta* Greene
Syns. *Haplopappus tenuisectus* (Greene) Blake

Asteraceae

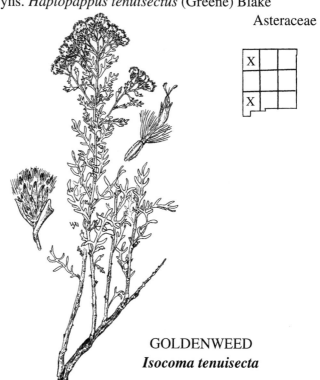

GOLDENWEED
*Isocoma tenuisecta*

22.    Leaves conspicuously petioled, the petiole 2.0 to 8.0 mm
       in length, leaves 0.8 to 5.0 cm in length, not pinnately
       cleft, but the leaves ovate to obovate or rhombic-ovate in
       outline, the lobes ovate to rounded or laciniate and not
       linear cleft ........................................................................... 23.

23.    Leaves conspicuously densely tomentose, 1.5 to 5.0 cm in length,
       margins irregularly lobed, lobes obtuse or rounded, the petioles
       2.0 to 5.0 cm in length; heads small, numerous and arranged in
       corymbose to paniculate inflorescences, the peduncles long and
       tomentose; the separate flowers are extremely inconspicuous. This
       densely gray shrub, seldom reaching 80.0 cm in height, is found
       over dry hills, gravelly mesas and in desert grasslands at 3,000 to
       6,000 ft. (910 to 1,830 m) in elevation. It may be found flower-
       ing over much of the growing season in the southern two-thirds
       of New Mexico. The common Spanish name, *Guayule*, which
       means rubber, is sometimes given to this species. This is not ab-
       solutely correct, but **Mariola** does contain some rubber. *P.
       argentatum*, found in Mexico and only in the Big Bend region of
       Texas, is the closely related species from which rubber has his-
       torically been extracted.

**Mariola** or **Guayule**, *Parthenium incanum* Kunth          Asteraceae

23.    Leaves 0.6 to 2.7 cm in length, the margins laciniate toothed or
       lobed, ovate to cuneate in outline; leaves and stems not conspicu-
       ously tomentose, but glabrous to puberulent with small dark glands
       obvious with a 10x hand lens; inflorescence an elongate, leafy,
       pyramidical raceme or panicle. This frequent shrub over the south-
       ern one-third of New Mexico, commonly reaching 1.0 m in height
       and uncommonly reaching 1.5 m, can be identified by the pale
       gray to almost white and fibrous bark. Found growing over dry
       slopes and in arroyos at 4,500 to 6,000 ft. (1,370 to 1,830 m) in
       elevation, it flowers late in the fall.

**Cutleaf Brickelbush**, *Brickellia laciniata* A. Gray          Asteraceae

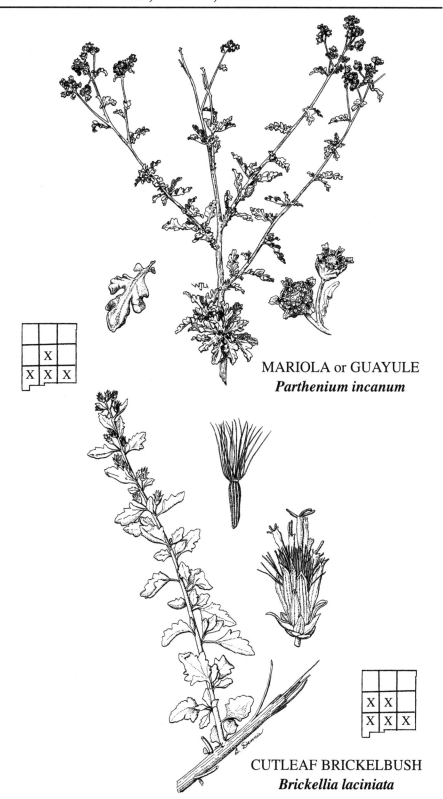

**MARIOLA or GUAYULE**
*Parthenium incanum*

**CUTLEAF BRICKELBUSH**
*Brickellia laciniata*

24. — Fruit a berry, several seeded and formed from single, perfect flowers. Currants, genus *Ribes* ....................................... 25.

24. Fruit an aggregate, multiple, achene or capsule; if an aggregate then formed from many separate pistils; if a capsule then formed from perfect flowers ................................. 32.

25. Flowers yellow, borne in racemes, petals yellow, occasionally with some red, hypanthium exserted to 10.0 mm in length and trumpet-shaped, extremely fragrant; leaves with 3 distinct lobes, glabrous above with a few hairs below, but never glandular; fruit glabrous, from dark red to black at maturity, sweet and edible. This common and attractive plant is found along the margins of streams, in alluvial areas and on moist slopes at 6,500 to 9,000 ft. (1,980 to 2,740 m) in elevation. Under favorable growing conditions it may reach 1.5 m in height. The bright yellow flowers that are produced in early spring, the tasty fruit and the attractive growth habit make this a much sought after plant for cultivation.

**Golden Currant**, *Ribes aureum* Pursh                    Grossulariaceae

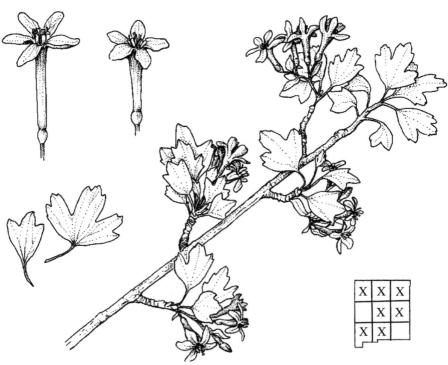

GOLDEN CURRANT
*Ribes aureum*

25.   Flowers white or pink ..................................................................... 26.

> 26.   Lower surfaces of the leaves covered with golden-yellow resinous glands or dots, leaves mostly 5-lobed with irregular serrate margins with callous tips; racemes drooping and producing 5 to 15 flowers; flower hypanthium 3.0 to 4.5 mm in length, sepals yellowish-white and surpassing the hypanthium and petals in length; berries black and glabrous. This uncommon shrub is rare over the northern half of New Mexico at 6,000 to 7,500 ft. (1,830 to 2,290 m) in elevation. Flowering in early spring, it is found in moist woods and adjacent to streams.

**Wild Black Currant,** *Ribes americanum* P. Miller

Grossulariaceae

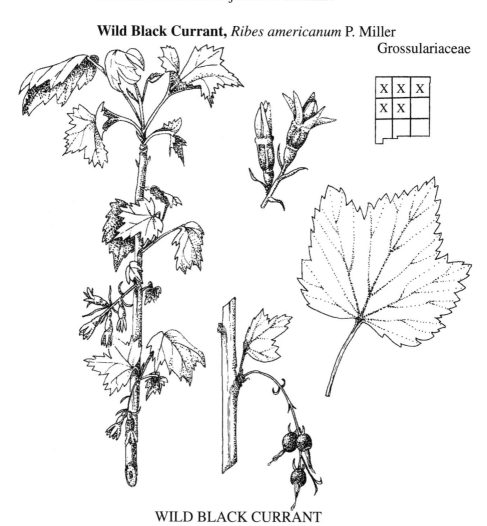

WILD BLACK CURRANT
*Ribes americanum*

26.   Lower surface of the leaves void of yellow resinous dots, some glands and dots may be present, but these not yellow, leaves 3- to 5-lobed .......................................................... 27.

27.   Hypanthium saucer-shaped and shallow, not more than 2.0 mm in length ................................................................................................ 28.

27.   Hypanthium tubular, cylindrical to campanulate, 3.0 mm or more in length ................................................................................................ 29.

28.   Racemes of 4 to 12 flowers, produced laterally, down the older stems, not terminal; petals pink to purple, hypanthium 1.0 mm or less in length, calyx lobes glandular and greenish to purplish, surpassing the petals; berries black and somewhat glandular, averaging about 10.0 mm in diameter. This is a locally abundant species of sunny mountain slopes at higher elevations from 8,500 to 11,500 ft. (2,590 to 3,500 m) in elevation. The plant is small with decumbent and prostrate branches.

**Colorado Currant**, *Ribes coloradense* Coville

Grossulariaceae

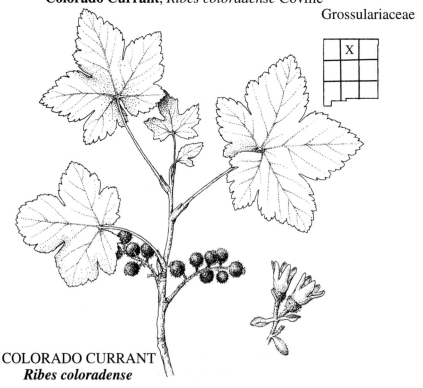

COLORADO CURRANT
*Ribes coloradense*

28. Racemes 4 to 8 flowered and terminal, not produced laterally and down the older stems; petals small and white, hypanthium 1.0 to 1.5 mm in length, calyx lobes 4.0 to 5.0 mm in length and slightly longer than the petals; berries black, glandular-pubescent, averaging more than 12.0 mm in diameter with some berries 3.0 cm in diameter; leaves distinctly 5-lobed, and appearing as fascicled at the tips of the branches, the lobes rounded. Flowering in May and June, this attractive and common species is found in moist woods, often among aspens and conifers at 7,000 to 11,500 ft. (2,130 to 3,500 m) in elevation.

**Rothrock Currant,** *Ribes wolfii* Rothrock      Grossulariaceae

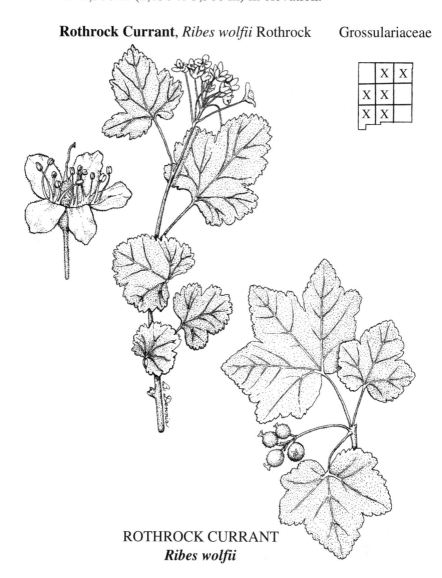

ROTHROCK CURRANT
*Ribes wolfii*

29.    Leaves deeply lobed, nearly half the distance to the midrib or slightly more and not strongly glandular-pubescent, 1.5 to 6.0 cm in width; flowers with reflexed sepals, petals pink to white, broader and shorter than the sepals. This common shrub may be unarmed or armed. It grows to 1.0 m in height and is common over the mountainous regions of New Mexico at 5,500 to 10,500 ft. (1,680 to 3,200 m) in elevation. Occurring in moist woods, flowers are produced in April and May. (Please see couplet 6, page 188 for further description and illustration.)

**Common Gooseberry** or **Whitestem Gooseberry**,
*Ribes inerme* Rydberg
Grossulariaceae

29.    Leaves obscurely lobed (you may need to study the leaves carefully to distinguish the lobes), appearing orbicular and glandular-pubescent ................................................................................ 30.

30.    Anthers lacking a cup-shaped gland at the apex; leaves sticky to the touch due to glandular-pubescence on both surfaces; flowers white, the hypanthium 5.0 to 7.0 mm long, about as broad as long; fruit black. This shrub, which grows to 1.0 m or more in height and is found at 6,000 to 7,200 ft. (1,830 to 2,200 m) in elevation, just might be closely related to the **Southwestern Black Currant.** The **Sticky Currant** is more common to the north of our range and to northwestern New Mexico. The **Southwestern Black Currant** is a more southern species. However, they appear to have many common characteristics.

**Sticky Currant**, *Ribes viscosissimum* Pursh    Grossulariaceae

30. Anthers with a cup-shaped gland at the apex; leaves glandular-pubescent, but not strongly viscid as in the **Sticky Currant** ............................................................................ 31.

31. Hypanthium approximately 2 times as long as wide or shorter, 3.0 to 4.0 mm in length, greenish white in color, the flowers produced from May through August; fruit black; leaves shallowly 3- to 5-lobed, the lobes crenate to dentate, and both surfaces are glandular-pubescent. This uncommon shrub has been reported to reach 2.0 m in height in southern and western New Mexico at 7,000 to 9,000 ft. (2,130 to 2,740 m) in elevation. The specific name, *mescalerium*, refers to the Mescalero Apache Indians who once lived in the range of this species.

**Southwestern Black Currant**, *Ribes mescalerium* Coville

Grossulariaceae

31. Hypanthium approximately 3 times as long as wide or longer, 6.0 to 8.0 mm in length, flowers pink; fruit red or orange-red and slightly glandular to smooth; leaves fragrant, shallowly 3- to 5-lobed, the lobes crenate, the length and width about the same distance. This common shrub, to 1.0 m in height, is widely scattered throughout New Mexico at 6,000 to 9,000 ft. (1,830 to 2,740 m) in elevation. Found in dry pine forests and gulches, and flowering from May through most of the summer months, this attractive plant is sought after for the fruit that is used in jellies and wines.

**Wax Currant**, *Ribes cereum* Douglas
       Syns. *R. inebrians* Lindley                    Grossulariaceae

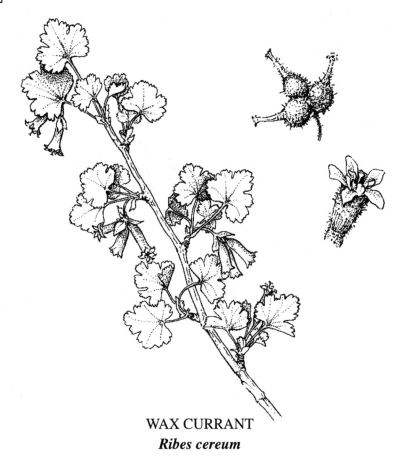

WAX CURRANT
*Ribes cereum*

32.     Flowers and fruit borne solitary, 1 or 2 on a leafy branch, or in corymbs; flowers perfect and complete, the petals white to off-pink; shrubs, often with shredding bark at maturity .............................................................................. 33.

32.     Flowers borne in catkins, pendulous or a drooping spike, or in a ball or head, forming achenes; floral parts absent or reduced in size, plants often monoecious or dioecious; mostly trees at maturity. (*Morus microphylla* commonly retains a shrub habit or may become a small tree.) .............. 36.

33.    Fruit an inflated capsule producing 2 or 3 follicle-like carpels that are dehiscent on 2 sutures; leaf blades usually longer than broad, 2.5 to 4.5 cm in length, petioles glabrous or only slightly pubescent; flowers 15 to 25 in a corymb. This shrub to 1.0 m or more in height is common over rocky slopes in dry and open woods. Flowering in June and July, it can be found from the foothills to the subalpine at 6,000 to 10,000 ft. (1,830 to 3,050 m) in elevation. This attractive species, with considerable tolerance for limited water, does well under cultivation.

**Mountain Ninebark**, *Physocarpus monogynus* (Torrey) Coulter

Rosaceae

MOUNTAIN NINEBARK
*Physocarpus monogynus*

33.    Fruit an aggregate of many drupelets formed from many separate pistils in each flower; leaf blades broader than long, petioles pubescent to glandular-pubescent; flowers solitary or in cymose clusters of less than 10 flowers ........................................................ 34.

34.    Mature leaves large, palmate and attractive averaging 8.0
       to 30.0 cm wide; flowers borne 2 to 9 in cymose clusters,
       petals white and showy; fruit red, the drupelets commonly
       eaten by birds, but not always tasty to humankind. This
       frequently planted shrub, 1.0 to 2.0 m in height, with shred-
       ding older bark, commonly occurs in the mountains at
       7,000 to 10,000 ft. (2,130 to 3,050 m) in elevation. It flow-
       ers during the summer months.

**Thimble Raspberry**, *Rubus parviflorus* Nuttall
        Syns. *Rubacer parviflorus* (Nuttall) Rydberg
                                                    Rosaceae

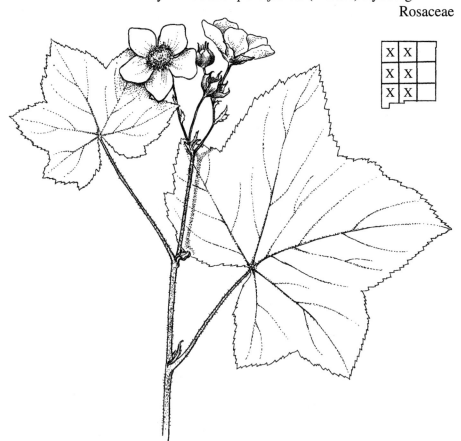

THIMBLE RASPBERRY
*Rubus parviflorus*

34.    Mature leaves averaging less than 8.0 cm wide; flowers
       and fruit borne solitary or 1 or 2 on leafy branches............... 35.

35. Leaves shallowly 3- or 5-lobed, lobes rounded, and some leaves not lobed with only palmate venation; flowers showy and solitary, with five white petals and many stamens, terminating the lateral branches. This common shrub, sometimes reaching 1.5 m in height at maturity, may also be decumbent and prostrate. It occurs in the foothills, canyons and on rocky slopes over the northern and western parts of New Mexico at 5,000 to 9,000 ft. (1,520 to 2,740 m) in elevation. Flowering in May and June, this species does not live up to the specific name, *deliciosus*; the dark purple fruit is anything but delicious.

**Boulder Raspberry,** *Rubus deliciosus* Torrey       Rosaceae

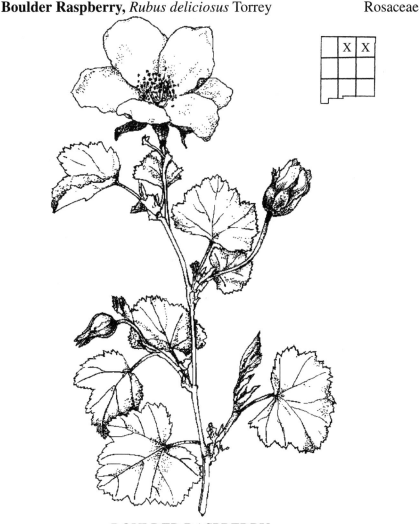

BOULDER RASPBERRY
*Rubus deliciosus*

35.    Leaves conspicuously 3-lobed, often with 2 small additional lat-
       eral lobes; flowers are attractive and conspicuous, borne sepa-
       rately or in small clusters of 2 or occasionally 3 per inflores-
       cence, petals number 5 and are showy, stamens are numerous;
       fruit is red, more than 1.5 cm in diameter, and looks delicious,
       but we have never tasted it. The known range of this rather large
       ascending shrub is different in that the distribution appears to be
       from the southwest corner to the northeast corner of New Mexico
       at 5,000 to 8,000 ft. (1,520 to 2,440 m) in elevation. It flowers
       throughout the growing season.

**New Mexico Raspberry**, *Rubus neomexicanus* A. Gray      Rosaceae

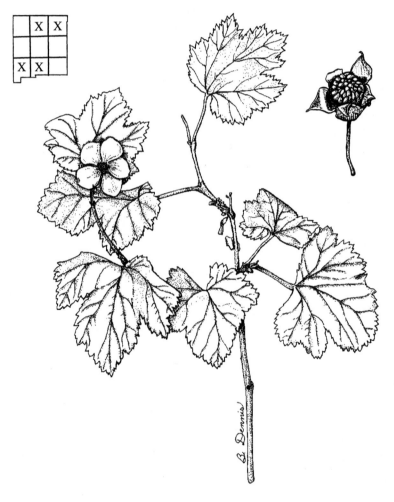

NEW MEXICO RASPBERRY
*Rubus neomexicanus*

36. Inflorescence a pendulous, globose head that is green in flower, becoming brown in fruit to produce many achenes, the heads remaining on the tree throughout the winter; petiole base hollow forming a hood over the lateral bud; bark on older branches and trunk scaling off to expose the white or greenish inner bark .............................................. 37.

36. Inflorescence a pendulous, elongate catkin that is green in flower, then producing either a number of yellow-brown capsules that in turn produce many seeds with long silky hairs at the base or a fleshy multiple fruit of many red, black or white drupes; petiole base not hollow, buds borne in the axils of the current leaves; bark smooth or forming fissures or ridges, but not scaling off .................................... 38.

37. Leaves 15.0 to 25.0 cm in width, divided into 5, sometimes 3 or 7, acute or acuminate lobes, the sinuses between the lobes extending about halfway or more to the base; leaves green above and tomentose to glabrous below, but not densely pubescent along the veins below; trees to 25.0 m in height at maturity; flowering from March through April. This attractive and conspicuous native tree is said to have been historically abundant in southwestern New Mexico at 4,500 to 6,000 ft. (1,370 to 1,830 m) in elevation. Today it appears to be less common along many of the same waterways and canyons.

**Arizona Sycamore** or **Arizona Plane-tree**, *Platanus wrightii*
S. Watson     Platanaceae

37. Leaves 8.0 to 20.0 cm in width, broadly ovate, shallowly divided into 5 short lobes with several teeth on each lobe, but not deeply divided to the base; leaves green above, greenish-white below and tomentose, with dense pubescence along the veins; trees to 30.0 m in height at maturity; flowering in April and May. This cultivated eastern species is becoming more widespread and abundant throughout New Mexico and the western states. It is slow growing but extremely long-lived and although a messy yard or garden tree, it is attractive as an ornamental.

**American Sycamore** or **American Plane-tree**,
*Platanus occidentalis* L.     Platanaceae

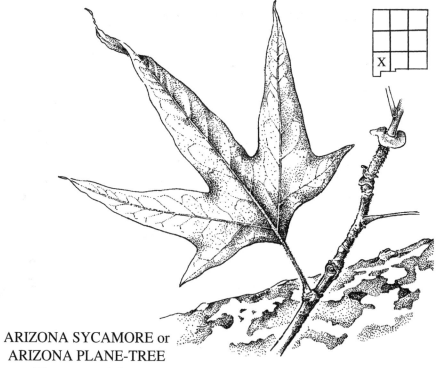

ARIZONA SYCAMORE or
ARIZONA PLANE-TREE
*Platanus wrightii*

AMERICAN SYCAMORE or
AMERICAN PLANE-TREE
*Platanus occidentalis*

38.    Inflorescence a pendulous, elongate drooping catkin that produces a number of ovoid tomentose capsules that in turn produce many minute seeds with long silky hairs at the base; leaves 4.0 to 8.0 cm in width with flattened petioles, variously lobed with 3 to 5 lobes to broadly toothed, upper surface dark green to blue-green, lower surface densely white tomentose; plants dioecious. This weedy, introduced tree has been known to grow to more than 25.0 m in height and it grows rapidly. At the same time it is short-lived because the wood is weak and storms often destroy it. It reproduces  asexually very rapidly from sucker shoots that come off the roots. Once introduced it is difficult to control, at the same time viable seeds are seldom produced.

**White Poplar**, *Populus alba* L.             Salicaceae

38.    Inflorescence a pendulous catkin that produces a fleshy multiple fruit of many red, black or white drupes; leaves ranging from 1- to 6-lobed to obliquely based and ovate or deeply notched and asymmetrical, but with 3 main veins from the base ........................................................................ 39.

39.    Petioles averaging less than 1.2 cm in length; mature leaf blades 7.5 cm or less in length and commonly palmately lobed, scabrous on both surfaces; variously lobed and not lobed; plant dioecious; staminate catkins (spikes) 1.0 to 2.0 cm in length, on short pedicels; pistillate catkins drooping, short, 1.0 to 1.8 cm in length; fruit a multiple of drupes (formed from several separate flowers), ranging in color from red to black at maturity, juicy and edible. This native shrub or small tree is relatively common over the southern half of New Mexico at 3,500 to 5,500 ft. (1,070 to 1,680 m) in elevation. Flowering in early spring, it is found in dry rocky soils, often of limestone and igneous origin.

**Texas Mulberry,** *Morus microphylla* Buckley        Moraceae

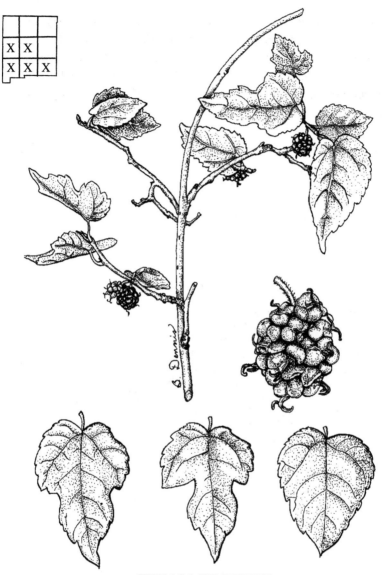

TEXAS MULBERRY
*Morus microphylla*

39.    Petioles averaging more than 1.2 cm in length; mature leaf blades 8.0 cm or more in length, glabrous or slightly pubescent on both surfaces, seldom slightly scabrous on the lower surface; variously lobed and not lobed; plant monoecious or dioecious; staminate catkins 1.0 to 2.5 cm in length, cylindric and drooping, pistillate catkins 1.2 to 2.0 cm in length, subglobose and drooping; fruit a multiple (formed from several separate flowers), ranging from white to pink, seldom turning black, sweet, juicy and edible. This

introduced tree, which may reach to 12.0 m at maturity, may attract more birds than even an ardent ornithologist can tolerate. Although native to China, this tree has become naturalized in much of North America and Europe. Another closely related introduced species, *Morus rubra* L., the **Red Mulberry**, may key to this point.

**White Mulberry**, *Morus alba* L. Moraceae

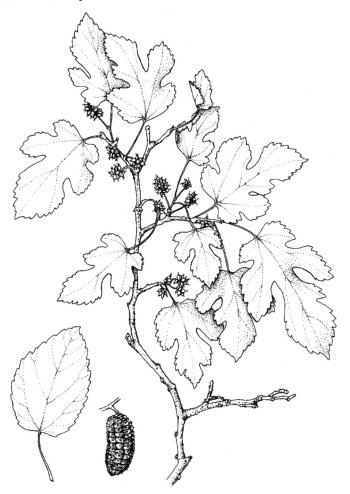

WHITE MULBERRY
*Morus alba*

40.    Plants with spines or thorns on stems .................................. 41.

40.    Plants without spines or thorns on stems ............................. 74.

41.     Plant a heavily branched mass of stiff, smooth, green, thick thorns to 6.0 mm in diameter and to 10.0 cm or more in length; leaves absent or if present then only scale-like, with photosynthesis occurring in the green stems and spines; flowers borne on slender pedicels in small lateral racemes in May through July. This robust shrub to 3.0 or possibly 4.0 m in height is easy to spot at 3,500 to 5,500 ft. (1,070 to 1,680 m) in elevation over the southern tier of counties. No other woody plant throughout New Mexico can be confused with this bundle of large green thorns.

**Crown-of-Thorns** or **Crucifixion Plant**, *Koeberlinia spinosa*
Zuccarini     Koeberliniaceae

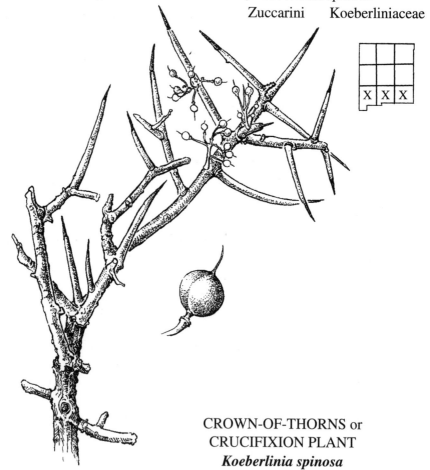

CROWN-OF-THORNS or
CRUCIFIXION PLANT
*Koeberlinia spinosa*

41.     Plants with spines and thorns, but these on stems and leaves or forming slender branches, not appearing to make up the entire plant; some true leaves present during the growing season, with photosynthesis occurring mostly in the leaves and young stems ...... 42.

42.     Leaf margins entire ................................................................ 43.

42.     Leaf margins toothed: serrate, dentate or crenate .................. 63.

43.     Leaves averaging less than 4.0 mm in width .................................... 44.

43.     Leaves averaging more than 4.0 mm in width ................................ 52.

44.     Fruit a fleshy 1-seeded drupe borne from a single flower; flowers inconspicuous in a small axillary cyme or solitary, perfect, but not always complete; leaves less than 15.0 mm in length, linear, oblong, oblanceolate to spatulate in shape and often in fascicles; branches often ending in sharp slender spines ..................................................... 45.

44.     Fruit a legume, 1-seeded globose pod, follicle, achene or utricle; flowers borne in heads, racemes, panicles or spikes ........ 47.

45.     Leaf margins strongly revolute, leaves small and linear-oblong, 2.0 to 12.0 mm in length and 1.0 mm in width, sessile and often fascicled; fruit an oblong, 1-celled drupe to 1.0 cm in length, with an exserted style, 4.0 to 7.0 mm in length, reddish-black to purplish-black at maturity; flowers solitary, small and yellowish. This shrub, from 1.0 to 3.0 m in height at maturity is characterized by elongate spine-tipped branches. It flowers in early spring and is abundant in the southern and southeastern counties of New Mexico at 3,500 to 5,000 ft. (1,070 to 1,520 m) in elevation.

**Javelinabush**, *Condalia ericoides* (Gray) M. C. Johnston
            Syns. *Microrhamnus ericoides* Gray           Rhamnaceae

45.     Leaf margins thickened and round in cross-section, but not revolute, leaves petiolate; fruit ovoid to ellipsoid, and sometimes beaked to less than 4.0 mm in length ..................................................... 46.

JAVELINABUSH
*Condalia ericoides*

46.    Fruit nearly sessile, black at maturity with a persistent
style; branchlets stout, very rigid, spiny throughout; leaves
oblanceolate to obovate, 3.0 to 5.0 mm in width, lateral
veins inconspicuous; flowers small and lacking petals,
borne in small cymes or umbels. This stiff shrub with
heavy spines, to 4.0 or 5.0 m in height at maturity, is infrequent in the southwest corner of New Mexico at 3,500
to 5,000 ft. (1,070 to 1,520 m) in elevation. Flowering in
late summer and fall, it occurs in dry canyons and on south-
facing slopes. (Please see distribution map, page 227.)

**Mexican Bluewood**, *Condalia mexicana* Schlechtendal
Rhamnaceae

46. Fruit distinctly pedicelled, larger than most when fleshy, 3.0 to 4.5 mm in diameter at maturity, commonly beaked and black in color; branchlets slender, spiny towards the apex; leaves spatulate, commonly in fascicles, 1.0 to 2.5 mm in width and 3.0 to 12.0 mm in length, lateral veins conspicuous. This relatively common species over southern New Mexico occurs on dry mesas at 3,500 to 5,500 ft. (1,070 to 1,680 m) in elevation. It flowers in late summer and fall.

**Squawbush**, *Condalia spathulata* A. Gray          Rhamnaceae

Some authorities consider this species distinct from *C. warnockii* M. C. Johnston, while others consider *C. warnockii* as a subspecies of the **Squawbush**.

MEXICAN BLUEWOOD
*Condalia mexicana*

SQUAWBUSH
*Condalia spathulata*

47. Fruit a legume with several seeds, or a legume-like, round pod with 1 seed and armed with sharp spines, in either case indehiscent; inflorescence a raceme; flowers purple to purple-pink to red ..................................................................................... 48.

47. Fruit an achene, utricle or follicle; inflorescence a head, panicle, spike or solitary; flowers white or yellowish.................................. 50.

48. Fruit a legume restricted into several segments (loment), but the fruit not separating at maturity and not spiny; shrub to 1.0 m in height, glabrous, but not pubescent or glandular; leaves small, 1.3 to 2.3 cm in length and elliptic; flowers numerous, in racemes, the corolla purple to pink, banner spreading and reflexed, stamens 10 and diadelphous. This introduced Asian species, which spreads rapidly by rhizomes along streams and *acequias* (irrigation ditches), is considered rare, but can become a serious problem. Occurring at 4,500 to 6,000 ft. (1,370 to 1,830 m) in elevation it flowers from May to July.

**Camelthorn**, *Alhagi maurorum* Medik
Syns. *A. camelorum* Fischer          Fabaceae

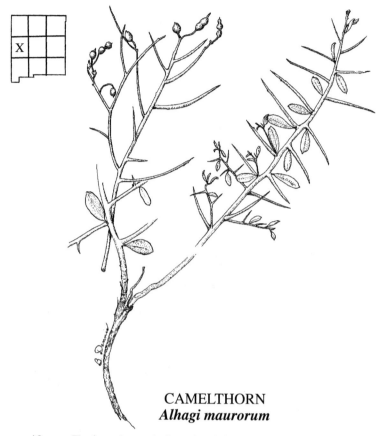

CAMELTHORN
*Alhagi maurorum*

48.    Fruit a 1 seeded pod, globose, thick-walled and spiny;
       shrubs low, 70.0 cm in height or less, herbage gray-pu-
       bescent and sometimes glandular ........................................ 49.

49.    Pubescence on the upper branches strigose and harsh, flowering
       branches sometimes densely glandular, this making the identifi-
       cation assured; barbs on the prickles of the fruit scattered and not
       confined to the apex of the barbs; 3 upper petals united at the
       base; leaves linear, commonly averaging less than 1.2 mm in
       width. This common shrub occurs in dry, sandy, scrub communi-
       ties and over rocky hillsides at 3,500 to 5,000 ft. (1,070 to 1,520
       m) in elevation. Limited in distribution to the southern counties,
       it may flower at any time during the growing season.

**Sticky Range Ratany** or **Little Leaf Krameria**, *Krameria erecta*
                              Willdenow *ex* J. A. Schultes
                    Syns. *K. parvifolia* Bentham
                          *K. glandulosa* Rose & Painter
                                          Krameriaceae

STICKY RANGE RATANY or
LITTLE LEAF KRAMERIA
*Krameria erecta*

49.    Pubescence on the upper branches tomentose and soft, flowering branches never glandular; barbs on the prickles of the fruit confined to the apex of the barbs; 3 upper petals free to the base and reflexed with 2 orange gland-like appendages inside the petals aiding in the identification; leaves linear, commonly averaging more than 1.5 mm in width. As with the previous species, this too is a dry, sandy, scrub communities species, but based on collection data it occurs at lower elevations of 3,500 to 4,000 ft. (1,070 to 1,220 m). It also flowers throughout the growing season and is confined to the southern counties. *K. grayi* in a tincture of the root or a strong decoction (tea) made from the leaves is one of the best plant astringents and topical hemostatics for sore gums and abcesses in the mouth.

**White Ratany** or **Chacate**, *Krameria grayi* Rose & Painter

Krameriaceae

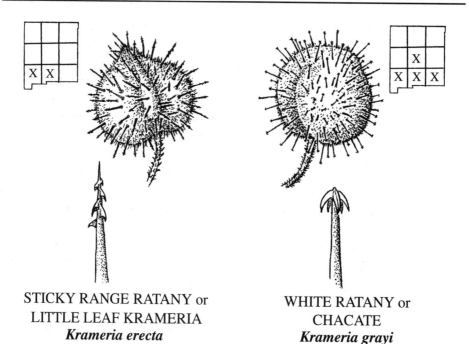

STICKY RANGE RATANY or
LITTLE LEAF KRAMERIA
*Krameria erecta*

WHITE RATANY or
CHACATE
*Krameria grayi*

One other more widespread member of this genus occurs in New Mexico. This is an herbaceous and prostrate species that grows from a woody base and has a similar southern range, but extends into the central part of the State. The **Trailing Krameria**, *Krameria lanceolata* Torrey, is found on open plains in sandy soils at 4,000 to 6,500 ft. (1,220 to 1,980 m) in elevation.

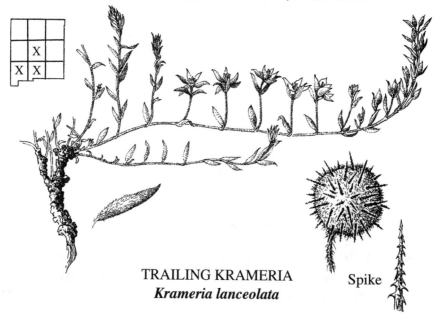

TRAILING KRAMERIA
*Krameria lanceolata*                    Spike

50.    Inflorescence a head of 5 to 9 flowers, surrounded by an involucre, heads solitary or in small corymbs; fruit an achene, the pappus white and soft; flowers perfect and yellow, with an inferior ovary; leaves linear to oblanceolate, often fascicled and sessile, the primary leaves developing into the curved rigid spines. This heavily tomentose shrub, seldom reaching 1.0 m in height at maturity, is confined to the northwest corner of New Mexico at 4,500 to 7,000 ft. (1,370 to 2,130 m) in elevation. Found predominantly in saline and alkaline soils, this rare species appears to flower throughout the growing season.

**Spiny Horsebush,** *Tetradymia spinosa* Hooker & Arnott

Asteraceae

SPINY HORSEBUSH
*Tetradymia spinosa*

50.    Inflorescence a cyme, a spike or the flowers borne solitary; fruit a utricle or follicle; flowers perfect or imperfect .................................................................................. 51.

51.     Young twigs light tan to brown or gray, rigid, terete, with some
        becoming spinescent; flowers imperfect and incomplete, perianth
        lacking, with male flowers and female flowers on separate plants
        (dioecious), or occasionally male and female flowers on the same
        plant (monoecious), not brightly colored, the staminate flowers
        develop into a spike, while the pistillate flowers are sessile, soli-
        tary or are borne in pairs; the fruit is a green to tan or somewhat
        reddish winged utricle. The plant will commonly have some leaves
        opposite and some alternate. This is a widely scattered species of
        alkaline soils occurring at 5,000 to 6,500 ft. (1,520 to 1,980 m) in
        elevation. (For a full description and illustration, please see Key
        VI, page 111.)

**Greasewood,** *Sarcobatus vermiculatus* (Hooker) Torrey
                                                    Chenopodiaceae

51.     Young twigs green, slender, stiff, angled, glabrous or glaucous
        and terminally spinescent; flowers perfect and complete, small
        and solitary, sepals 5, petals 5 and white, stamens 7 to 9, pistil 1;
        fruit a broadly ovoid follicle. Rare in New Mexico, **Spiny
        Greasebush** is usually found on dry limestone cliffs and hills. It
        has been reported and collected from the eastern and southeast-
        ern parts of the State to the southwest corner at 4,500 to 5,500 ft.
        (1,370 to 1,680 m) in elevation.

**Spiny Greasebush**, *Glossopetalon spinescens* A. Gray
                                                    Crossosomataceae

52.     Fruit a large, green aggregate, measuring 8.0 to 13.0 cm
        in diameter at maturity, made up of many 1-seeded drupe-
        lets, the juice milky white; leaves broad-ovate to ovate-
        lanceolate, 6.0 to 12.0 cm in length and 3.0 to 6.0 cm in
        width, green and lustrous, petiole 2.5 to 5.0 cm in length;
        dioecious; the staminate flowers on long axillary racemes,
        the pistillate flowers in globose dense heads. These ro-
        bust and thorny introduced trees commonly reach 20.0 m
        in height and appear rather nondescript until the large,
        heavy fruit is mature. Native to the states east of New
        Mexico, historically the most important use of this tree
        was planting as a hedge row to control cattle and sheep.

**Osage Orange** or **Hedge Apple**, *Maclura pomifera*
                    (Rafinesque) Schneider          Moraceae

SPINY GREASEBUSH
*Glossopetalon spinescens*

OSAGE ORANGE or
HEDGE APPLE
*Maclura pomifera*

52.    Fruit a much smaller berry, drupe, capsule, utricle or winged seed, all less than 2.0 cm in diameter ...................... 53.

53.    Fruit a berry, these borne singly, in pairs or in small fascicles ......... 54.

53.    Fruit a drupe, capsule, utricle or winged seed; inflorescence a cyme, raceme, panicle, spike, solitary or in axillary clusters............. 57.

54.    Leaves oblong to obovate, leathery, glabrate and dark green above and woolly-villous beneath, 1.4 to 2.5 cm in width and 2.0 to 6.0 cm in length, spines borne along the stems and at the tips of the branches; flowers fragrant and perfect in few flowered fascicles, borne on pubescent pedicels, corolla white, petals 5- and 3-lobed, stamens 5 fertile and 5 sterile; fruit lustrous black, borne on slender peduncles. This robust shrub to 3.0 m at maturity is rare in southwest New Mexico at 4,000 to 6,000 ft. (1,220 to 1,830 m) in elevation. Flowering in June and July, it can be found locally abundant in isolated locations along streams and arroyos.

**Woolly Buckthorn**, *Sideroxylon lanuginosum* Michaux
ssp. *rigidum* (A. Gray) T. D. Pennington
Syns. *Bumelia lanuginosa* (Michaux) Persoon
Sapotaceae

54.    Leaves linear to elliptic or oblanceolate, light or glaucous green in color, 0.3 to 1.2 cm in width and 1.0 to 6.0 cm in length; fruit globose to ovoid and red in color............. 55.

55.    Older stems commonly reddish-brown, flowers averaging 2.0 mm in length, greenish-white to greenish-yellow with some purple in veins, calyx lobes 2/3 as long as the corolla tube or 2.0 mm long, pedicels about 10.0 mm in length; leaves 1.0 to 4.0 cm in length and fascicled; fruit bright red, tomato-shaped berries. This common shrub can be found widely scattered over dry hills and plains throughout New Mexico at 4,000 to 7,000 ft. (1,220 to 2,130 m) in elevation. Usually about 1.0 m in height, it may reach 2.0 m and become an attractive cultivated plant.

**Pale Wolfberry** or **Tomatillo**, *Lycium pallidum* Miers
Solanaceae

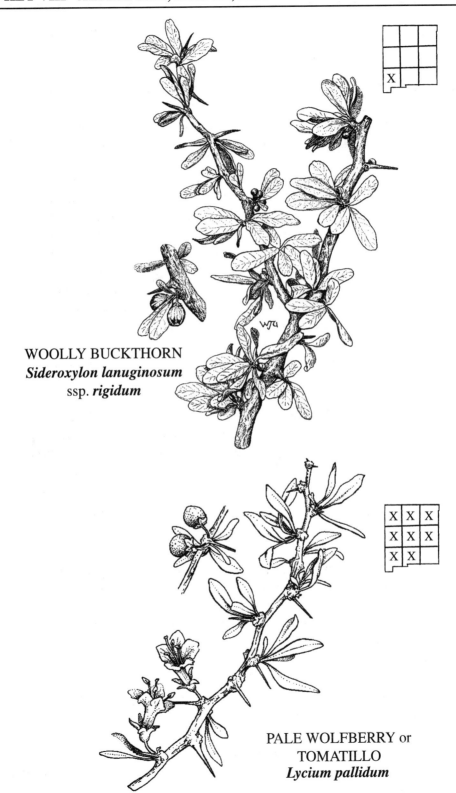

WOOLLY BUCKTHORN
*Sideroxylon lanuginosum*
ssp. *rigidum*

PALE WOLFBERRY or
TOMATILLO
*Lycium pallidum*

55. Older stems commonly gray to light brown, flowers averaging 1.6 mm in length or less, purple or white tinged with lavender, calyx lobes less than 2/3 as long as the tube, or less than 2.0 mm long, pedicels less than 6.0 mm in length .......................................... 56.

56. Leaves oblanceolate to spatulate and somewhat linear, averaging more than 4.0 mm in width, and 1.0 to 5.0 cm in length; corolla lobes ciliate to lanate, greenish-white to light purple or lavender, flowers borne in fascicles; spines stout and abundant or sometimes absent; fruit bright red, fleshy and juicy. An infrequent species of drier areas at lower elevations ranging from 3,500 to 5,500 ft. (1,070 to 1,680 m), our records are from alkaline soils in the major river drainages in the southern part of the State.

**Torrey Wolfberry**, *Lycium torreyi* A. Gray          Solanaceae

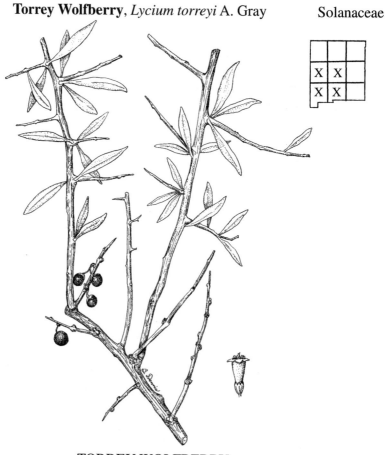

TORREY WOLFBERRY
*Lycium torreyi*

56.     Leaves in small fascicles of 2 or 4 leaves, linear and spatu-
        late, averaging less than 3.0 mm in width and 1.0 to 2.5
        cm in length; corolla lobes only slightly ciliate or gla-
        brous, white to blue to lavender, flowers borne solitary or
        2 to 3 in a fascicle; spines slender often needle-like; fruit
        bright red and very juicy. The range of this uncommon
        shrub appears to be limited to the southern part of New
        Mexico at 3,500 to 5,000 ft. (1,070 to 1,520 m) in eleva-
        tion. Flowering dates are not well established. Some au-
        thorities separate this species into two subspecies, but
        based on our present knowledge this is not possible at
        this time.

        **Berlandier Wolfberry**, *Lycium berlandieri* Dunal

                                                            Solanaceae

57. Fruit a capsule; flowers and fruit borne in terminal racemes or
    narrow panicles, usually at the ends of the branches ........................ 58.

57. Fruit a drupe, utricle or winged seed and samara-like; flowers
    seldom terminal, usually borne down the stem, back from the
    stem apex, often with leaves beyond the inflorescence .................... 59.

        58.     Flowers and leaves not usually appearing at the same time,
                flowers appearing first followed by leaves; flowers bright
                crimson, to 2.5 cm in length, perfect, regular and tubular,
                borne in panicles or racemes, 5.0 to 20.0 cm in length;
                stems numerous, conspicuously grooved, cane-like, 1.5
                to 5.0 m long, radiating whip-like from a common base;
                leaves oblanceolate to spatulate, thick and leathery, 1.5
                to 4.0 cm in length; fruit an ovoid capsule producing many
                winged seeds. This attractive and unique shrub is con-
                fined to the southern one-third of the State at 4,000 to
                6,500 ft. (1,220 to 1,980 m) in elevation. Usually found
                on dry, rocky, well-drained soils and south-facing slopes,
                the flowers develop from March through June, followed
                by the leaves.

        **Ocotillo**, *Fouquieria splendens* Engelmann      Fouquieriaceae

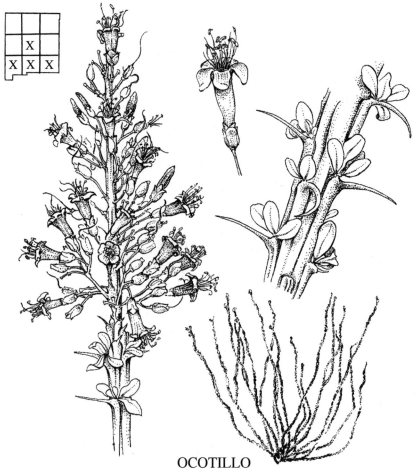

OCOTILLO
*Fouquieria splendens*

58.  Flowers produced in the summer following the produc-
     tion of leaves in the early spring, both present at the same
     time; leaves with three main veins from the base that are
     more obvious when observed from the lower surface, this
     surface white-tomentose, the upper surface green to gray-
     green and pubescent; flowers small, white, the sepals, pet-
     als and stamens 5-merous, ovary and styles 3-lobed; fruit
     a 3-lobed, small dry capsule. This common low shrub,
     seldom reaching 1.0 m in height, is widely scattered
     throughout New Mexico at 5,500 to 9,500 ft. (1,680 to
     2,900 m) in elevation. It may flower over the entire grow-
     ing season, often forming thickets in forested areas.

**Buckbrush** or **Fendler Ceanothus**, *Ceanothus fendleri*
                              A. Gray      Rhamnaceae

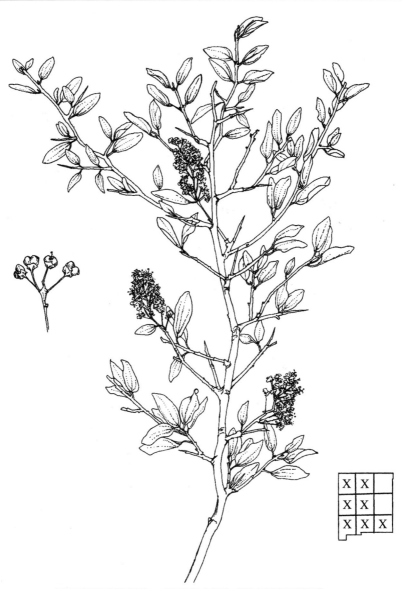

BUCKBRUSH or FENDLER CEANOTHUS
*Ceanothus fendleri*

59.      Fruit a utricle, fruiting bracts in pairs and orbicular or obovate, formed on each side of the mature seed and enclosing it; plants dioecious; inflorescence a spike or panicle or an axillary cluster; plants of semiarid habitats .................................................................. 60.

59.      Fruit a 1-seeded drupe, fruit not surrounded by paired bracts; flowers perfect or sometimes monoecious or polygamous; inflorescence a cyme or flowers solitary ................................................... 61.

60.    Leaves orbicular-ovate, about as wide as long, petiolate to nearly sessile, scurfy, not on a short spur bending around the bud; staminate flowers on spikes and the perianth 5-parted, pistillate flowers solitary or several in leaf axils. Considered by some authorities to be perennial, this spiny species produces woody stems well above the soil level to 1.0 m in height. It is found in dry alkaline soils over the western and especially the northwestern portion of New Mexico at 4,500 to 7,000 ft. (1,370 to 2,130 m) in elevation. A relatively rare species with a more northern range throughout North America, our records are poor and incomplete.

**Spiny Saltbush**, *Atriplex confertifolia* (Torrey & Fremont)
S. Watson      Chenopodiaceae

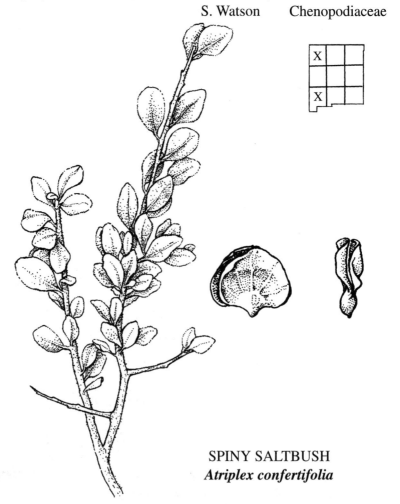

SPINY SALTBUSH
*Atriplex confertifolia*

60.  Leaves oblanceolate to spatulate, 4 times longer than wide, sessile, on a short spur that bends around the bud; flowers in terminal and axillary spicate panicles and imperfect. This yet uncollected shrub in New Mexico, to 1.5 m in height, has a record of occurring on dry plains and hills at 4,500 to 7,500 ft. (1,370 to 2,290 m) in elevation in adjacent states. Although the distribution and known geography of this species would indicate it can be expected to occur in the northwestern corner of New Mexico, there are no records of sightings or collections. We include this short description here for those individuals who might be fortunate enough to locate it.

**Hop Sage**, *Grayia spinosa* (Hooker) Moquin-Tandon
Syns. *Atriplex grayi* Collotzi *ex* W. A. Weber
Chenopodiaceae

HOP SAGE
*Grayia spinosa*

61.     Spines commonly paired at the nodes, and stipular, averaging
        less than 2.0 cm in length; leaves less than 2.5 cm in width and
        4.5 cm in length, the leaf base oblique, with 3 main veins from
        the base, coarsely toothed or entire; flowers greenish-white and
        lacking a corolla; fruit a 1-seeded, yellow or orange, fleshy drupe.
        This evergreen shrub, seldom reaching more than 1.5 m in height,
        is confined to the southern and southwestern counties of New
        Mexico at 3,200 to 4,500 ft. (980 to 1,370 m) in elevation. It
        occurs over dry rocky terrain and mesas, and occasionally in and
        along the margins of arroyos.

**Desert Hackberry** or **Granjeno**, *Celtis pallida* Torrey      Ulmaceae

DESERT HACKBERRY
or GRANJENO
*Celtis pallida*

61.     Spines commonly borne singly, not paired, 1 spine borne at each node or formed at the tips of the branches, averaging more than 2.0 cm in length; leaves with 1 main vein and the leaf base attenuate, cuneate or obtuse, but never oblique ................................... 62.

    62.     Leaves averaging more than 4.0 cm in length, 0.8 to 2.5 cm in width, lanceolate to narrowly ovate with 1 main vein, entire, upper surface green, covered with scale-like stellate pubescence, lower surface silvery white, densely covered with scale-like stellate hairs; stems not obviously grooved, reddish, coated with gray, scaly pubescence, becoming glabrous with spines present or absent, when present variable in length, commonly 2.0 to 6.0 cm; flowers in clusters of 1 to 3, hypanthium tubular and silvery-yellow above, calyx 4 lobed, petals absent; fruit a drupe, yellow to brown and densely covered with silver scales. Native to Eurasia, the **Russian Olive** is commonly planted in yards and as a windbreak, but it has escaped cultivation and is widely scattered over the State, especially in low, moist and sandy areas.

    **Russian Olive**, *Elaeagnus angustifolia* L.          Elaeagnaceae

RUSSIAN OLIVE
*Elaeagnus angustifolia*

62.     Leaves averaging less than 2.5 cm in length, 0.4 to 0.7 cm in width, elliptic, ovate or narrowly oblong with 3 main veins, entire to serrate, glabrous to puberulent, pale green on both surfaces; stems grayish green, grooved and glaucous with stout spines to 7.0 cm in length; flowers inconspicuous, in small axillary cymes of 2 to 7 flowers; drupe globose, blue to black in color, covered with a bloom at maturity. Occurring in the southern tier of counties at 3,500 to 5,000 ft. (1,070 to 1,520 m) in elevation, this uncommon shrub may flower at various times throughout a single growing season. The fact that the leaves are extremely variable in shape and margins, and that various forms of this species have been described by several different scientific names, leads to considerable confusion in making an identification. (Please see couplet 68, page 248 for further description.)

**Lote Bush** or **Graythorn**, *Ziziphus obtusifolia* (Hooker)
A. Gray
Syns. *Condalia obtusifolia* (Hooker) Weberbauer
*C. lycioides* (A.Gray) Weberbauer

Rhamnaceae

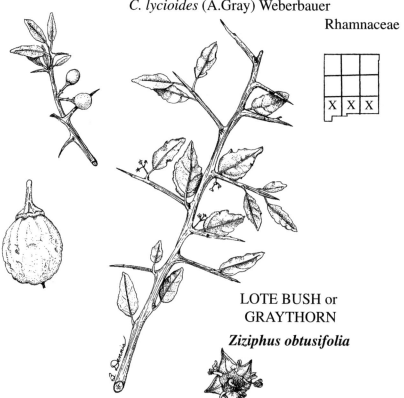

LOTE BUSH or
GRAYTHORN

*Ziziphus obtusifolia*

63.     Spines 2 or 3 at the nodes, commonly stipular, averaging less
        than 2.0 cm in length; fruit a drupe or a berry .................................. 64.

63.     Spines borne singly at the nodes or on exserted modified stems
        averaging more than 2.0 cm in length; fruit a drupe or a pome......... 67.


        64.     Spines paired at the nodes and stipular with some stems
                exserted and forming spines; leaves alternate, 3 main veins
                from the base, but not fascicled and not spine tipped; fruit
                a 1-seeded drupe; wood and inner bark never yellow............ 65.

        64.     Spines 3 at the nodes and stipular; leaves unifoliate and
                fascicled, 1 main vein from the base with some leaves
                spine tipped; fruit a several seeded berry; wood and inner
                bark yellow; flower with 6 separate sepals, 6 separate
                petals, 6 stamens, each anther opening by 2 apical valves,
                and the ovary superior .......................................................... 66.


65.     Leaf bases oblique, some leaves entire and some 3-toothed to-
        ward the apex; fruit a 1-seeded, yellow or orange, fleshy drupe,
        less than 1 cm in length. (For a full description and illustration of
        this native shrub, the **Desert Hackberry,** please see couplet 61,
        page 242.)

        **Desert Hackberry** or **Granjeno**, *Celtis pallida* Torrey       Ulmaceae


65.     Leaf bases obtuse, cuneate to slightly oblique, most leaves widely
        serrate and glandular tipped; fruit a 1- or 2-seeded, orange to
        brown, fleshy drupe, 2.0 to 3.0 cm in length, edible as it comes
        from the tree or dried and preserved; spines present or absent,
        when present axillary and much shorter than the leaves, hooked
        or curved, stems never exserted to form spines. This introduced
        and cultivated tree may reach to 15.0 m in height at maturity. It is
        considered native to Syria, and it occurs in moist soils through-
        out many parts of Asia, Africa and Europe where it is thought to
        have numerous medicinal uses.

        **Jujube**, *Ziziphus jujuba* P. Miller
                Syns. *Z. zizyphus* (L.) Karsten                Rhamnaceae

66.    Inflorescence a raceme averaging more than 9 flowers, commonly 10 or more; fruit red or purple, averaging 8.0 to 12.0 mm in length; second year twigs gray. This cultivated and widely escaping species is the alternate host of the black stem rusts of wheat and several cultivated grasses. By eliminating the **Common Barberry** the rust could not survive. For many years the Department of Agriculture had an eradication policy to eliminate this plant from the wheat growing regions of the central states, consequently, it is far less common than it once was.

**Common Barberry**, *Berberis vulgaris* L.          Berberidaceae

COMMON BARBERRY
*Berberis vulgaris*

66. Inflorescence a raceme averaging less than 9 yellow flowers, commonly less than 8; fruit scarlet red, 4.0 to 6.0 mm in length, 1- to 3-seeded; second year twigs a varnished reddish-brown. This native shrub seldom reaches more than 1.0 m in height. It is frequently found in river valleys, on shaded hillsides and in canyons at 6,000 to 8,500 ft. (1,830 to 2,600 m) in elevation over the northern half of New Mexico.

**Fendler Barberry**, *Berberis fendleri* A. Gray     Berberidaceae

FENDLER BARBERRY
*Berberis fendleri*

67.    Mature leaves averaging less than 2.5 cm in length and less than
       1.0 cm in width; fruit a drupe with 1 to 3 stones ............................. 68.

67.    Mature leaves averaging more than 2.5 cm in length and more
       than 1.0 cm in width; fruit a drupe with 1 stone or a pome .............. 69.

    68.    Fruit with 1 stone, blue to black in color, and covered
           with a bloom; flowers inconspicuous, in small axillary
           cymes of 2 to 7 flowers; twigs grayish green, grooved,
           with stout leaf-bearing spines, to 7.0 or 8.0 cm in length;
           leaves elliptic, ovate or narrowly oblong with 3 main veins,
           entire to serrate, glabrous to puberulent, and pale green
           on both surfaces. (For a full description and illustration
           of this diverse native shrub please see couplet 62, page
           244.)

           **Lote Bush** or **Graythorn**, *Ziziphus obtusifolia* (Hooker)
                                                                A. Gray
                    Syns. *Condalia obtusifolia* (Hooker) Weberbauer
                         *C. lycioides* (A. Gray) Weberbauer
                                                           Rhamnaceae

    68.    Fruit with 3 stones, the stones commonly indehiscent,
           drupe dark blue to black and juicy; flowers small but not
           inconspicuous, in terminal panicles or spikes, sometimes
           axillary, white in color, with 5 sepals and petals and com-
           plete; leaves opposite or alternate, orbicular to obovate
           or elliptical, margins entire to serrulate, petiole short. Our
           only collections of this rare, low growing shrub are from
           Guadalupe Canyon in Hidalgo County, growing in allu-
           vial soil on the steep banks of an intermittent stream at
           5,400 ft. (1,650 m) in elevation.

           **Wright Sageretia**, *Sageretia wrightii* S. Watson   Rhamnaceae

69.    Fruit a 1-seeded plum-like drupe; carpel 1, ovary solitary, simple
       and 1-celled; lenticels horizontal and prominent .............................. 70.

69.    Fruit an apple-like pome; carpels several, commonly 5, united,
       enclosed and adnate to the hypanthium (calyx tube) which be-
       comes more or less fleshy; lenticels oval and not horizontal but
       sometimes prominent or obscure ........................................................ 71.

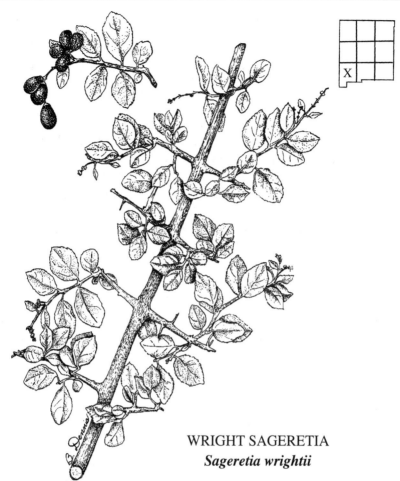

WRIGHT SAGERETIA
*Sageretia wrightii*

70.  Flowers in clusters of 2 to 5 on the end of a spur or from lateral buds, pedicels 8.0 to 14.0 mm long; leaves glabrous on both surfaces, teeth lacking glands at their tips, oval to obovate, 6.0 to 10.0 cm long and 3.0 to 5.0 cm wide, 2 glands often present at the base of the leaves or top of the petiole; petals white, ovate, 9.0 to 12.0 mm in length; fruit 2.2 to 2.7 cm in length, purple to red, flesh sweet, juicy and edible. This common North American shrub or small tree occurs in a wide range of habitats including woodlands, stream banks, thickets and in fence rows. The spine-tipped, purplish twigs and sweet smelling flowers in April and May make it easy to identify at 4,000 to 7,500 ft. (1,220 to 2,300 m) in elevation. (Please see couplet 231, page 414 for further description.)

**Wild Plum**, *Prunus americana* Marshall          Rosaceae

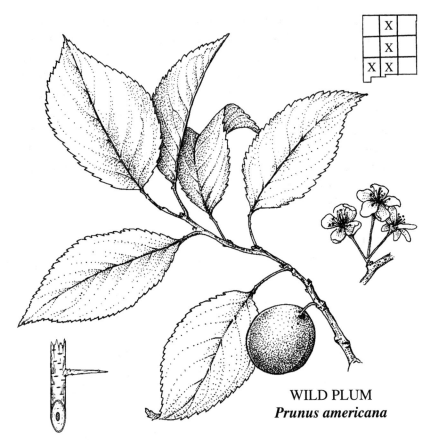

WILD PLUM
*Prunus americana*

70.    Flowers in clusters of 2 to 4 from the buds of the previous
       year, pedicels 7.0 to 10.0 mm long; leaves pubescent on
       the lower surface, teeth with glands at their tips, leaves
       elliptic to lanceolate, 2.0 to 6.0 cm long and 1.0 to 2.5 cm
       wide, 2 glands common at the junction of the leaf and the
       petiole; petals white, obovate, 3.5 to 6.0 mm in length;
       fruit 2.0 to 2.2 cm in length, red to yellow or with yellow-
       ish dots, flesh tangy to sour, juicy and edible. This infre-
       quent shrub or small tree, to 2.0 m in height, is confined
       to the eastern edge of New Mexico at 4,500 to 6,500 ft.
       (1,370 to 1,980 m) in elevation. Often forming thickets,
       it occurs in pastures, along prairie stream banks, in old
       fields, and generally sandy soils. New Mexico appears to
       be the western edge of its range. (Please see couplet 231,
       page 413 for further description.)

**Sand Plum**, *Prunus angustifolia* Marshall
       Syns. *P. watsonii* Sargent                    Rosaceae

71. Fruit averaging more than 2.0 cm in diameter at maturity, mature carpels papery and soft cartilaginous; leaves permanently pubescent to tomentose on the lower surface, ovate-oblong to broadly elliptic, 6.0 to 9.0 cm in length and 3.0 to 6.0 cm in width, coarsely serrate; flowers showy, rose-colored, in corymbs or umbel-like cymes of 2 to 5 flowers, styles 5, connate at the base, 2 ovules in each carpel, stamens many. This introduced and commonly cultivated species of lawns and gardens is closely related to the apple tree, except for the sometimes spinescent branches and the attractive pink flowers of early spring that characterize the **Crabapple**.

**Crabapple**, *Malus ioensis* var. *ioensis* (Wood) Britton
Syns. *Pyrus ioensis* (Wood) Bailey

Rosaceae

CRABAPPLE
*Malus ioensis* var. *ioensis*

71.    Fruit averaging less than 2.0 cm in diameter at maturity, carpels
       1 to 5, hard and bone-like, each enclosing 1 nutlet; flowers white
       to pink, solitary or commonly in corymbs, styles distinct, 1 ovule
       in each carpel, calyx tube with 5 lobes, urn-shaped, petals 5, sta-
       mens 5 to 20 in 1 to 3 series; native species to New Mexico are
       here described. **Hawthorn** or **Red Haw,** genus *Crataegus* ............. 72.

       72.    Leaves elliptic to lanceolate and mostly acute to acumi-
              nate at the apex, about twice as long as wide, finely and
              evenly serrate to crenately-serrate, with no notched mar-
              gins; stamens 10 or more; spines averaging less than 2.5
              cm in length or absent; fruit with 5 nutlets, dark red to
              dark crimson, becoming black and lustrous. Collections
              would indicate that this species is confined to canyons
              and adjacent to streams in the western, central and north-
              ern parts of the State at 6,500 to 8,500 ft. (1,980 to 2,590
              m) in elevation.

       **River Hawthorn**, *Crataegus rivularis* Nuttall          Rosaceae

              RIVER HAWTHORN
              *Crataegus rivularis*

72. Leaves ovate to oblong-ovate to rhombic, less than twice as long as wide, coarsely or finely serrate to double serrate or incised, often with shallowly notched or weakly lobed margins; stamens 8 or less; spines averaging more than 2.5 cm in length ............................................................... 73.

Our knowledge of the genus *Crataegus* is extremely limited and confusing. The following couplet is based on the available literature. Our field collections do not necessarily support this dichotomy. Also, another described species of limited range in southwestern New Mexico, *Crataegus wootoniana* Eggleston, appears to be very similar to *C. erythropoda*. In *C. wootoniana* the leaf margins almost form distinct lobes. Considerable field and laboratory study will be required to clarify these problems.

73. Petioles and lower surface of leaves pubescent at maturity, especially on the veins; marginal teeth not strongly glandular tipped; spines averaging more than 3.5 cm in length; inflorescence a corymb and flat-topped; fruit with 2 to 4 nutlets, pedicels of the fruit villous. This species has been collected at one location in the Gila National Forest and it is presently being described for publication (Phipps & O'Kennon). This collection appears to be widely separated from the described range of *C. macracantha*, which is a more northern species.

**Western Hawthorn**, *Crataegus macracantha* Loddiges var. *huffii*
Phipps & O'Kennon
Rosaceae

73. Petioles and leaves glabrous at maturity; marginal teeth with black glandular tips; spines averaging between 2.5 and 3.5 cm in length; leaves coarsely serrate and only occasionally notched; inflorescence a raceme to a corymb; fruit red to purplish-brown or black, with 5 nutlets. This appears to be a more northern species in New Mexico, found along streams at 6,500 to 8,000 ft. (1,980 to 2,440 m) in elevation. However, some of the more southern collections of this taxon from the Gila National Forest, that have been identified as *C. wootoniana*, appear to be *C. erythropoda*.

**Red Haw**, *Crataegus erythropoda* Ashe                    Rosaceae

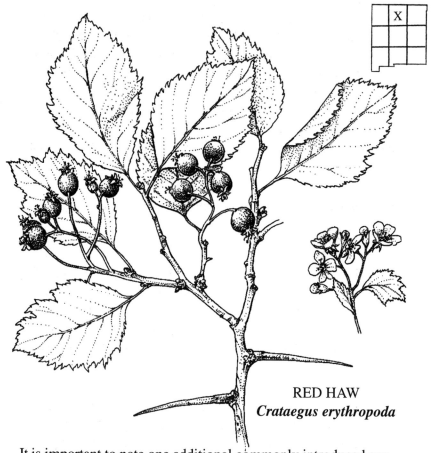

RED HAW
*Crataegus erythropoda*

It is important to note one additional commonly introduced species that will key directly to this point. This is the **Fire Thorn** or
**Pyracantha,** *Pyracantha coccinea* M. Roemer, (Syn. *Cotoneas-
ter pyracantha* (L.) Spach). This shrub, which may grow to several meters, is commonly cultivated in lawns and gardens over
much of New Mexico. The fruit is a bright scarlet pome that provides winter food for a wide range of birds; leaf blades are ellip-
tic-oblanceolate, both surfaces are glabrous, bright green and
glossy above; flowers are small, white and borne in cymes.

74.    Inflorescence a head of several to many flowers, each clus-
       ter of flowers surrounded or subtended by an involucre
       of bracts; heads may contain all ray flowers, all disk flow-
       ers, or a combination of disk and ray flowers, flowers
       may be perfect, imperfect or sterile, corolla 5-parted, sta-
       mens commonly fused by their anthers into a tube, ovary
       inferior; fruit an achene .... Aster or Composite family,
       Asteraceae ........................................................................... 75.

74.    Inflorescence a panicle, raceme, cyme, corymb, spike, catkin (ament), umbel or flowers solitary, individual flowers with basic parts, but lacking an involucre of bracts; flowers perfect or imperfect, corolla 4- or 5-parted, stamens seldom if ever fused by their anthers, ovary inferior or superior; fruit variable ...................................................... 121.

75.    Leaves averaging less than 5.0 mm in width at maturity or absent ......76.

75.    Leaves averaging more than 5.0 mm in width at maturity .............. 110.

76.    Leaves arising from a woody, well developed caudex, with herbaceous perennial stems extending less than 10.0 to 15.0 cm above the soil level, forming a basal rosette of leaves or the leaves imbricated along the lower portion of the short stem; heads scapose on an exserted peduncle......... 77.

76.    Leaves arising from obvious woody stems extending well above the soil level, caulescent, forming true shrubs with the leaves scattered along the stems; heads not scapose, but arranged variously over the plant .................................. 78.

77.    Leaves densely crowded at the base, narrowly oblanceolate, 3.0 to 10.0 cm in length and 1.0 to 5.0 mm in width, not obviously glandular; involucre approximately 1.0 cm in height, phyllaries linear in 2 to 3 series with the inner series shorter, the receptacle chaffy; ray flowers yellow, numbering 20 to 40 and pistillate but commonly infertile; disk flowers yellow, many, perfect and fertile; plants 30.0 to 50.0 cm in height. This species is reported in the literature to occur in New Mexico, but no record can be found in the major state herbaria. If it does occur it is probably confined to the southern one-third of the State at 4,500 to 5,500 ft. (1,370 to 1,680 m) in elevation.

**New Mexico Encelia,** *Encelia scaposa* A. Gray        Asteraceae

77.    Leaves closely imbricated along the basal portion of the stem to one-third the total length, mostly entire, but occasionally with a few short lobes, linear-lanceolate to oblanceolate, averaging about 10.0 cm in length and 2.0 to 6.0 mm in width, commonly glandular-punctate; involucre 0.4 to 0.7 cm in height, phyllaries 4.5 to 6.0 mm in length; ray flowers yellow, 3-lobed, numbering 10 to 15, pistillate and fertile; disk flowers yellow, numbering 25 to 30 and staminate; plants 15.0 to 30.0 cm in height. This common species of high, dry, limestone hills may be found over the eastern two-thirds of New Mexico at 4,500 to 5,000 ft. (1,370 to 1,520 m) in elevation. It flowers early in the spring.

**Bitterweed**, *Tetraneuris scaposa* var. *scaposa* (DeCandolle)
Greene

Syns. *Hymenoxys scaposa* (DeCandolle) Parker

Asteraceae

BITTERWEED
*Tetraneuris scaposa* var. *scaposa*

78.      Leaves averaging less than 1.0 cm in length ......................... 79.

78.      Leaves averaging more than 1.0 cm in length ...................... 83.

79.      Heads borne in racemes, laterally down the stems and sessile, not confined to the tips of the branches; leaves fasciculate, linear to spatulate, 0.5 to 1.0 cm in length and 0.3 to 0.5 cm in width, margins entire to toothed; shrubs unisexual, dioecious; both pistillate and staminate heads 15 to 20 flowered, color tawny to light yellow. This low shrub is relatively common over the southern half of New Mexico at 3,500 to 6,000 ft. (1,070 to 1,830 m) in elevation. Flowering throughout the growing season, it occurs in dry, hilly country. This species has been reported to have some medicinal value; at the same time it is thought to be toxic to sheep and cattle.

**Yerba-de-pasmo**, *Baccharis pteronioides* DeCandolle      Asteraceae

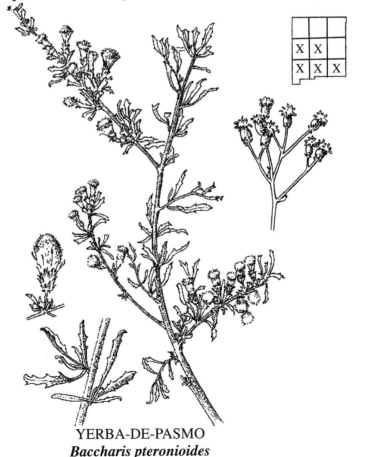

YERBA-DE-PASMO
*Baccharis pteronioides*

79.      Heads borne terminally at the tips of the branches, on a peduncle
         or in an elongated panicle, seldom sessile; leaves not fasciculate,
         but borne separately along the stems ................................................. 80.

    80.      Leaves and some stems covered with distinctive resinous
             glands or punctate, strongly aromatic; ray flowers present,
             3 to 10 in number, bright yellow in color ............................. 81.

    80.      Leaves and stems covered with a tomentum, a resinous
             and glabrous coating, or densely hispid, with stiff hairs,
             but not strongly punctate; ray flowers absent ...................... 82.

81.      Heads borne on exserted, naked peduncles, extending above the
         leaves 3.0 to 8.0 cm in length; ray flowers bright yellow, pistil-
         late and fertile, 9 to 12 in number; disk flowers yellow, perfect
         and fertile, 20 to 25 in number; stems seldom reaching 50.0 cm
         in height at maturity; leaves linear, punctate with large orbicular
         oil glands, thus the plants are strongly aromatic. This more south-
         ern species of Mexico and the Chihuahuan Desert flowers over a
         large part of the growing season and occurs at 4,500 to 6,000 ft.
         (1.370 to 1,830 m) in elevation. Found in dry, rocky soils of south-
         ern New Mexico, it is sought after by Indians for its medicinal
         properties.

         **False Damianita** or **Mariola**, *Chrysactinia mexicana* A. Gray
                              Syns. *Pectis taxifolia* Greene
                                                      Asteraceae

81.      Heads not borne on exserted peduncles, but on short peduncles,
         less than 1.0 cm in length and growing directly from the leafy
         stems; ray flowers conspicuous, bright yellow, 2 to 6 in number;
         disk flowers yellow and 8 to 18 in number; stems commonly
         reaching 1.0 m or more in height at maturity; leaves linear to
         acerose and rigid, covered with many resinous glands and viscid,
         thus exuding a strong turpentine-like odor. Flowering in the fall,
         this attractive shrub is common over southern and southwestern
         New Mexico at 3,500 to 6,000 ft. (1,070 to 1,830 m) in elevation.
         It occurs in the Chihuahuan Desert over dry hills and in rocky
         canyons.

         **Turpentine Bush**, *Ericameria laricifolia* (A. Gray) Shinners
                              Syns. *Haplopappus laricifolius* A. Gray
                                                      Asteraceae

FALSE DAMIANITA or MARIOLA
*Chrysactinia mexicana*

TURPENTINE BUSH
*Ericameria laricifolia*

82.    Shrub to 70.0 cm in height at maturity, with the branches spreading, the twigs canescent-tomentose; leaves lanceolate to oblanceolate, persistent, canescent and sometimes crowded toward the ends of the branches, from less than 1.0 cm to more than 3.0 cm in length; shrubs producing bisexual flowers; heads 4-flowered on short peduncles commonly in clusters at the ends of the branches. This common species is more northern in its distribution in New Mexico. Occurring at 5,500 to 7,800 ft. (1,680 to 2,380 m) in elevation in rocky and sandy soils on the plains, it flowers in late summer and into the fall. The Hopi Indians have used this species as a medicinal plant for several hundred years to treat digestive and uterine disorders. (Please see couplet 109, page 287 for further description.)

**Gray Horsebush**, *Tetradymia canescens* DeCandolle
Syns. *T. inermis* Nuttall                    Asteraceae

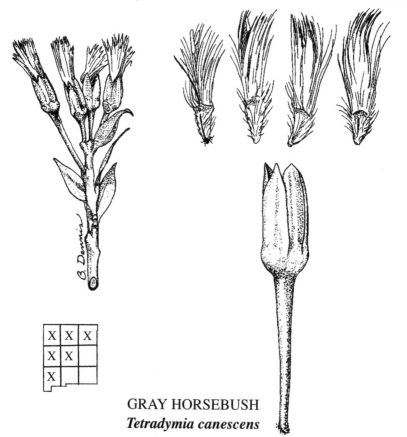

GRAY HORSEBUSH
*Tetradymia canescens*

82.     Slender shrub to 3.0 m in height at maturity, with the branches erect in broom-like clusters, the twigs glabrous, resinous and striate; leaves linear, relatively few, with considerable range in length, often scale-like and absent to 1.5 cm in length; shrubs dioecious, the flowers unisexual with male and female flowers on separate plants; heads of more than 4 flowers, discoid and solitary on elongate and nearly leafless branches. This rare shrub has only been collected in the southwest corner of New Mexico at 4,000 to 6,500 ft. (1,220 to 1,980 m) in elevation. Flowering throughout the growing season, when adequate moisture is available, this desert species tends to grow in and adjacent to arroyos and into the hills at higher elevations. (Please see couplet 92, page 270 for further description.)

**Broom Baccharis** or **Desert Broom**,

*Baccharis sarothroides* A. Gray

Asteraceae

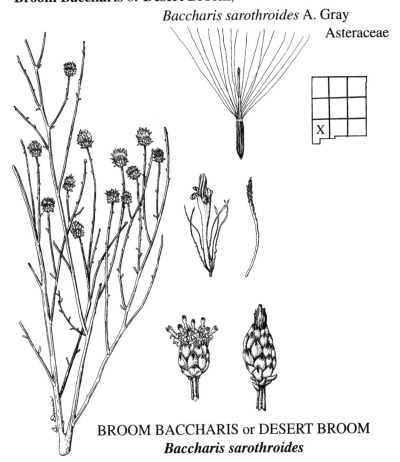

BROOM BACCHARIS or DESERT BROOM
*Baccharis sarothroides*

The **Hispid Baccharis**, *Baccharis brachyphylla* A. Gray, a rather weak and slender, suffrutescent subshrub, with widely scattered leaves, measuring less than 1.0 cm in length and 2.0 mm in width and covered with stiff hairs will key to this point. The heads contain 10 to 15 flowers and are arranged in elongated panicles. This low, upright and rare species, to 75.0 cm in height, has been treated as a perennial by some authors. It is found in sandy soils on mesas in the southern tier of counties and in the Franklin Mountains at 3,000 to 4,000 ft. (910 to 1,220 m) in elevation. It flowers throughout the growing season.

83.      Ray and disk flowers present. Ray flowers are the ligulate or strap shaped flowers commonly located around the margin of the head in the Aster family. In the following species the marginal ray flowers in the heads may be obscure and require a 10x hand lens for distinguishing and counting. (Please see the illustrations in the Illustrated Glossary) ................................................................... 84.

83.      Ray flowers absent, heads made up of all disk flowers. (Please see Illustrated Glossary) ................................................................... 89.

     84.      Heads scattered along the stems in small, globose, axillary clusters, not topping the plant, flowers off-yellow to whitish to gray, disk and ray flowers difficult to distinguish without a hand lens, ray flowers not always obvious ................................................................... 85.

     84.      Heads borne at the tips of the branches, sometimes in small axillary clusters, but generally topping the plant; flowers from bright yellow to dusty yellow in color; the ray flowers not always obvious ................................................................... 86.

85.      Heads and upper stems green to whitish or yellowish, but lacking tomentum, commonly unisexual but sometimes bisexual; staminate heads more common and including 5 to 12 flowers and pistillate heads less common including only a single flower and rather unique in appearance; flowers whitish to gray in color; involucre papery, forming wing-like structures around the ovary and fruit; leaves linear-filiform, 2.0 to 8.0 cm in length; stems

slender to 2.0 m in height. This species is frequently found in sandy, desert soils along stream banks and in arroyos over the southern half of New Mexico at 3,000 to 4,000 ft. (910 to 1,220 m) in elevation.

**Burro Bush**, *Hymenoclea monogyra* Torrey & A. Gray          Asteraceae

BURRO BUSH
*Hymenoclea monogyra*

85.     Heads and upper stems covered with tomentum of silvery-canescent, woolly hairs, these becoming tan with age; heads commonly bisexual, racemose or paniculate, with 3 to 5 flowers per head; pappus absent or weakly present, ray flowers yellowish-white and obscure; leaves finely filiform, villous-tomentose, and often revolute to the point of appearing almost terete. This shrub often reaching 0.5 to 1.0 m in height at maturity, is common throughout New Mexico at 3,500 to 6,000 ft. (1,070 to 1,830 m) in elevation. It flowers in late summer and into the fall, occurring over dry plains and hills, in sandy soils and in areas of dunes. (Please see couplet 108, page 286 for further description.)

**Sand Sage** or **Threadleaf Sage**, *Artemisia filifolia* Torrey
Syns. *Oligosporus filifolius* (Torrey) W. A. Weber

Asteraceae

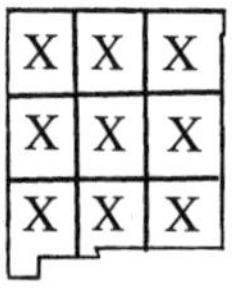

| X | X | X |
|---|---|---|
| X | X | X |
| X | X | X |

SAND SAGE
or THREADLEAF SAGE
*Artemisia filifolia*

86.    Heads 8.0 to 13.0 mm in height, containing a total of more than 18 flowers, corymbose; ray flowers 5 to 8, rays exserted, long and showy, extending 8.0 to 12.0 mm beyond the head; leaves narrow, 4.0 to 10.0 cm in length, glabrous to puberulent, but not resinous, punctate or scabrous; achenes silky-canescent. This mostly herbaceous perennial, growing from a woody base, could have been omitted from this publication. But over the southern part of New Mexico it may be woody to 15.0 or 20.0 cm above the soil. Widely scattered at 6,000 to 9,000 ft. (1,830 to 2,740 m) in elevation, it is more common in the northern part of the State and infrequent in the southern counties. It may flower over a large part of the growing season. (Please see couplet 19, page 201 for further description and distribution map.)

**Broom Groundsel**, *Senecio spartioides* Torrey &
A. Gray                    Asteraceae

86.    Heads 2.0 to 6.0 mm in height, containing 15 flowers or fewer; ray flowers 1 to 9, rays short and hardly extending beyond the head; leaves narrow, 2.0 to 5.0 cm in length, slightly glandular to punctate, scabrous or pubescent, but not glabrous ........................................................................ 87.

87.    Pappus in both disk and ray flowers absent or reduced to a microscopic ring; leaves lanceolate to oblanceolate, 2.0 to 5.0 cm in length and 2.0 to 6.0 mm in width; total disk and ray flowers numbering 11 to 15, of which about 6 are ray flowers; heads 4.0 to 6.0 mm in height. This perennial plant, which is only woody at or near the base may reach 80.0 cm in height. Often mistaken for **Snakeweed**, *Gutierrezia*, it is limited in its range to the southern one-third of New Mexico at 4,000 to 6,000 ft. (1,220 to 1,830 m) in elevation.

**Nakedseed Weed** or **Tatalencho**, *Gymnosperma glutinosum*
(Sprengel) Lessing
Syns. *Selloa glutinosa* Sprengel
Asteraceae

NAKEDSEED WEED
or TATALENCHO
*Gymnosperma glutinosum*

87.  Pappus in both disk and ray flowers of short or elongate scales;
     leaves linear, 0.5 to 7.0 cm in length and 1.0 to 4.0 mm in width;
     total disk and ray flowers numbering 2 to 12, of which 1 to 4 are
     ray flowers; heads 2.0 to 5.0 mm in height. The following two
     species are difficult to distinguish under the best of conditions
     and there is considerable confusion in the literature as to whether
     these are a single species or two distinct species. They are both
     widely scattered over New Mexico and the western states at 3,000
     to 8,000 ft. (910 to 2,440 m) in elevation, in disturbed, dry and
     overgrazed soils .................................................................................. 88.

88. Heads with 3 to 5 ray flowers and 3 to 6 disk flowers, disk flowers perfect; involucres averaging 2.0 to 3.0 mm in width; heads cylindrical in loose clusters.

**Broom Snakeweed**, *Gutierrezia sarothrae* (Pursh)
Britton & Rusby
Syns. *Xanthocephalum sarothrae* (Pursh) Shinners
Asteraceae

BROOM SNAKEWEED
*Gutierrezia sarothrae*

88.    Heads with 1, seldom 2 or 3, fertile ray flowers and 1 or 2 disk flowers, usually staminate; involucres averaging less than 1.5 mm in width; heads narrowly cylindrical in tight clusters.

**Threadleaf Snakeweed**, *Gutierrezia microcephala*
(DeCandolle) A. Gray
Syns. *G. sarothrae* var. *microcephala*
(DeCandolle) L. Benson
*Xanthocephalum microcephalum*
(DeCandolle) Shinners
Asteraceae

89.    Disk flowers purplish to lavender and numerous in each head; anthers with slender tail-like appendages extending from the base, these between the filaments; corollas 5-lobed in the central flowers and 4-lobed in the more numerous outer flowers; leaves linear to lanceolate, 1.0 to 6.0 cm in length and 2.0 to 6.0 mm in width, and sessile with few exceptions. This shrub to 3.0 or more m in height is characterized by erect, straight branches and appressed silky pubescence. Infrequent along streams and in arroyos over the southern half of New Mexico at 3,000 to 4,000 ft. (910 to 1,220 m) in elevation, this species flowers in the fall. There are reports in the literature that this plant was used by Native Americans to form the shafts of arrows and for medicinal purposes.

**Arrowweed**, *Pluchea sericea* (Nuttall) Cavanilles
Syns. *Tessaria sericea* (Nuttall) Shinners    Asteraceae

89.    Disk flowers yellow to white to green, but never purplish, ranging from 3 or 4 to many in a head; anthers lacking tail-like appendages from the base ........................................................................ 90.

90.    Style branch lobes glabrous within and pubescent on the outer surface; involucral bracts in several series and more or less herbaceous; receptacle naked. (Tribe Astereae including the following genera: *Baccharis*, *Chrysothamnus*, *Ericameria* and *Isocoma* ........................................................ 91.

ARROWWEED
*Pluchea sericea*

90. Style branches with a ring of hairs at the flattened tips or with the lobes hairy on both surfaces of extended, rounded tips; involucral bracts in 1, 2 or several series, herbaceous or membranous; receptacle naked or chaffy. (Includes the following species: *Artemisia cana, Artemisia filifolia, Porophyllum scoparium, Porophyllum gracile, Tetradymia canescens* and *Tetradymia filifolia*) .................. 105.

91.     Flowers unisexual and plants dioecious, with male and female
        flowers on separate plants. genus *Baccharis* ..................................... 92.

91.     Flowers perfect, with male and female reproductive parts in each
        flower and on the same plant. However, some flowers may be
        sterile ................................................................................................. 96.

> 92.     Plants growing upright from the base in broom-like clus-
>         ters to 3.0 m in height; stems lacking leaves or with the
>         leaves to 2.5 cm in length, narrow and commonly ob-
>         scure, strongly striated and resinous; heads solitary at the
>         tips of elongate, upright branches and forming panicles;
>         achenes less than 2.0 mm in length and 10 nerved. This
>         infrequent, robust, evergreen shrub appears to be confined
>         to the southwest corner of New Mexico at 4,000 to 6,500
>         ft. (1,220 to1,980 m) in elevation. Occurring from dry
>         washes and along streams to grasslands in the hills, it may
>         flower over most of the growing season. (Please see cou-
>         plet 82, page 261 for description and illustration.)

> **Broom Baccharis** or **Desert Broom**,
> *Baccharis sarothroides* A. Gray
> Asteraceae

> 92.     Plants spreading from the base, not in broom-like clus-
>         ters, seldom reaching more than 2.0 m in height; stems
>         with leaves obvious and easily distinguished from the
>         stems ................................................................................ 93.

93.     Pappus of female flowers reddish-brown or purplish and in sev-
        eral series; achenes 3.0 to 5.0 mm in length and scabrous; plants
        herbaceous from a heavy woody base and taproot, commonly
        less than 1.0 m in height at maturity; leaves linear to oblanceolate,
        averaging less than 1.8 cm in length, the upper leaves awl-shaped;
        heads solitary and borne in panicles on slender, weak branches.
        This is another questionable and infrequent shrub that occurs in
        the dry plains and hills of New Mexico at 4,500 to 6,500 ft. (1,370
        to 1,980 m) in elevation. Flowering in the spring and summer it
        may die back to the soil level in cold, dry winters.

**Wright Baccharis**, *Baccharis wrightii* A. Gray                Asteraceae

93.   Pappus of female flowers white to off-white, seldom whitish-pink, and in 1 or 2 and occasionally 3 series; achenes less than 3.0 mm in length and glabrous; plants true shrubs, commonly 1.0 to 2.0 m in height at maturity ............................................................... 94.

94.   Achenes 4- or 5-ribbed, pistillate pappus in fruit not elongate and scarcely or not surpassing the styles; pistillate heads with approximately 30 flowers, borne in terminal, rounded panicles; leaf margins seldom entire, but sharply spinulose to spinulose-serrate; leaves with only 1 midvein and no lateral veins or nerves; leaves linear-lanceolate to linear-oblanceolate, 2.0 to 8.0 cm in length and 0.2 to 0.8 mm in width. This rare, woody species occurs on rocky slopes in the southwest quarter of New Mexico at 5,000 to 8,000 ft. (1,520 to 2,440 m) in elevation. Flowering in August and September, this shrub may reach more than 1.0 m in height.

**Arizona Baccharis**, *Baccharis thesioides* Humboldt,
Bonpland, Kunth          Asteraceae

94.   Achenes 8 to 10 ribbed, pistillate pappus in fruit elongate, surpassing the styles by 3.0 or more mm; leaf margins entire to remotely toothed to dentate, but never spinulose; leaves with only 1 midvein or with 1 main vein and 2 lateral veins or nerves; stems striate-angled, shrubs reaching to 2.0 m in height. There is some question as to whether the following two species are biologically isolated or are a single species. Based on field collections *B. salicina* is more widespread over New Mexico in moist soils and in valleys, while *B. neglecta* is limited to the southern counties in drier habitats. Both occur between 4,500 to 6,000 ft. (1,370 to 1,830 m) in elevation ................. 95.

ARIZONA BACCHARIS
*Baccharis thesioides*

95.    Female involucre 3.0 to 5.0 mm in height; pappus averaging about
       10.0 mm in length; leaves narrowly linear to narrowly elliptic,
       entire to serrate, commonly 1 nerved or with faint lateral nerves.

       **Roosevelt Weed** or **Jara Dulce**, *Baccharis neglecta* Britton

                                                                    Asteraceae

95.    Female involucre 5.0 to 8.0 mm in height; pappus averaging about
       4.0 mm in length; leaves oblanceolate to oblong, serrate with the
       teeth set some distance apart, commonly 3 nerved. (Please see
       illustration on page 273.)

       **Willow Baccharis**, *Baccharis salicina* Torrey & A. Gray

                                                                    Asteraceae

WILLOW BACCHARIS
*Baccharis salicina*

96. Throat of the disk corollas expanded and sharply flaring from a short basal tube that is well defined, corollas yellow, 4.0 to 6.0 mm in length; involucres 4.0 to 6.2 mm in height; disk flowers numbering 7 to 16; heads borne in crowded cymes; leaves linear to slightly oblanceolate, 2.0 to 6.5 cm in length and 2.0 to 4.0 mm in width, usually entire with the lower leaves sometimes serrate, glabrous to slightly pubescent and often glutinous. Although appearing woody throughout, this is a subshrub, to 80.0 cm in height, and growing from a woody taproot in our area.

Often locally abundant, this species is found most commonly in alkaline and gypsum soils along roadsides and on overgrazed dry plains and ranges, at 3,500 to 6,000 ft. (1,070 to 1,830 m) in elevation. It may flower throughout the growing season.

**Jimmy Goldenweed**, *Isocoma pluriflora* (Torrey & A. Gray) Greene
Syns. *I. wrightii* (A. Gray) Rydberg
*Haplopappus pluriflorus* (Torrey & A. Gray) Hall
*H. heterophyllus* (A. Gray) Blake
Asteraceae

JIMMY GOLDENWEED
*Isocoma pluriflora*

96.    Throat of the disk corolla gradually expanded, the basal tube poorly delimited or not well defined ............................ 97.

97.    Phyllaries not in vertical files or rows, variable and spreading; the 5 lobes of the disk corolla obviously unequal; leaves glandular-dotted, wedge shaped to spatulate or oblanceolate and sessile, 3.0 to 18.0 mm in length; disk flowers 12 to 30 per head, yellow and maturing in September and October; achene 4- or 5-ribbed, 4 angled and silky-pubescent. This rare species is limited in distribution to cliffs and ledges in the southwestern corner of New Mexico at 4,500 to 7,000 ft. (1,370 to 2,130 m) in elevation. There is some confusion in the literature as to the possible varieties of this species that might be expected in New Mexico. (Please see couplet 117, page 296 for further description.)

**Goldenbush**, *Ericameria cuneata* (A. Gray) McClatchie    Asteraceae

97.    Phyllaries in well-marked vertical files, 4 or 5 in series; the 5 lobes of the disk corolla almost equal or slightly less than equal. **Rabbitbrush**, genus *Ericameria* ...................................................... 98.

        98.    Branches and young twigs covered with a felt-like tomentum of white to gray to yellowish weak hairs, that may be scraped from the stems with a sharp knife ........................... 99.

        98.    Branches and young twigs glabrous to somewhat pubescent, but not tomentose. The bark of some older stems may be gray but this should not be confused with tomentum ............................................................................... 100.

99.    Heads arranged in leafy terminal racemes, these somewhat branching down the stems, becoming paniculate; outer involucral bracts prolonged into slender herbaceous tips, involucres 9.0 to 15.0 mm in height; leaves sessile, 0.6 to 6.0 cm in length and 1.0 to 2.0 mm in width, 1-nerved, green, but not tomentose; heads of 5 to 20 yellow flowers. This species of **Rabbitbrush** is moderately low, seldom reaching 60.0 cm in height, and appears to be limited in range to the northwest and northcentral portion of New Mexico at 5,500 to 9,500 ft. (1,680 to 2,900 m) in elevation. It flowers in late summer and fall.

**Parry Rabbitbrush**, *Ericameria parryi* (A. Gray) Nesom & Baird
        Syns. *Chrysothamnus parryi* (A. Gray) Greene
                                    Asteraceae

PARRY RABBITBRUSH
*Ericameria parryi*

99.    Heads arranged in leafy cymes or corymbs, appearing somewhat flat-topped or rounded at the ends of the branches; outer involucral bracts obtuse to acute and lacking herbaceous and elongated tips; involucres 6.0 to 11.0 mm in height; leaves sessile, filiform, linear to broadly linear and occasionally tomentose, 2.0 to 8.0 cm in length and 1.0 to 8.0 mm in width, 1- to 3-nerved or leaves absent; heads of mostly 5 to 6 yellow flowers. This is one of the most diverse shrubs throughout the western states. As many as 19 ecological races of this single species have been identified by some authorities, and these races may range from 15.0 cm to 3.0 m in height. This complex species commonly occurs throughout New Mexico from the dry plains and hills to stream margins and dry stream beds at 4,000 to 8,000 ft. (1,220 to 2,440 m) in elevation. It flowers in the late summer and fall.

**Rubber Rabbitbrush**, *Ericameria nauseosa* (Pallas *ex* Pursh)
Nesom & Baird
Syns. *Chrysothamnus nauseosus* (Pallas *ex* Pursh) Britton
Asteraceae

100.    Involucres 9.0 to 13.0 mm in height at maturity, bracts strongly keeled, arranged in straight vertical rows ............. 101.

100.    Involucres 5.0 to 8.0 mm in height at maturity, bracts only moderately keeled, the vertical rows not sharply defined.... 102.

101.    Leaves linear, 1.5 to 2.5 mm in width over the length of the leaf, 1-nerved; corollas 10.0 to 14.0 mm in length and yellow; shrubs 30.0 to 90.0 cm in height at maturity; involucral bracts keeled, in vertical ranks, with a green to brown spot near the apex. This densely branched shrub is locally common in dry hills and sandy soils at 5,000 to 6,500 ft. (1,520 to1,980 m) in elevation in eastern and southern New Mexico. Like most woody members of the Asteraceae it flowers in the fall. Three subspecies of this species have been described in our range. One subspecies, *E. pulchella* ssp. *baileyi* (Wooton & Standley) L. C. Anderson, can be easily identified by the cilia along the margins of the leaves.

**Southwest Rabbitbrush**, *Ericameria pulchella* (A. Gray)
L. C. Anderson
Syns. *Chrysothamnus pulchellus* (A. Gray) Greene
Asteraceae

RUBBER RABBITBRUSH
*Ericameria nauseosa*

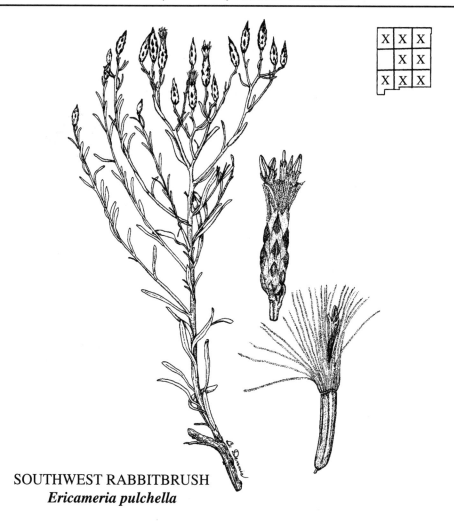

SOUTHWEST RABBITBRUSH
*Ericameria pulchella*

101.    Leaves oblanceolate to spatulate, 2.0 to 3.0 mm in length at the
        widest point, 1-nerved; corollas 7.0 to 9.0 mm in length and yel-
        low; shrubs 10.0 to 40.0 cm in height at maturity; involucral bracts
        keeled to boat-shaped, 5 vertical ranks, lacking a well defined
        spot near the apex of the bracts. This scabrulose subshrub is ir-
        regularly branched from a decumbent woody base. An infrequent
        species over the northwest quarter of New Mexico at 5,500 to
        7,500 ft. (1,680 to 2,290 m) in elevation, this plant grows in dry
        habitats over rocky slopes, on cliffs and on the plains. It may
        flower over the growing season as moisture becomes available.

**Dwarf Rabbitbrush**, *Ericameria depressa* (Nuttall)
L. C. Anderson
Syns. *Chrysothamnus depressus* Nuttall
Asteraceae

DWARF RABBITBRUSH
*Ericameria depressa*

102.  Achenes sparsely pubescent when young to glabrous at
      maturity; leaves linear to linear-spatulate or linear-oblan-
      ceolate ................................................................................. 103.

102.  Achenes densely hairy throughout their development;
      leaves linear to linear-lanceolate ........................................ 104.

103.    Plants to 30.0 cm in height at maturity; young branches glabrous; leaves averaging 1.0 to 2.8 cm in length and 1.0 to 2.5 mm in width, linear to very narrowly oblanceolate, 1-nerved, flat to twisted; bracts obscurely keeled in poorly defined vertical rows; heads of 5 to 8 yellow flowers borne in tight, small cymes. This more northern and infrequent species is found over dry hills, in the valleys and on the plains at 5,000 to 8,000 ft. (1,520 to 2,440 m) in elevation. Flowering occurs in the fall.

**Vasey Rabbitbrush**, *Ericameria vaseyi* (A. Gray)
L. C. Anderson
Syns. *Chrysothamnus vaseyi* (A. Gray) Greene
Asteraceae

103.    Plants 50.0 to 100.0 cm in height at maturity; young branches puberulent, becoming glabrous at maturity; leaves averaging 2.5 to 5.0 cm in length and 1.0 to 3.0 mm in width, linear-oblanceolate to narrowly spatulate, 1-nerved, and flat; rarely several ray flowers may develop; disk flowers commonly about 5, yellow. This rare species appears to be confined to the southeastern counties of New Mexico, entering the State from Texas through the Guadalupe Mountains. Flowering in August and September, it has been collected in the San Andres Mountains at less than 7,000 ft. (2,130 m) in elevation.

**Guadalupe Mountains Rabbitbrush**, *Ericameria spathulata*
(L. C. Anderson) L. C. Anderson
Syns. *Chrysothamnus spathulatus* L. C. Anderson
Asteraceae

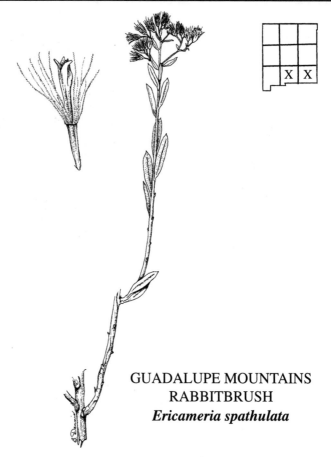

GUADALUPE MOUNTAINS
RABBITBRUSH
*Ericameria spathulata*

104.   Plants to 30.0 cm in height at maturity; leaves 0.5 to 1.2 mm in width and 0.5 to 3.5 cm in length, linear to fili-form, 1-nerved, flat, glabrous or scabrous-ciliolate on the margins; flowers yellow, about 5 per head; heads in loose to compact cymes; phyllaries glabrous and in about 3 in-distinct ranks; achenes densely hairy. This low shrub is usually divided into 2 subspecies based on the lengths of the leaves and the lengths of the peduncles on the heads. Whether one single species or one species with two sub-species, this taxon occurs in the northwest and northcentral part of New Mexico in dry, rocky and sandy alkaline soils, on the plains and in the hills, at 5,000 to 8,000 ft. (1,520 to 2,440 m) in elevation. It flowers in the fall.

**Green's Rabbitbrush**, *Ericameria filifolia* (Rydberg)
L. C. Anderson
Syns. *Chrysothamnus greenei* (A. Gray) Greene
Asteraceae

GREEN'S RABBITBRUSH
*Ericameria filifolia*

104.   Plants from 40.0 cm to more than 2.0 m in height at maturity; leaves commonly 1.0 to 5.0 mm in width, seldom
to 7.5 mm in width, and 2.0 to 5.0 cm in length, linear to
linear-lanceolate, 1- to 5-nerved, flat or often twisted, glabrous to puberulent and sometimes viscid; flowers yellow, about 5 per head; heads in terminal rounded or flat-
topped cymes; achenes densely to sparsely hairy. This
diverse species is widely scattered throughout New
Mexico at 5,000 to 7,000 ft. (1,520 to 2,130 m) in elevation. Flowering in late summer and fall, it commonly occurs over dry hills, mesas and the associated valleys. Based
on the level of pubescence on the stems and leaves and
the width of the leaves, some authorities have described
4 to 6 subspecies and/or varieties within this species. We
will not follow this procedure in this treatment.

**Sticky Rabbitbrush**, *Ericameria viscidiflora* (Hooker)
L. C. Anderson
Syns. *Chrysothamnus viscidiflorus* (Hooker) Nuttall
Asteraceae

STICKY RABBITBRUSH
*Ericameria viscidiflora*

105.   Heads solitary on long, exserted, leafless peduncles, often 2.0 or
       more cm above the leafy stems; leaves mostly alternate, but usu-
       ally some leaves opposite on each plant; plants perennial and
       suffrutescent or subshrubs, and glabrous ........................................ 106.

105.   Heads clustered or solitary, not on long, exserted, leafless pe-
       duncles, but with the heads distributed, on leafy stems, vertically
       down the stems, or heads forming a flat-topped inflorescence on
       leafy stems; leaves practically all alternate; plants woody well
       above the soil level, usually tomentose to white-canescent ............. 107.

106. Flowers yellow, commonly numbering more than 40 per head; phyllaries 7 to 9; achenes 3.7 to 5.5 mm in length. Based on collections this is an uncommon species in southern New Mexico at 3,500 to 4,500 ft. (1,070 to 1,370 m) in elevation. It may be locally abundant in dry arroyos and over limestone hills, and found flowering throughout the growing season when moisture is available.

**Shrubby Poreleaf**, *Porophyllum scoparium* A. Gray

Asteraceae

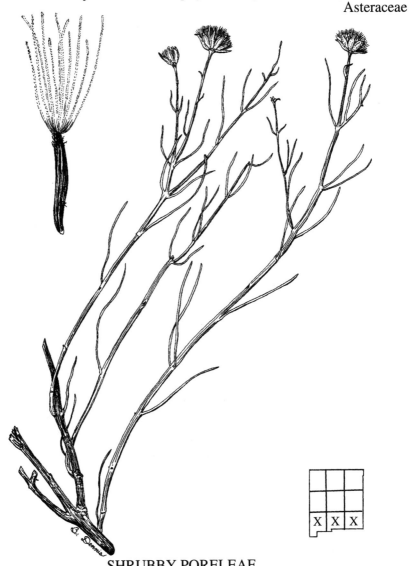

SHRUBBY PORELEAF
*Porophyllum scoparium*

106.    Flowers purple to white with dark purple streaks, commonly numbering 10 to 30 per head or occasionally only 5; phyllaries 4 to 6; achenes 5.7 to 10.3 mm in length. Either this is an extremely rare species in New Mexico or it is being overlooked. Since it occurs both to the east in northern Texas, to the west in Arizona and California and northern Mexico, it is probably being overlooked. It is reported to flower throughout the growing season at 3,000 to 4,000 ft. (910 to 1,220 m) in elevation in dry desert grasslands.

**Slender Poreleaf**, *Porophyllum gracile* Bentham     Asteraceae

107.   Leaves less than 1.0 mm in width, filiform .................................... 108.

107.   Leaves more than 1.0 mm in width, linear to lanceolate or oblanceolate ....................................................................................... 109.

108.    Flowers per head commonly 4, ray flowers absent; heads apical, terminating the branches; leaves not fascicled, to 3.5 cm in length. This rare, much branched and irregular shrub may reach to 65.0 cm at maturity. It occurs at 4,700 to 7,000 ft. (1,430 to 2,130 m) in elevation in isolated canyons over southcentral and western New Mexico. It flowers in July and August.

**Threadleaf Horsebush**, *Tetradymia filifolia* Greene
Asteraceae

108.    Flowers per head commonly 3 to 9, with 1 to 3 ray flowers and 2 to 6 disk flowers; heads racemose to paniculate, produced down the stem, rather than at the apex; leaves often fascicled, to 5.0 cm in length. (This species should have keyed out earlier in this key due to the presence of ray flowers, but it is included again at this point because it is easy to miss these very small marginal flowers. See couplet 85, page 264 for a full description and illustration.)

**Sand Sagebrush** or **Threadleaf Sagebrush**,
*Artemisia filifolia* Torrey
Syns. *Oligosporus filifolius* (Torrey) W. A. Weber
Asteraceae

THREADLEAF HORSEBUSH
*Tetradymia filifolia*

109. Heads borne on terminal, short peduncled, cymes; flowers per head commonly 4 and yellow, ray flowers absent; leaves 0.5 to 3.5 cm in length, linear to lanceolate or narrowly oblanceolate, occasionally in shorter fascicles, entire, and woolly-canescent. This is a much-branched western shrub, from 30.0 cm to 70.0 cm in height, found on dry plains in rocky and sandy soils, over northern and western New Mexico at 5,500 to 7,800 ft. (1,680 to 2,380 m) in elevation. It flowers from July to September. (Please see couplet 82 and illustration on page 260.)

**Gray Horsebush**, *Tetradymia canescens* DeCandolle
Syns. *T. inermis* Nuttall     Asteraceae

109.    Heads borne on leafy panicles extending down the stems 15.0 or more cm; flowers per head commonly 6 to 20, yellow to white, ray flowers absent; leaves 2.0 to 9.0 cm in length, linear to linear-lanceolate, not fasciculate, entire, occasionally with 1 or 2 marginal teeth, and white- to gray-canescent. This is a robust shrub to 1.5 m in height, that extends from the northern Great Plains into northcentral New Mexico. Found in dry soils or bordering prairie creeks at higher elevations of from 5,000 to 9,300 ft. (1,520 to 2,840 m), it flowers from July through September. Thought to have medicinal value, when crushed the leaves have a typical smell of sage.

**Silver Sagebrush**, *Artemisia cana* Pursh          Asteraceae

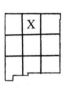

SILVER SAGEBRUSH
*Artemisia cana*

110.    Leaves 5 or more times longer than wide, linear, lan-
        ceolate, narrowly oblanceolate, narrowly obovate to nar-
        rowly elliptic, attenuate, sessile, or with the petiole much
        reduced and not distinctly different from the extended
        blade ............................................................................ 111.

110.    Leaves 4 or less times longer than wide, ovate, deltoid,
        oblong, spatulate, wedge-shaped to broadly elliptic, peti-
        ole present, commonly obvious .......................................... 116.

111.  Ray and disk flowers in each head or flowers in each head all
      ray-like and 2-lipped with the outer lip exserted and ligulate, flow-
      ers bisexual and fertile .................................................... 112.

111.  Ray flowers absent, heads made up of all disk flowers, flowers
      unisexual and plants dioecious, with male and female flowers on
      separate plants. The following 3 couplets that identify 4 species
      of the genus *Baccharis* are based chiefly on the pistillate or fe-
      male plants. However, the distribution, shrub characteristics and
      leaf morphology will be helpful in making an identification .......... 113.

112.    Heads radiate, bell-shaped, made up of both disk and ray
        flowers, ray flowers numbering 2 to 8 and disk flowers
        numbering 15 to 25; leaves lanceolate or narrowly ellip-
        tic, 7.0 to 10.0 cm in length and 0.8 to 1.1 cm in width,
        upper surface dark green and the lower surface pale green,
        entire to serrate; involucral bracts 7 to 9 in number and
        5.0 to 7.0 mm in length; achenes tan to brown in color,
        slightly pubescent and 3.0 mm in length. This shrub, mea-
        suring 0.5 to 1.5 m in height is characterized by brown to
        gray older branches, and green younger branches, these
        usually glabrous. It is found in well-drained soils in can-
        yon bottoms and flood plains in the southwest corner of
        New Mexico at 4,000 to 5,000 ft. (1,220 to 1,520 m) in
        elevation. Rarely collected on the Mexico-U.S. border,
        this pungent smelling species flowers from February
        through April.

        **Jarilla** or **Willow-Leaf Groundsel**, *Senecio salignus*
                                        DeCandolle      Asteraceae

JARILLA or WILLOW-LEAF GROUNDSEL
*Senecio salignus*

112.  Heads made up of all ray-like flowers, with 9 to 14 flowers per head; corolla bright yellow, 2-lipped, the inner lip erect and 2-toothed, the outer lip spreading and 3-toothed; leaves lanceolate to oblanceolate, acuminate and narrowed to the stem, 2.5 to 8.0 cm in length and 0.5 to 1.2 cm in width, both surfaces green, the lower surface pubescent with some glandular, entire to remotely denticulate, involucral bracts not imbricate but in 2 series; achenes glandular pubescent to densely hairy, 4.0 to 8.5 mm in length. This suffrutescent perennial, which becomes woody with age, can be found on rocky hills and in canyons at 3,500 to 5,000 ft. (1,070 to 1,520 m) in elevation, in the southern counties of New Mexico. Reaching to almost 1.5 m in height at maturity, it may flower over a long growing season from February to late October.

**American Trixis**, *Trixis californica* Kellogg          Asteraceae

AMERICAN TRIXIS
*Trixis californica*

113.   Leaf margins sharply and evenly spinulose-serrate to ciliate; leaves predominately 1-nerved, 2.0 to 8.0 cm in length and 1.5 to 8.0 mm in width, linear-lanceolate to linear-oblanceolate, only slightly glutinous if at all; heads in numerous, rounded, terminal paniculate cymes, pistillate heads of approximately 30 flowers, the involucre 4.0 to 6.0 mm in height; achenes with 4 or 5 ribs. This woody species is rarely collected on rocky slopes in the southwest quarter of New Mexico at 5,000 to 8,000 ft. (1,520 to 2,440 m) in elevation. Flowering in August and September, this shrub may reach more than 1.0 m in height. (Please see couplet 94, page 271 for further description, and page 272 for illustration.)

**Arizona Baccharis**, *Baccharis thesioides* Humboldt, Bonpland,
                                                    Kunth            Asteraceae

113.   Leaf margins entire to coarsely or remotely toothed, sometimes below the middle, but never spinulose-serrate to ciliate; leaves predominantly 3-nerved, leaves 1.5 to 12.0 cm in length and 3.0 to 20.0 mm in width, linear to lanceolate to oblong or obovate, slightly to heavily glutinous ............................................................ 114.

114.   Plants woody only at the base, the younger branches herbaceous; achenes 5-nerved; pappus scant and rather rigid, not especially elongating in fruit and not exceeding the stigmas, 3.5 to 5.0 mm in length; leaves linear to lanceolate, 5.0 to 12.0 cm in length and 4.0 to 18.0 mm in width, apex acuminate, base narrowed to a short petiole, margin coarsely and often remotely toothed to entire, surface glabrous and glutinous; heads in large, round, terminal panicles. This extremely common and successful riparian species in New Mexico and the Southwest, is found in low moist areas and adjacent to streams and ponds at 3,500 to 5,000 ft. (1,070 to 1,520 m) in elevation. It flowers throughout the growing season and may reach a mature height of 1.0 to 3.5 m.

**Seepwillow Baccharis**, *Baccharis salicifolia*
                          (Ruiz-Lopez & Pavon) Persoon
                          Syns. *B. glutinosa* Persoon
                                                    Asteraceae

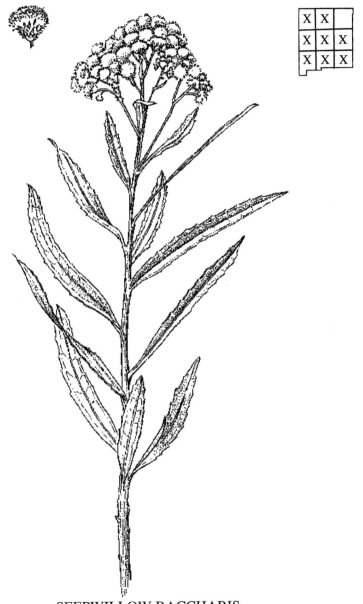

SEEPWILLOW BACCHARIS
*Baccharis salicifolia*

114.  Plants woody throughout; achenes 10-nerved; pappus copious and soft, elongating in fruit and much longer than the stigmas, 8.0 to 13.0 mm in length. The following 2 species have often been confused in the literature and we cannot be certain this treatment will improve the situation ........................................................................................... 115.

115.    Pistillate involucral bracts acute, 5.0 to 6.5 mm in height; pistil-
        late heads 5.0 to 10.0 mm in width; pappus less than 10.0 mm in
        length; leaves 1.4 to 8.0 cm in length and 4.0 to 17.0 mm in width,
        elliptic to oblanceolate or linear, base sessile or cuneate to a short
        petiole, entire to few teeth or slightly lobed; heads borne in pan-
        iculate clusters. If herbarium collections are correct, this is a rela-
        tively common and widespread species of moist soils and along
        stream banks at 4,000 to 6,000 ft. (1,220 to 1,830 m) in eleva-
        tion. It tends to flower in the spring and early summer. Some-
        what glutinous, this heavily branching shrub may reach to 2.5 m
        in height. (Please see couplet 95, page 272, for description and
        illustration on page 273.)

        **Willow Baccharis**, *Baccharis salicina* Torrey & A. Gray     Asteraceae

115.    Pistillate involucral bracts obtuse, 7.0 to 8.5 mm in height; pistil-
        late heads 3.0 to 5.0 mm in width; pappus more than 11.0 mm in
        length; leaves 1.3 to 8.5 cm in length and 3.0 to 20.0 mm in width,
        spatulate-oblanceolate to elliptic or linear, base cuneate to a short
        petiole or sessile, entire to irregularly toothed and more or less
        glutinous; heads numerous, often forming pyramidal panicles.
        Occurring in moist habitats similar to the previous species, this
        robust species appears to be confined to the southern portions of
        New Mexico at 3,500 to 6,500 ft. (1,070 to 1,980 m) in elevation.
        Also, it tends to flower later in the growing season, well into the
        fall.

        **Emory Baccharis**, *Baccharis emoryi* A. Gray                 Asteraceae

116.    Leaves with 1 main vein, sessile or attenuate, or with peti-
        oles averaging less than 6.0 mm in length .......................... 117.

116.    Leaves with 3 main veins or with a main vein and 2 or
        more lateral veins, petioles commonly averaging more
        than 6.0 mm in length ........................................................ 118.

**EMORY BACCHARIS**
*Baccharis emoryi*

117. Leaves elliptic to oblong or ovate to oval, 1.2 to 3.5 cm in length and 0.6 to 1.8 cm in width, veins strongly reticulate but not heavily glandular dotted, margins entire; heads borne in corymbs or panicles, 12 to 20 disk flowers per head, yellow and often nodding, ray flowers absent; achenes 5.0 to 7.0 mm in length, pappus a pair of slender and unequal awns. This common shrub of dry sandy and gravelly soils in the Chihuahuan Desert will usually reach 1.0 to 2.0 m in height. Found in the southern half of New Mexico at 3,000 to 5,500 ft. (910 to 1,680 m) in elevation, it flowers from mid-July into late fall.

**Tarbush,** *Flourensia cernua* DeCandolle                    Asteraceae

TARBUSH
*Flourensia cernua*

117.  Leaves wedge-shaped to widely obovate to more or less spatulate, base attenuate, veins not strongly reticulate, but heavily glandular-punctate, the margins somewhat crenate and uneven, 0.7 to
1.9 cm in length and 0.3 to 1.2 cm in width; heads borne in terminal cymes, usually discoid, but some radiate flowers may be
present, 12 to 30 in number, yellowish; achenes 2.5 to 3.0 mm in
length, hairy. This species is extremely rare in the very southwestern corner of New Mexico at 4,000 to 7,000 ft. (1,370 to
2,130 m) in elevation. The limited collections indicate that it occurs on rocky ledges and flowers late in the growing season. There
may be 2 separate subspecies in the State, but of this we cannot
be certain. (Please see couplet 97, page 275 for further description.)

**Goldenbush**, *Ericameria cuneata* (A. Gray) McClatchie

Asteraceae

118.    Heads solitary, on a long, naked, hispid-scabrous peduncle, discoid or radiate, ray flowers sometimes absent; flowers yellow; leaves oblong to ovate, entire or remotely few toothed, usually near the base, 1.2 to 3.0 cm in length and 0.5 to 1.7 cm in width, covered with white hairs; achenes black, obcordate, margins pubescent, awns absent or 1 or 2 in number. This western shrub, to 1.5 m in height, is covered with a dense, very rough pubescence. Although common in Arizona and southern California, to date this species appears to be rare and confined to Hidalgo and Grant Counties in southwestern New Mexico at 4,000 to 4,600 ft. (1,220 to 1,400 m) in elevation. Collections have been on gentle rocky slopes and in loose sand and gravel in arroyo bottoms. It appears to flower in May and June.

**Bush Encelia**, *Encelia frutescens* A. Gray       Asteraceae

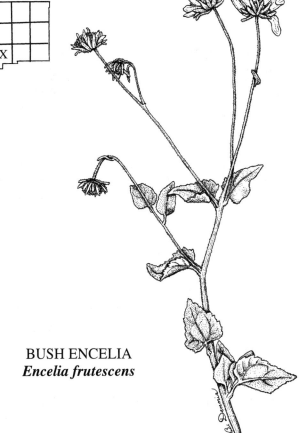

BUSH ENCELIA
*Encelia frutescens*

118.    Heads in panicles, or small clusters at the tips of the branches or laterally; leaves deltoid-ovate, rhombic-ovate, triangular-acuminate to deltoid-lanceolate, margins toothed ............................................................................ 119.

119.    Phyllaries and peduncles glandular-viscid; stems, leaves, leaf margins and phyllaries often purple or purple tinged; leaves deltoid-ovate or rhomboid-ovate, 2.5 to 11.0 cm in length and 1.5 to 9.0 cm in width, and glandular-puberulent; heads in panicles, 8.0 to 12.0 mm in height, containing about 15 flowers. This subshrub is confined to the southwest corner of New Mexico at 3,500 to 5,500 ft.(1,070 to 1,680 m) in elevation. Usually found in moist, alluvial soils, adjacent to streams and in canyons, this species flowers in September and October.

**Purple Brickellia**, *Brickellia floribunda* A. Gray        Asteraceae

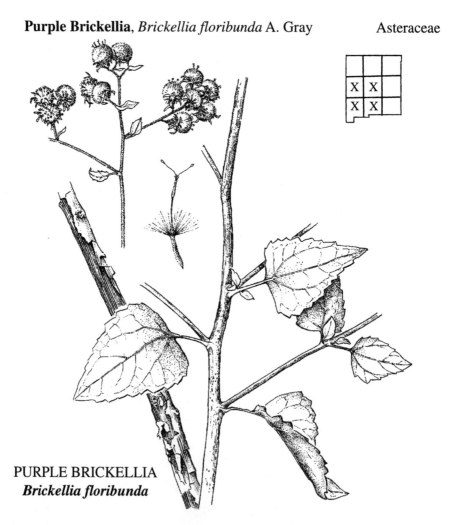

PURPLE BRICKELLIA
*Brickellia floribunda*

119.     Phyllaries and peduncles not glandular-viscid; stems, leaves, leaf margins and phyllaries dark or light green, the phyllaries may have some purple striations; range not confined, but widely scattered over New Mexico ................................................................ 120.

    120.     Leaves lanceolate, base truncate, sub-cordate to slightly hastate, tending to acute or acuminate at the apex, margins coarsely toothed, 2.5 to 10.0 cm in length and 1.5 to 8.0 cm in width; heads in panicles, 20 to 40 flowers per head, 1.0 cm or more in length; flowers cream-colored; plants subshrubs from a woody base. Occurring in canyons and rocky slopes at 4,500 to 10,000 ft. (1,370 to 3,050 m) in elevation, this is a relatively common species throughout much of New Mexico. Flowering from July through October, it can be found from the piñon-juniper to the pine, spruce and fir forests of higher elevations.

**Brickelbush**, *Brickellia grandiflora* (Hooker) Nuttall

Asteraceae

BRICKELBUSH
*Brickellia grandiflora*

120. Leaves deltoid-ovate, cordate to truncate at base, rounded to acute at the apex, margin dentate to crenate, 1.2 to 5.5 cm in length and 1.0 to 5.0 cm in width; heads cymose or solitary to several in the axils of the leaves, 8 to 20 flowers per head, 1.0 cm or less in length; flowers cream-colored; plants woody. More tolerant of drier climates, this common shrub is found over dry slopes and on rocky mesas in the foothills over much of New Mexico at 4,000 to 8,800 ft.(1,220 to 2,680 m) in elevation. It flowers from July through October.

**California Brickelbush**, *Brickellia californica*
(Torrey & A. Gray) A. Gray
Asteraceae

CALIFORNIA BRICKELBUSH
*Brickellia californica*

121.   Fruit an acorn which is a nut subtended only partially by a cup-like involucre of imbricate, woody scales; sepals and petals reduced and inconspicuous; plants monoecious; inflorescence of staminate flowers in aments, inflorescence of pistillate flowers solitary or in small clusters or reduced spikes. Fagaceae - Oak Family ...................................................................................... 122.

121.   Fruit variable, including achene, berry, capsule, drupe, follicle, nutlet, pome, legume, samara or utricle, but never an acorn with cup-like woody scales; inflorescence variable; plants monoecious, dioecious or with perfect flowers ..................................................... 138.

### THE OAKS

The following section of this key (couplets 122 through 137) is to the family Fagaceae, genus *Quercus*, and includes the 16 species of Oaks that have been described for New Mexico. In preparing these materials we relied heavily on the vegetative characteristics. However, considering the high rate of hybridization within the genus, many field observations and collections fall somewhere between the species here defined. Through this key and the illustrations we have attempted to define the central morphological tendencies for the gene pool of each of the included species. Also, as indicated in the introduction and bibliography, I have relied heavily on the research and assistance of Richard Spellenberg and Leslie Landrum in the preparation of this key. At the same time, we take full responsibility for errors and omissions.

122.   Leaves deeply or shallowly lobed, the sinuses between the lobes 25 percent or more of the distance from the tips of the lobes to the midvein ................................................. 123.

122.   Leaves entire, toothed or only shallowly lobed, the sinuses between the lobes less than 25 percent of the distance from the tips of the lobes to the midvein.................... 126.

123.    Lobes rounded, never spinose at the tips and the leaves elliptic in outline, the sinuses between the lobes reaching 50 percent or more of the distance from the tips of the lobes to the midveins, leaves 4.5 to 17.0 cm in length, commonly averaging 7.0 cm or more in length and 3.0 to 12.0 cm in width, slightly pubescent, deciduous; acorns 1.4 to 2.5 cm in length, borne solitary or in clusters of 2 or 3, the cap covering one-third to one-half of the acorn. This common shrub or small tree is widely scattered over New Mexico at 6,000 to 8,500 ft. (1,830 to 2,590 m) in elevation. It can be found in canyons, along streams and in dry montane forests with ponderosa pines. Flowering in April and May, the acorns are not mature until the fall. (Please see couplet 11, page 193 for further description and illustration.)

**Gambel Oak**, *Quercus gambelii* Nuttall                    Fagaceae

123.    Lobes mostly spinose and acute, seldom rounded at the tips, the sinuses between the shallow lobes commonly reaching to less than 50 percent of the distance from the tips of the lobes to the midveins, leaves averaging 6.5 cm or less in length and pubescent ..................................................................................... 124.

124.    Mature acorns averaging more than 1.3 cm in length, borne solitary or in pairs, becoming mature in mid-July and into August or September; leaves lobed, 2.5 to 8.0 cm in length and 1.2 to 5.5 cm in width, densely woolly on the lower surface and moderately woolly above. Occurring at 3,500 to 4,500 ft. (1,070 to 1,370 m) in elevation, it is restricted to sandy soils, on the plains and over sand dunes in southeastern New Mexico. It spreads by rhizomes to form large clones. This uncommon shrub often reaches from 0.5 to 1.0 m in height at maturity. In the past some authorities have placed the **Havard Shin Oak** and the following two species in one species, the **Waxleaf Oak**, *Q. undulata*. (Please see couplet 12, page 194 for description and illustration.)

**Havard Shin Oak**, *Quercus havardii* Rydberg

                                                                 Fagaceae

124. Mature acorns averaging less than 1.2 cm in length; leaves 1.5 to 7.0 cm in length and 0.6 to 5.5 cm in width; commonly occurring in piñon-juniper and ponderosa pine forests or on limestone hillsides, sometimes in clones; shrubs from 1.0 to 2.0 m at maturity or becoming small trees to 7.0 m in height; widely scattered over New Mexico. The following 2 species are part of a "complex of confusion" in the literature and without additional field and laboratory work may not be adequately delineated in these descriptions ............................................................................ 125.

125. Leaves shallowly lobed or toothed, undulately crisped, very tiny stellate hairs whose branches are almost straight and appressed to the epidermis, and with larger stellate hairs, the branches running in many directions, 1.5 to 7.5 cm in length and 0.8 to 4.0 cm in width, the teeth mucronate-tipped. More commonly found in the southern half of New Mexico at 5,000 to 7,000 ft. (1,520 to 2,130 m) in elevation, this shrub to 2.0 m in height occurs on rocky limestone slopes and in canyons.

**Sandpaper Oak,** *Quercus pungens* Liebmann
　　　Syns. *Q. undulata* var. *pungens* (Liebmann) Engelmann
　　　　　　　　　　　　　　　　　　　　　　　　Fagaceae

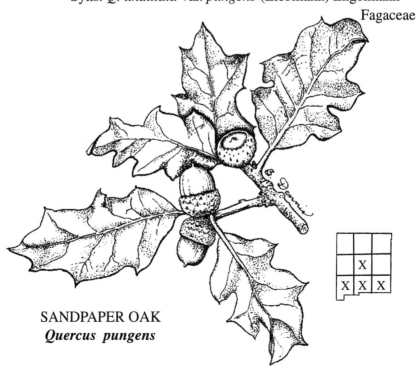

SANDPAPER OAK
*Quercus pungens*

125. Leaves shallowly lobed, coarsely toothed or entire, not undulately crisped, but flat, and not harsh to the touch, scattered stellate-pubescence on the upper surface and somewhat pubescent on the lower surface, 1.5 to 6.5 cm in length and 0.6 to 3.0 cm in width, the teeth mucronate-tipped. Widely scattered over dry slopes and canyons throughout New Mexico at 5,500 to 8,500 ft. (1,680 to 2,590 m) in elevation, this low shrub, ranging in size from 1.0 to 2.0 m in height at maturity, may rarely become a small tree to several meters. This extremely variable taxon appears to be the result of complex hybridization between *Q. gambelii* and *Q. grisea*, however this is not well understood.

**Waxleaf** or **Vasey Oak**, *Quercus undulata* Torrey          Fagaceae

Another rare and closely related species, **Vasey Shin Oak**, *Quercus vaseyana* Buckley, has been reported from the southeast corner of New Mexico, but these reports are in question.

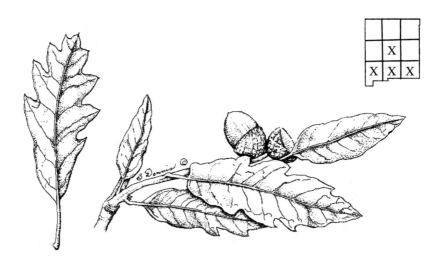

WAXLEAF or VASEY OAK
*Quercus undulata*

127.  Leaf margin spinose to dentate-spinose with 1 to 8 spines on each side of the leaf, leaves somewhat leathery with reticulate veins below, oblong to ovate to elliptic in outline, gray-green in color, glabrous to slightly pubescent on the upper surface and densely stellate-tomentose on the lower surface; acorns 1.2 to 2.5 cm in length with the cupule covering a fourth to a third of the nut. This widespread and relatively abundant species is usually a shrub or small tree to 3.0 m in height. It is found from the grasslands and deserts to the upper piñon-juniper forests at 4,000 to 8,000 ft. (1,220 to 2,440 m) in elevation. It flowers in the spring from early April into June.

**Scrub Live Oak**, *Quercus turbinella* Greene          Fagaceae

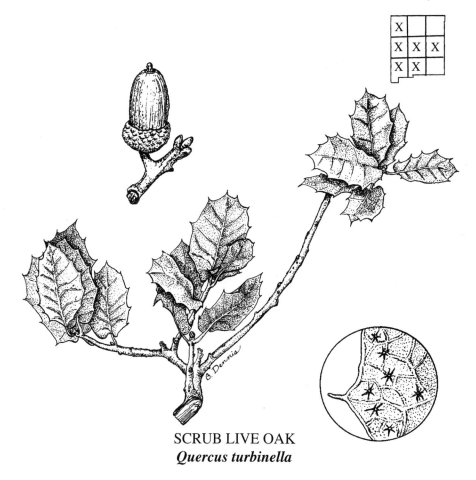

SCRUB LIVE OAK
*Quercus turbinella*

127.  Leaf margin entire, or with a few widely serrate or shallowly toothed leaves, but not spinose ...................................................... 128.

128.    Leaves averaging close to 2.0 cm in length, 1.0 to 3.5 cm
in length and 0.4 to 1.5 cm in width, green to yellow-
green in color, glabrous on the upper surface and sparsely
pubescent with glandular hairs on the lower surface, ob-
long-oblanceolate to ovate to elliptic; acorns 1.0 to 1.5
cm in length, the cupule one-third to one-half the total
length. This rare shrub or small tree to 3.0 m in height is
limited to the southwest corner of New Mexico in Hidalgo
County at 4,000 to 6,500 ft. (1,220 to 1,980 m) in elevation. Flowering in April and May, it has been collected
adjacent to the Geronimo Trail and in the Peloncillo Mountains.

**Toumey Oak**, *Quercus toumeyi* Sargent               Fagaceae

128.    Leaves averaging close to 3.0 cm or slightly more in
length, 1.6 to 4.0 cm in length, and 0.9 to 2.5 cm in width,
dull gray-green in color, stellate-pubescent on the upper
surface and stellate-pubescent to tomentose on the lower
surface, oblong to elliptic or ovate; acorns 1.0 to 1.2 cm
in length, the cupule covering one-third to one-half of the
total length. This is a common shrub or more often a tree
ranging from 1.0 to 10.0 m in height over much of New
Mexico. Occurring at elevations of 4,700 to 7,200 ft.
(1,430 to 2,200 m), the **Gray Oak** is part of the forest,
woodland and savanna vegetation of the State.

**Gray Oak**, *Quercus grisea* Liebmann               Fagaceae

129.    Lower surface of the leaves with a layer of white waxy cuticle,
appearing glaucous, or densely gray- or white-tomentose or red-
dish-tomentose when young to blue-tomentose at maturity; margins of leaves predominantly entire, occasionally with a few scattered teeth on some leaves or margins slightly undulate, but most
leaves not toothed, serrate or dentate, the tips of a few leaves
may be emarginate on the **Mexican Blue Oak** ............................ 130.

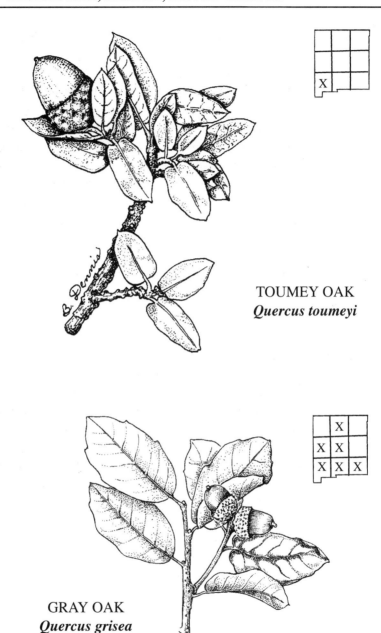

TOUMEY OAK
*Quercus toumeyi*

GRAY OAK
*Quercus grisea*

129.    Lower surface of the leaves lacking a layer of white waxy cu-
        ticle, not densely gray- to white-tomentose or reddish-tomentose
        when young to blue-tomentose at maturity; occasionally with
        some pubescence confined on the midvein, the tips of leaves not
        noticeably emarginate; margins of leaves predominantly toothed,
        serrate, dentate or obviously undulate, occasionally entire leaves
        will be present, but in reduced numbers .......................................... 133.

130.    Veins on the lower leaf surfaces conspicuous with reticu-
        late veinlets, this lower surface reddish-tomentose when
        young, both surfaces becoming blue to bluish- or green-
        tomentose to quite glabrous at maturity and the upper sur-
        face blue-green and shiny at maturity; leaves 2.5 to 6.0
        cm in length and 1.0 to 2.5 cm in width, oblong to obo-
        vate to elliptic, the apex rounded to acute, and sometimes
        emarginate, occasionally with 2 or 3 teeth at the apex;
        acorns 0.8 to 1.8 cm in length, the cupule enclosing about
        one third of the fruit. This small tree to 8.0 m in height at
        maturity is rare and confined to the southwest corner of
        New Mexico at 4,000 to 6,500 ft. (1,220 to 1,980 m) in
        elevation. It is found in forested canyons and on rocky
        slopes in the mountains.

**Mexican Blue Oak**, *Quercus oblongifolia* Torrey        Fagaceae

MEXICAN BLUE OAK
*Quercus oblongifolia*

130.    Veins and veinlets on the lower leaf surfaces not conspicu-
        ous due to a covering of gray- or white-tomentum and/or
        stellate hairs, or lower surface may be glaucous when
        leaves are mature due to a prominent waxy cuticle and
        little or no pubescence, but lower surface not reddish when
        young or blue to bluish-green at maturity ......................... 131.

131.    Lower leaf surface glaucous when leaves are mature due to a prominent waxy cuticle layer, this resulting in a paler lower surface in comparison to the upper lustrous, dark green leaf surface, in young leaves the lower surface is often covered with orange, glandular hairs; leaves ovate to elliptic or broadly lanceolate in outline, entire or some early leaves on young stems with 1 to 4 sharply triangular teeth ending in stiff spines, 1.5 to 5.0 cm in length and 1.0 to 3.0 cm in width; acorns 2.0 to 2.7 cm in length, the cupule 5.0 to 7.5 mm in length. This shrub or small tree to 8.0 m in height at maturity is found in riparian areas, canyons, steep cliffs and coniferous forests from 3,500 to 7,500 ft. (1,070 to 2,350 m) in elevation. A rare and not well known species in southwest New Mexico, it appears to be confined to the Apache Box area in Grant County. The **Palmer Oak**, *Q. palmeri*, will sometimes have a waxy cuticle layer on the lower leaf surface, but the leaf margins will have exserted spines which will distinguish it from the **Canyon Live Oak** that may occasionally have weak spines on the margin. (Please see couplet 133, pg. 312.)

**Canyon Live Oak**, *Quercus chrysolepis* Liebmann          Fagaceae

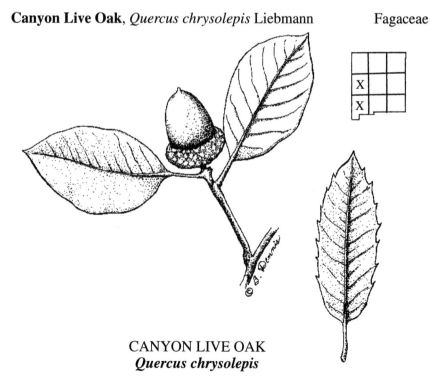

CANYON LIVE OAK
*Quercus chrysolepis*

131.    Lower leaf surface gray- to white-tomentose or with white stellate hairs, lower surface much whiter than the upper surface ......... 132.

132.    Mature leaves lanceolate to elliptic, apex acute, base rounded to cuneate, margin entire and revolute, 4.0 to 12.0 cm in length, averaging more than 4.5 cm in length at maturity and 0.8 to 3.5 cm in width, leaves dark green or yellow-green and often lustrous on the upper surface; acorns solitary or paired, 1.2 to 2.0 cm in length, the cupule covering about one-third of the fruit and white-tomentose on the inner surface and somewhat so on outer surface. Infrequent, but locally abundant in oak and coniferous forests at 5,000 to 8,000 ft. (1,520 to 2,440 m) in elevation, this attractive shrub or small tree to 10.0 m in height is found in moist canyons and on higher slopes. It flowers in early spring and occurs over the southern and southwestern third of New Mexico.

**Silverleaf Oak** or **Whiteleaf Oak**, *Quercus hypoleucoides*
                                   A. Camus               Fagaceae

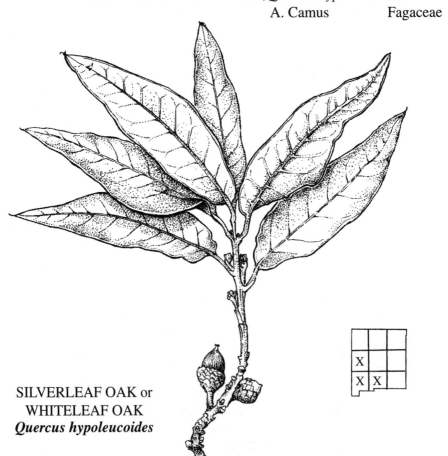

SILVERLEAF OAK or
WHITELEAF OAK
*Quercus hypoleucoides*

132.    Mature leaves oblong to elliptic to obovate, apex more
        rounded than acute, base rounded to slightly cuneate,
        margin entire to slightly undulate or minutely revolute,
        2.0 to 6.5 cm in length, averaging less than 4.5 cm in
        length at maturity and 1.2 to 3.5 cm in width, leaves usu-
        ally dark green and shiny on the upper surface; acorns
        solitary or 2 or 3 in a cluster 0.8 to 1.5 cm in length, the
        cupule covering one-half to one-third of the fruit, gla-
        brous or essentially so on the inner surface and reddish
        brown to tomentose on the outer surface. This infrequent
        shrub or small tree to 5.0 m in height is usually found
        growing in dry, well-drained, limestone soils. It appears
        to be restricted to Lea and Eddy Counties and the
        Guadalupe Mountains at 5,000 to 6,000 ft. (1,520 to 1,830
        m) in elevation.

**Mohr Shin Oak**, *Quercus mohriana* Buckley *ex* Rydberg
                                                    Fagaceae

The **Gray Oak**, *Quercus grisea*, may also key to this point.
This species has a wide range of variability in leaf size
and marginal teeth. The leaves are gray-green on both
surfaces and may have some minute stellate-pubescence
on both surfaces. (Please see the full description at couplet 128, pg. 306 and illustration, page 307.)

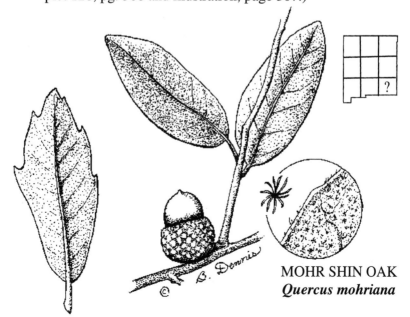

MOHR SHIN OAK
*Quercus mohriana*

133.    Leaves with exserted spines on margins, the spines 2.0 to 3.0
        mm in length or longer, appearing to radiate from near the center
        of the leaves that are orbicular to suborbicular or ovate in out-
        line, 1.5 to 6.0 cm in length and 1.0 to 4.4 cm in width, com-
        monly less than 2x as long as wide; the lower surfaces of the
        leaves may be covered with orange, glandular hairs when young
        and glaucous to glabrate with white, waxy cuticle at maturity as
        in the previous **Canyon Live Oak**, *Quercus chrysolepis*, the up-
        per surface a lustrous dark green when fresh. See couplet 131 to
        compare these 2 species. This shrub to 1.0 m, possibly 2.0 m, in
        height is extremely rare on the far western edge of New Mexico.
        There is some question as to the occurrence of this species in
        New Mexico. However, one specimen was found from the Apache
        Box area of Grant County at 5,100 to 5,400 ft. (1,550 to 1,650 m)
        in elevation.

**Palmer** or **Dunn Oak**, *Quercus palmeri* Engelmann
                    Syns. *Q. dunnii* Kellogg                              Fagaceae

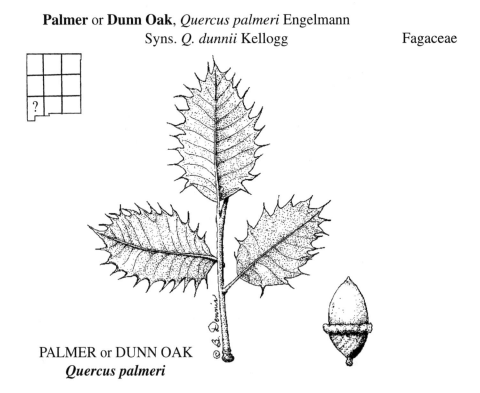

PALMER or DUNN OAK
    *Quercus palmeri*

133.    Leaves ranging from undulate to serrate, dentate, mucronate or
        entire, but not with exserted spines around the entire margin of
        the leaf, outlines of the leaves may range from elliptic to lan-
        ceolate, obovate to oblong ............................................................ 134.

134.  Leaf margins regularly dentate-undulate, with 6 to 10 teeth evenly distributed on each side of the leaf, lanceolate, oblong to obovate in shape, 9.0 to 14.0 cm in length and 2.5 to 7.5 cm in width, lustrous, dark green and glabrous on the upper surface, dull gray-green with some tomentum or a glaucous bloom on the lower surface and deciduous; acorns borne solitary or in pairs 12.0 to 20.0 mm in length, with the cupule covering about half of the fruit. This attractive tree, from 5.0 to 16.0 m in height, is found in the Guadalupe and Capitan Mountains in the southeastern corner of New Mexico at 5,000 to 7,200 ft. (1,520 to 2,200 m) in elevation. Flowering in April and May, it occurs on slopes and adjacent to streams in protected canyons in southern mountains.

**Chestnut** or **Chinquapin Oak**, *Quercus muehlenbergii*
Engelmann                    Fagaceae

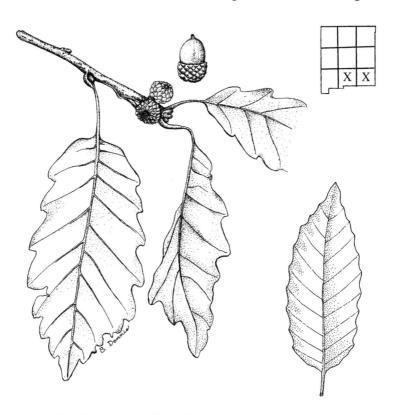

CHESTNUT or CHINQUAPIN OAK
*Quercus muehlenbergii*

134.     Leaf margins irregularly dentate to undulate, serrate, mucronate, to shallowly lobed or entire, with 6 or fewer teeth unevenly distributed on each side of the leaf or distributed from about the middle of the leaf towards the apex ..................................................................................... 135.

135.     Teeth unevenly distributed over the length of the leaf; leaves commonly averaging 3.0 cm or less in width, not prominently reticulate on the lower surface ................................................................ 136.

135.     Teeth unevenly distributed from the middle or upper two-thirds of the leaf to the apex, the lower half of the leaf usually entire or slightly undulate; leaves commonly averaging more than 3.0 cm in width, prominently reticulate on the lower surface ..................... 137.

136.     Toothed leaves only mucronate-tipped or rounded, never aristate-tipped; leaves pubescent beneath with tightly appressed minute stellate hairs, appearing glabrous to the naked eye, but pubescent under the handlens, oblong to elliptic in outline, coarsely 3 to 6 toothed on each margin or undulate to entire to shallowly lobed, 1.5 to 6.5 cm in length and 0.6 to 3.0 cm in width; acorns brown at maturity, 0.8 to 1.3 cm in length, the cupule covering about one-third of the fruit. This shrub or rarely a small tree to 5.0 m in height is widely scattered over the State, but is common in southcentral New Mexico. It is extremely variable in morphology and may be the result of complex hybridization. Flowering in early spring, it is commonly found on dry rocky slopes at 5,500 to 8,500 ft. (1,680 to 2,590 m) in elevation. (Please see couplet 125, page 304 for description and illustration.)

**Waxleaf** or **Vasey Oak**, *Quercus undulata* Torrey

Fagaceae

136.   Toothed leaves more aristate-tipped and never rounded;
       leaves glabrous and appearing shiny on both surfaces with
       a few stellate hairs, and often stiff branched hairs in tufts
       in vein axils along the midvein or at the base of the leaf,
       lanceolate to oblong-lanceolate in outline, coarsely 2 to 4
       toothed on each margin or entire, but not lobed or undu-
       late, 2.0 to 7.5 cm in length and 0.8 to 3.0 cm in width;
       acorns dark brown to black at maturity, 1.0 to 1.2 cm in
       length, the cupule covering about one-fourth to one-third
       of the fruit. This more southern species is found on the
       plains and in piñon-juniper and oak woodlands at 4,000
       to 6,500 ft. (1,220 to 1,980 m) in elevation. Although not
       common it can be locally abundant, and the shiny, lan-
       ceolate leaves make it relatively easy to identify.

**Emory Oak**, *Quercus emoryi* Torrey            Fagaceae

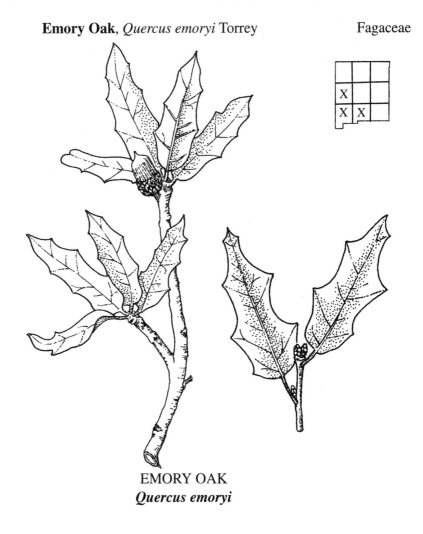

EMORY OAK
*Quercus emoryi*

137.    Mature leaves obovate to suborbicular, usually not over 2.0 to 2.5 times as long as wide, 3.0 to 10.0 cm in length and 1.5 to 6.0 cm in width, margin often with 3 to 9 teeth, these usually more abundant over the apical one-half of the leaf, lower surface of leaves partially covered with stellate and glandular hairs, the glandular hairs with several arms; acorns borne on elongated peduncles, 1.5 to 6.3 cm in length, acorns 1.2 to 2.0 cm in length, the cupule covering about one-third of the total length. This shrub or small tree is commonly found in canyons and along steep slopes in oak and coniferous forests at 4,500 to 8,000 ft. (1,370 to 2,440 m) in elevation. Flowering in the spring and producing fruit each fall, collections have been limited to the southwest corner of the State.

**Netleaf Oak**, *Quercus rugosa* Née

        Syns. *Q. reticulata* Humboldt & Bonpland        Fagaceae

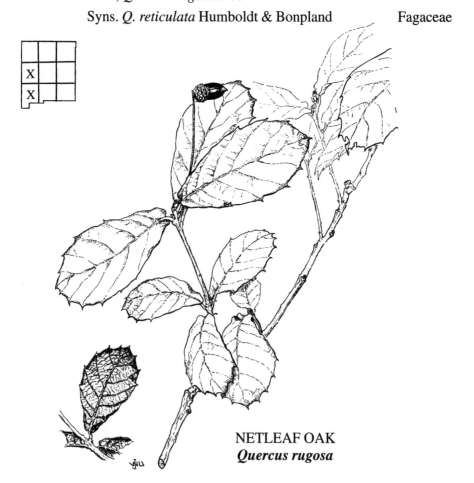

NETLEAF OAK
*Quercus rugosa*

137. Mature leaves oblong to narrowly obovate or oblanceolate, usually 2.5 times or more longer than wide, 3.0 to 12.5 cm in length and 1.2 to 6.0 cm in width, margins slightly revolute with 3 to 12 bluntly mucronate teeth, especially toward the apex, or rarely some leaves entire, upper and lower surfaces of the leaves sparsely pubescent to glabrous; acorns borne on short peduncles, less than 2.0 cm in length, or practically sessile, acorn 0.8 to 1.4 cm in length, the cupule covering about one-third of the total length. Probably rare to infrequent in New Mexico, and commonly confused with the **Gray Oak**, *Quercus grisea*, which is much more common. Field collections and herbarium materials limit the **Arizona White Oak** to the southwest corner and southern border of the State. This shrub or relatively large tree to 15.0 m in height is found along rocky stream beds and in alluvial habitats at 4,500 to 6,800 ft. (1,370 to 2,070 m) in elevation.

**Arizona White Oak**, *Quercus arizonica* Sargent      Fagaceae

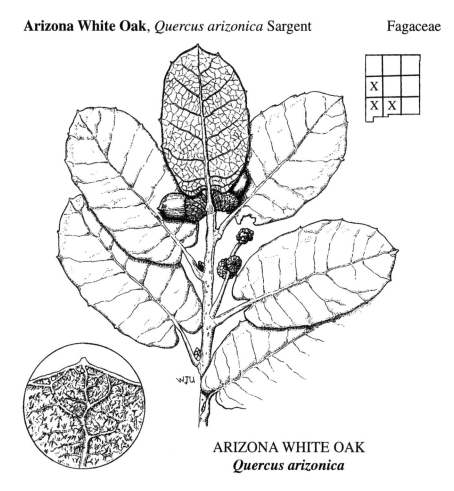

ARIZONA WHITE OAK
*Quercus arizonica*

138.    Buds enclosed by a single hoodlike scale; mature indi-
        vidual seeds covered with long hairs; flowers unisexual,
        borne in catkins (aments) that are usually erect or only
        slightly pendulous, lacking a perianth; fruit a capsule
        which is not septicidal; plants dioecious trees or shrubs.
        **Willows**, genus *Salix* ............................................................ 139.

138.    Buds with several overlapping scales or bud scales lack-
        ing; flowers perfect or imperfect, borne solitary or in any
        of several inflorescence types, but if in catkins (aments)
        then usually pendulous rather than erect; leaves broad,
        scale-like or absent; fruit an achene, berry, drupe, utricle,
        samara, follicle, legume, pome, aggregate, multiple or cap-
        sule (then usually septicidal); plants monoecious, dioe-
        cious or with perfect flowers ............................................. 164.

## THE WILLOWS

We here describe the **Willows**, genus *Salix*, of the family
Salicaceae. Because the willows are dioecious, with male (staminate) and female (pistillate) flowers on separate plants, and the
leaves often developing with, before or after the flowers, correct
identification can be a challenge. Identification will often require
the collection of male and female plants in flower, female plants
in fruit and vegetative plants with mature leaves. Because the
willows are excellent indicators of the biologic health of riparian
or other ecosystems, they are extremely important in the study of
ecology. The Spanish explorers' word for the profusion of  willows they found growing along rivers in the southwest was
*mimbres,* thus we have the Mimbres River and the Mimbreño
culture that lived in this region 700 years ago.

139.    Plants depressed shrubs, prostrate or creeping, less than 10.0 cm,
        or seldom to 15.0 cm in height at maturity; species confined to
        the alpine and rarely in the subalpine ............................................. 140.

139.    Plants trees or shrubs, more than 10.0 cm in height at maturity,
        unless heavily grazed; species not confined to the higher eleva-
        tions of the alpine and subalpine, but found at practically all el-
        evations in New Mexico ................................................................. 141.

140.  Catkins on short lateral shoots, not on the terminal shoots of the season, male catkins 1.0 to 2.5 cm in length, female catkins 2.0 to 7.0 cm in length, usually with 10 or fewer flowers; leaves slightly glaucous beneath but not reticulate, dark green on upper surface, the apex tending toward acute, margin entire; styles of pistillate flowers 0.5 mm in length or longer; scales of the catkins pilose, brown to black; capsules villous, 4.0 to 8.0 mm in length; plants with long, heavy, woody horizontal stems, rooting at the nodes. Restricted to alpine, rocky summits above 11,000 ft. (3,350 m) in elevation, this distinctive species is confined to the highest mountain peaks in northcentral New Mexico. It commonly flowers and quickly produces fruit in the short summer growing season of late June and July.

**Alpine Willow,** *Salix arctica* Pallas
Syns. *S. petrophila* Rydberg              Salicaceae

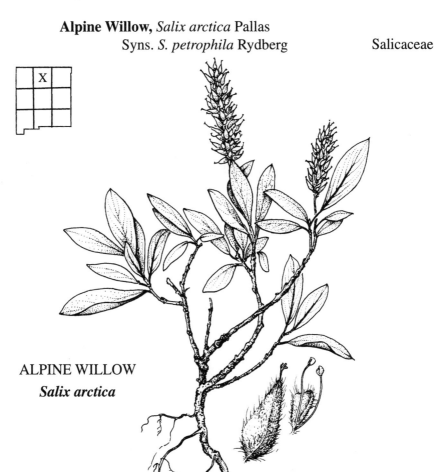

ALPINE WILLOW
*Salix arctica*

140.  Catkins at the tips of the terminal shoots of the season, both male and female catkins 1.0 to 2.0 cm in length, usually with 10 or more flowers; leaves glaucous and reticulate veined beneath, green on upper surface, the apex tending toward obtuse to rounded, margin entire; styles of pistillate flowers lacking or less than 0.5 mm in length; scales of the catkins glabrous or nearly so and green; capsules densely tomentose, 3.0 to 4.0 mm in length; plants with short stems and the leaves clustered at the ends of creeping, slender branches, rooting along the branches. More common in the wettest areas of the tundra and often associated with melting snow and snowbank communities, this species occurs at 11,000 to 12,500 ft. (3,350 to 3,660 m) in elevation. It flowers and fruits in June through early August, and will be completely covered by the first significant snowfall.

**Snow Willow,** *Salix reticulata* ssp. *nivalis* (Hooker)
A. & D. Löve & Kapoor
Syns. *S. nivalis* var. *saximontana*
(Rydberg) Schneider          Salicaceae

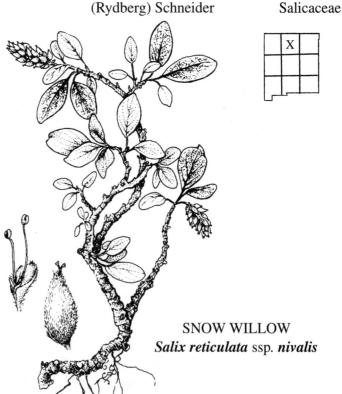

SNOW WILLOW
*Salix reticulata* ssp. *nivalis*

141.   Leaf blade narrowly linear to narrowly oblong, averaging 2.0 to
       8.0 mm in width, 6.0 or more times longer than wide .................... 142.

141.   Leaf blades broader, not narrowly linear, but lanceolate, elliptic,
       ovate, oblanceolate to obovate, averaging more than 8.0 mm in
       width ........................................................................................ 143.

       142.   Petioles 1.0 to 3.0 mm in length; leaves 1.3 to 3.6 cm in
              length and 1.5 to 4.0 mm in width, margins entire or re-
              motely denticulate; staminate flowers in densely flow-
              ered catkins 0.7 to 2.0 cm in length, stamens 2, filaments
              hairy; pistillate flowers in densely to loosely flowered
              catkins 0.8 to 2.0 cm in length, ovaries silky to pilose
              becoming glabrous with age; capsules pilose to glabrate,
              6.0 mm in length. Usually growing as a shrub to less than
              6.0 m, this species may be found as a tree, from one trunk,
              growing to 10.0 m or more in height. A more southern
              species, it is frequently found at lower elevations, from
              4,000 to 6,000 ft. (1,220 to 1,830 m). It occurs in *cienegas*
              and along irrigation ditches and rivers and flowers from
              March through May. It has been observed flowering again
              in August and September.

       **Yewleaf Willow,** *Salix taxifolia* Kunth          Salicaceae

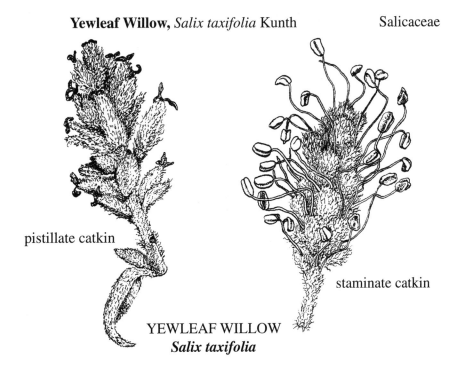

       pistillate catkin

                                                          staminate catkin

              YEWLEAF WILLOW
              *Salix taxifolia*

YEWLEAF WILLOW
*Salix taxifolia*

142.   Petioles 2.0 to 7.0 mm in length; leaves 3.0 to 14.0 cm in
       length and 2.0 to 12.0 mm in width, margins entire or
       remotely toothed; staminate flowers in densely flowered
       catkins 0.9 to 6.0 cm in length, stamens 2, filaments hairy;
       pistillate flowers in loosely flowered catkins 2.0 to 8.0
       cm in length, ovaries glabrous to sparsely silky; capsules
       glabrous, 4.0 to 5.0 mm in length. This is one of the most
       common and widespread willows in New Mexico. Oc-
       curring at 3,500 to 7,500 ft. (1,100 to 2,300 m) in eleva-
       tion, it commonly forms thickets along streams, can be
       found in roadside ditches and is important to riparian com-
       munities. Usually found growing as a shrub from 0.5 to
       3.0 m in height, it has been reported to 6.0 m in height,
       forming small trees.

**Coyote** or **Sandbar Willow**, *Salix exigua* Nuttall
                          Syns. *S. interior* Rowlee      Salicaceae

|   |   |   |
|---|---|---|
| X | X | X |
| X | X |   |
| X | X | X |

COYOTE or SANDBAR WILLOW
*Salix exigua*

143.    Plants large trees at maturity, more than 8.0 m in height, usually
        with a single large trunk or occasionally with 2 or 3 large trunks
        from a single root system ................................................................ 144.

143.    Plants shrubs or small trees at maturity, usually less than 6.0 m in
        height, with several stems, often spreading by rhizomes, and
        shorter than the typical tree ........................................................... 150.

144.    Upper and lower leaf surfaces green when mature, lower
        leaf surfaces sometimes a lighter shade of green, but never
        glaucous, leaves narrowly lanceolate to narrowly oblan-
        ceolate, 6.5 to 13.0 cm in length and 9.5 to 15.0 mm in
        width, 4.0 times longer than wide, apex acuminate, mar-
        gin finely serrate, 5 to 10 teeth per cm; leaves and flow-
        ers maturing at the same time from March through May;
        younger twigs yellowish, older wood dark gray; stami-
        nate catkins with many flowers, 3.5 to 7.0 cm in length,
        stamens 3 to 8; pistillate catkins loosely flowered, 2.2 to
        6.5 cm in length, ovaries glabrous to slightly villous; cap-
        sules glabrous to finely pubescent, 3.0 to 8.0 mm in length.
        This relatively abundant tree in southern and western New
        Mexico is found along arroyos, streams and rivers at 4,500
        to 7,000 ft. (1,370 to 2,130 m) in elevation. Commonly
        growing to 15.0 m in height, it has been reported to reach
        30.0 m.

**Goodding's Black Willow**, *Salix gooddingii* Ball
Syns. *S. nigra* Marshall

Salicaceae

144.    Upper leaf surfaces green and lower leaf surfaces glau-
        cous at maturity, otherwise the following six species are
        similar and several hybrids have been described among
        these taxa ......................................................................... 145.

145.  Branches strongly pendulous, often reaching to or near the ground,
      or the crown globose and spherical; both species introduced and
      cultivated as ornamentals forming attractive trees for lawns and
      gardens ...................................................................................... 146.

145.  Branches neither strongly pendulous nor forming a globose crown;
      branches erect and spreading, species native or introduced, com-
      monly cultivated ......................................................................... 147.

staminate flower

GOODDING'S BLACK WILLOW
*Salix gooddingii*

146. Branches strongly pendulous, "weeping", often reaching
to or near the ground; trunk often dividing near the base
to produce several large branching trunks, thus producing a large umbrella-shaped tree; leaves narrowly lanceolate, often sickle-shaped, 7.0 to 14.0 cm in length and
0.9 to 1.8 mm in width, 6.5 to 13.0 times longer than wide,
glaucous on the lower surface, green to dull green on the
upper surface. This commonly cultivated large tree to 15.0
m or more in height, is found in lawns and gardens, around
old farm sites and escaping cultivation. Thought to be

native to China, this alien species will often require additional water if it is to survive throughout most of New Mexico.

**Weeping Willow**, *Salix babylonica* L.                    Salicaceae

WEEPING WILLOW
*Salix babylonica*

146.    Branches forming a globose or spherical crown; trunk seldom dividing near the base, usually extending to 1.0 to 2.0 m before spreading into many ascending branches, these usually bright yellow when young, becoming brown to gray with age and finally forming the globose or spherical crown; leaves narrowly lanceolate to linear-lanceolate, 5.0 to 12.0 cm in length and 10.0 to 15.0 mm in width, glaucous on the lower surface, bright green to yellow-green on the upper surface. This attractive tree to 15.0 m or more in height is commonly cultivated in lawns and gardens over southern New Mexico. Native to Asia and requiring less water than the **Weeping Willow,** this species is becoming very popular throughout the Southwest. Some authorities consider *Salix matsudana* a subspecies of *Salix babylonica*.

**Globe Willow**, *Salix matsudana* Koidzumi            Salicaceae

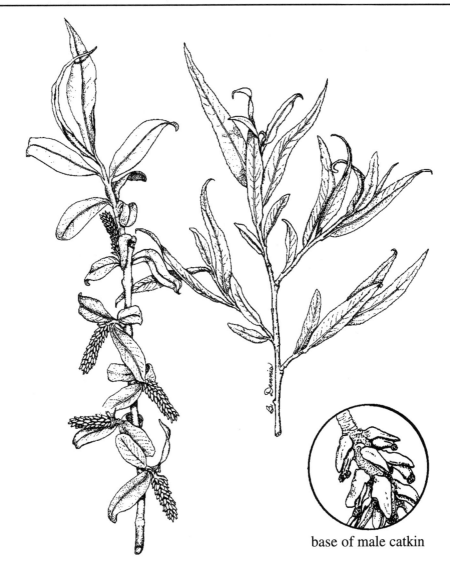

base of male catkin

GLOBE WILLOW
*Salix matsudana*

147. Leaf margins finely toothed, averaging 8 to 12 teeth per cm; these species native to New Mexico; stamens 3 to 6 ................................ 148.

147. Leaf margins coarsely toothed, averaging 5 to 8 teeth per cm; these species introduced to New Mexico, cultivated and commonly escaping cultivation; stamens 2 ............................................. 149.

148.    Mature leaves averaging more than 2.0 cm in width; young
        twigs tending towards yellow or grayish-yellow; leaves
        broadly lanceolate to ovate-lanceolate, long acuminate at
        the apex, yellow-green to green on the upper surface and
        somewhat glaucous on the lower surface, but not ex-
        tremely so, 5.5 to 13.0 cm in length and 2.2 to 3.6 cm in
        width; stamens commonly numbering 3 to 9; staminate
        catkins 3.8 to 6.0 cm in length and densely flowered; pis-
        tillate catkins 2.5 to 10.0 cm in length; capsules glabrous,
        3.0 to 8.0 mm in length. This native tree, often reaching
        10.0 to sometimes 25.0 m at maturity, is commonly found
        over much of the United States, including New Mexico.
        It is found along streams and rivers in rich alluvial soils,
        as well as being cultivated where additional water can be
        provided. Occurring at 4,000 to 7,900 ft. (1,220 to 2,410
        m) in elevation, it has been reported to hybridize with
        *Salix gooddingii.*

**Peachleaf Willow,** *Salix amygdaloides* Andersson    Salicaceae

PEACHLEAF WILLOW
*Salix amygdaloides*

148.    Mature leaves averaging less than 2.0 cm in width; young twigs tending towards reddish-brown or purple; leaves narrowly lanceolate to oblanceolate, long acuminate at the apex, bright green on the upper surface and silvery-white on the lower surface, 5.5 to 15.0 cm in length and 0.9 to 2.2 cm in width; stamens commonly numbering 3, occasionally 4 or 5; staminate catkins 1.2 to 6.0 cm in length; pistillate catkins 1.5 to 5.4 cm in length; capsules glabrous, 2.0 to 3.0 mm in length. This relatively small native tree, seldom reaching more than 9.0 m at maturity, is infrequently found in southern and southwestern New Mexico at 4,500 to 7,400 ft. (1,370 to 2,260 m) in elevation. It is chiefly a riparian species of dry washes in oak woodlands throughout Mexico and appears to be limited to warmer climates.

**Bonpland Willow,** *Salix bonplandiana* Kunth        Salicaceae

149.    Mature leaves averaging less than 2.2 cm in width, 1.0 to 2.4 cm in width and 4.0 to 9.0 cm in length, silky on both surfaces due to numerous soft appressed hairs, lacking raised glands at the base of the blade; branchlets spreading, yellow-green, pubescent, never extremely brittle; capsules ovoid-conic, 3.0 to 4.5 mm in length, glabrous and sessile or subsessile. This more commonly introduced species often escapes cultivation in urban and rural areas. A large tree to 25.0 m in height, this plant is known to hybridize with the following. Also, some authorities consider the following species to be a variety of *Salix alba.*

**White Willow,** *Salix alba* L.        Salicaceae

149.   Mature leaves averaging more than 2.2 cm in width, 2.0 to 3.5
cm in width and 7.0 to 15.0 cm in length, glabrous and lacking
pubescence above and glaucous below, commonly with a few
raised glands at the base of the blade; branchlets spreading, greenish to dark red, glabrous, very brittle at the base, thus the common name; capsules narrowly conic, 4.0 to 6.0 mm in length,
glabrous and on pedicels. This and the previous species were introduced into the United States from Europe in colonial times
and have continued to broaden their range along streams and rivers. **Crack Willow** is often planted for shade and as a windbreak
in the western states.

**Crack Willow**, *Salix fragilis* L.                    Salicaceae

CRACK WILLOW
*Salix fragilis*

150.   Mature twigs strongly pruinose or glaucous, covered with
a powdery white or bluish waxy coating or bloom, the
coating may be removed by rubbing the stem .................... 151.

150.   Mature twigs not noticeably pruinose or glaucous, often
glabrous to pubescent and ranging in color from yellow
to red or brown, but not covered with a waxy coating or
bloom ................................................................................ 153.

151.    Capsules on pistillate plants glabrous; mature leaves long and
        narrow, tending toward broadly linear to broadly oblanceolate or
        lanceolate, 5.0 to 12.0 cm in length and 8.0 to 22.0 mm in width,
        commonly averaging more than 6.5 cm in length, lower leaf sur-
        face lighter green, glabrous to glaucous or rarely slightly tomen-
        tose; bracts subtending flowers dark brown or black; staminate
        catkins appearing before the leaves, 1.5 to 3.0 cm in length, scale
        hair long and pilose; anthers 2 and yellow. This robust and com-
        mon shrub, sometimes reaching 4.0 m at maturity, occurs in mon-
        tane thickets along rivers and creeks and adjacent to intermittent
        streams at 5,200 to 8,500 ft. (1,600 to 2,600 m) in elevation. Wide-
        spread over New Mexico, it may start flowering as early as mid-
        March in southern counties. It is closely related to the **Blue Wil-
        low,** *S. drummondiana,* and the two taxa may be ecotypes of a
        single species. The **Blue Willow** is commonly found at higher
        elevations above 7,500 ft. (2,300 m).

**Bluestem Willow**, *Salix irrorata* Andersson                Salicaceae

BLUESTEM WILLOW
*Salix irrorata*

151.  Capsules on pistillate plants pubescent; mature leaves elliptic to oblanceolate, glaucous and silvery appressed pubescent on the lower surface and green to dark green and/or finely hairy on the upper surface, commonly averaging less than 6.5 cm in length...... 152.

152.  Catkins subglobose, 5.0 to 20.0 mm in length, on pubescent, leafy peduncles; bracts subtending flowers yellowish, often with red tips; leaves elliptic to oblanceolate, 2.0 to 7.0 cm in length and 5.0 to 15.0 mm in width, dark green above and glabrate to glaucous beneath, silky-pubescent on both surfaces, margins entire to slightly serrate to revolute, leaves appearing with the flowers; axillary buds not strongly conspicuous. Found in the montane to subalpine life zones at 6,500 to 9,500 ft. (1,980 to 2,900 m) in elevation, this locally abundant species occurs along mountain streams and rivers, in sedge meadows and on lake shores. Flowering in April and May, it seldom reaches more than 3.0 m at maturity, but it has been known to reach 5.0 m.

**Geyer's Willow**, *Salix geyeriana* Andersson          Salicaceae

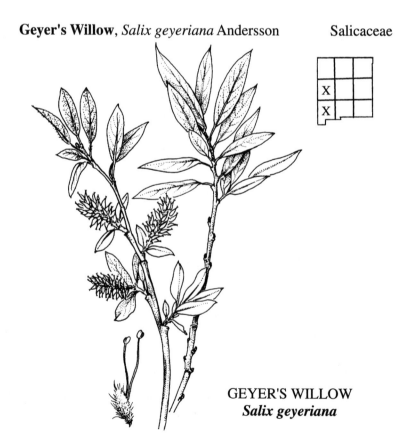

GEYER'S WILLOW
*Salix geyeriana*

152. Catkins elongate, 10.0 to 60.0 mm in length, usually sessile or nearly so; bracts subtending flowers dark brown or black; leaves elliptic to oblanceolate, 2.0 to 9.0 cm in length and 5.0 to 20.0 mm in width, dark green above, only sparingly pubescent and often silvery pubescent to hairy below, margins mostly entire to slightly dentate-crenate or undulate, leaves appearing after the flowers; stamens 2 and red or red-tipped. Occurring along streams in the montane and subalpine, usually above 7,500 ft. (2,300 m) in elevation, this species has been found growing with **Geyer's Willow,** as well as other high elevation species. As previously stated, *S. drummondiana* appears to be closely related to *S. irrorata.*

**Blue Willow** or **Silver Willow,** *Salix drummondiana* Barratt
Syns. *S. subcoerulea* Piper
Salicaceae

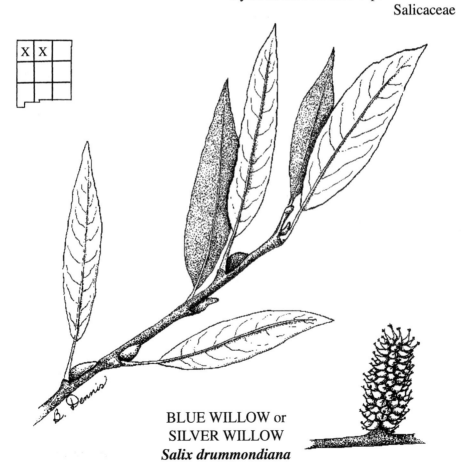

BLUE WILLOW or
SILVER WILLOW
*Salix drummondiana*

153. Ovaries of pistillate flowers and capsules pubescent ...................... 154.

153. Ovaries of pistillate flowers and capsules glabrous........................ 158.

    154. Flowers precocious, appearing before the leaves, catkins not usually subtended by young leaves, with leafy shoots arising after the catkins ........................................................ 155.

    154. Flowers coetaneous, appearing with the leaves, catkins usually subtended by young leaves and arising on the young leafy shoots ............................................................. 156.

155. Willow growing throughout the forests and not confined to the margins of streams and lakes, but growing along roadsides, in gravel and open woods; first year twigs covered with a gray, velvet pubescence (not pruinose); leaves 4.0 to 12.0 cm in length and 12.0 to 40.0 mm in width, obviously obovate to oblanceolate, margins revolute, entire, glandular dotted to somewhat serrate; male catkins 2.0 to 6.0 cm in length, scales dark and long-pilose; female catkins 2.5 to 6.5 cm in length, scales dark and long-pilose, pedicels 0.8 to 2.0 mm in length; capsules 7.0 to 10.0 mm in length and slightly stalked. This common, large shrub or small tree, to 8.0 m in height at maturity, has been collected from 7,000 to 10,000 ft. (2,130 to 3,050 m) in elevation. It occurs in most of the better wooded areas throughout New Mexico, including the National and State Forests.

**Scouler's Willow,** *Salix scouleriana* Barratt     Salicaceae

155. Willow limited to moist areas, growing adjacent to streams, around subalpine bogs, and in wet areas on the tundra, seldom, if ever, growing in the dry areas of the forests and open woods; first year twigs glabrous or nearly so, turning purple to black with age; leaves 2.0 to 5.0 cm in length and 0.7 to 2.2 mm in width, oblong to elliptic to somewhat obovate, margins flat to revolute, entire to crenate; male catkins 1.0 to 3.0 cm in length, scales dark brown and white-pilose; female catkins 1.5 to 4.5 cm in length, scales dark brown and white-pilose, pedicels 0.2 to 0.8 mm in length; capsules 4.0 to 7.0 mm in length and sessile. This shrub, to 3.0 m in height at maturity, occurs on the high mountain slopes and mountain summits in the northern part of New Mexico at 10,000 to 13,000 ft. (3,050 to 4,000 m) in elevation.

**Planeleaf Willow,** *Salix planifolia* Pursh
    Syns. *S. phylicifolia* var. *monica* (Bebb) Schneider     Salicaceae

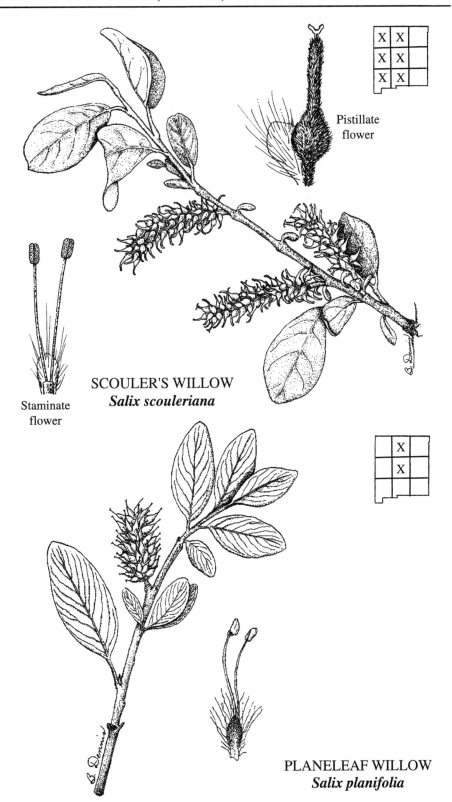

Pistillate
flower

Staminate
flower

SCOULER'S WILLOW
*Salix scouleriana*

PLANELEAF WILLOW
*Salix planifolia*

156.   Floral bracts yellow to pale brown or pale green and persistent; pedicels of flowers 2.5 to 4.8 mm long; leaves 3.0 to 8.0 cm in length and 15.0 to 35.0 mm in width, elliptic to oblanceolate or obovate, broadest at or above the middle and pointed at both ends, lower surface glaucous, densely to sparsely tomentose or silky, upper surface dull and darker green, pubescent with shorter silky hairs than the lower surface, margins flat to rarely revolute, entire to somewhat crenate or serrate; twigs pubescent when young; male catkins 0.6 to 2.5 cm in length, scales yellow, often with reddish tips; stamens 2 and the anthers yellow; female catkins 1.0 to 7.0 cm in length, scales yellow, often with reddish tips; capsules 4.0 to 9.0 mm in length and silky pubescent. This is a common willow over western and southern New Mexico at 7,000 to 9,400 ft. (2,130 to 2,850 m) in elevation. It is usually found growing along streams and lake shores from the ponderosa pine forest to the lower subalpine. It flowers in the spring from April through June.

**Bebb Willow,** *Salix bebbiana* Sargent
   Syns. *S. depressa* ssp. *rostrata* (Richardson) Hiitonen
                                                          Salicaceae

156.   Floral bracts dark tan to brown or black and persistent; pedicels of flowers absent to 2.0 mm long. (The following two plants are morphologically very similar and may be ecotypes of a single species.) ......................................... 157.

157.   Petioles 1.0 to 3.0 mm in length; catkins 0.5 to 2.2 cm in length and developing on branchlets 2.0 to 10.0 mm in length; pedicels absent or less than 0.5 mm long; leaves on sterile twigs 2.5 to 3.5 cm in length and 6.0 to 13.0 mm in width, oblong-elliptic to oblanceolate, margins entire, upper and lower surfaces tomentose, the lower surface densely so. This rare but locally abundant shrub to 1.0 m in height should probably be identified by the common name, **Subalpine Willow**. Practically confined from 8,500 to 11,500 ft. (2,600 to 3,510 m) in elevation, it forms thickets that are usually adjacent to mountain streams or in wet meadows.

**Barrenground Willow,** *Salix brachycarpa* Nuttall            Salicaceae

BEBB WILLOW
*Salix bebbiana*

BARRENGROUND
WILLOW
*Salix brachycarpa*

157.    Petioles 3.0 to 12.0 mm in length; catkins 1.5 to 5.0 cm in length
and developing on branchlets 5.0 to 25.0 mm in length; pedicels
0.5 to 2.0 mm long; leaves on sterile twigs 2.5 to 7.0 cm in length
and 15.0 to 25.0 mm in width, oblong-ovate to elliptic, margins
entire, upper surface dark green and the lower surface glaucous,
neither surface densely tomentose. Commonly reaching more than
1.0 m in height, but seldom more than 2.0 m, this robust shrub is
found in the subalpine and alpine at 10,000 to 12,000 ft. (3,050
to 3,660 m) in elevation. It is limited to the most northern counties of New Mexico and has a short flowering season in late June
and July.

**Grayleaf Willow,** *Salix glauca* L.                    Salicaceae

158.    Bracts subtending the flowers pale yellow or creamy-
white, showy and persistent; stamens yellow, 3 to 7, usually 4 or 5 per flower; twigs glabrous, lustrous and reddish-brown; leaves 5.0 to 15.0 cm in length and 1.2 to 3.3
cm in width, lanceolate to oblanceolate, apex long-acumi-
nate, dark green and shiny above, margins finely serrulate;
yellow glands at the base of the blade; stipules commonly
persist; catkins 1.7 to 10.0 cm in length; capsules 4.0 to
8.0 mm in length and glabrous. This infrequent and poorly
defined shrub or small tree to 11.0 m has a range that
continues to be confusing in New Mexico. It is more commonly found in the montane, but it may occur in a wide
range of life zones. Usually found between 5,500 and
9,500 ft. (1,680 to 2,900 m) in elevation, along stream
margins, in sandy soils and wet meadows, the attractive
staminate plants and large leaves will usually cause the
observant botanist to stop for a more serious look.

**Pacific Willow** or **Shining Willow**, *Salix lucida*
                    Muehlenberg          Salicaceae

Two subspecies have been identified for the **Pacific Willow** or **Shining Willow** based chiefly on the lower leaf surface. If the leaves are strongly glaucous on the lower surface, and the plant is a small tree it is thought to be *Salix lucida* ssp. *lasiandra* (Bentham) E. Murray. If the leaves are not glaucous on the lower surface, but only a lighter green than the upper surface, and the plant is a shrub it is thought to be *Salix lucida* ssp. *caudata* (Nuttall) E. Murray.

PACIFIC WILLOW or
SHINING WILLOW
*Salix lucida*

158.   Bracts subtending the flowers dark in color, brown, black
       or darker yellow or tan; stamens 2 per flower .................... 159.

159.    Mature leaves not glaucous on the lower surface, but sometimes
        pale green.................................................................................. 160.


159.    Mature leaves glaucous on the lower surface ................................. 161.



The distinction between the following two species is not clear in
New Mexico. The **Tall Blueberry Willow,** *S. boothii*, has been
collected and is better defined than the **Myrtle-leafed Willow,** *S.*
*myrtillifolia*. Based on herbarium specimens, *S. myrtillifolia* has
probably never been collected in New Mexico.



160.    Shrubs or small trees, 1.0 to 3.5 m in height; rarely occur-
        ring in wet meadows and along streams in the subalpine
        from 9,000 to 10,000 ft. (2,740 to 3,050 m) in elevation;
        leaves 3.0 to 10.0 cm in length and 8.0 to 30.0 mm in
        width, oblong to elliptic to lanceolate, apex acute, mar-
        gins entire to serrate with serrations often gland tipped
        and the glands running down the petiole, petiole 3.0 to
        15.0 mm in length, lower leaf surface glabrous or pilose,
        but not glaucous, upper leaf surface shiny and glabrous
        often with white to rusty hairs along the mid-vein, stipules
        small and rudimentary if present; staminate catkins 2.0 to
        6.0 cm in length; pistillate catkins 1.0 to 7.0 cm in length;
        capsules 4.0 to 8.0 mm in length.

        **Tall Blueberry Willow,** *Salix boothii* Dorn
                    Syns. *S. pseudocordata* (Andersson) Rydberg
                    *S. novae-angliae* Andersson            Salicaceae



160.    Shrubs, seldom to 1.0 m in height, decumbent; rarely oc-
        curring, if at all, at about 9,000 ft. (2,740 m) in elevation
        and higher in New Mexico; leaves 2.5 to 5.0 cm in length
        and 10.0 to 30.0 mm in width, oblanceolate to obovate to
        elliptic, apex acute to obtuse, margins serrate with serra-
        tions often gland tipped, petiole 2.0 to 8.0 mm in length,

lower leaf surface glabrous, but not glaucous, upper leaf surface glabrous, stipules small and rudimentary if present; staminate catkins 1.0 to 4.0 cm in length; pistillate catkins 1.0 to 4.0 cm in length; capsules 4.0 to 7.0 mm in length.

**Myrtle-leafed Willow,** *Salix myrtillifolia* Andersson

Syns. *S. pseudocordata* (Andersson) Rydberg

Salicaceae

TALL BLUEBERRY WILLOW
*Salix boothii*

161.   Pedicels of mature capsules 2.0 to 4.5 mm in length; twigs yellow to grayish-yellow, becoming reddish on the sunny side of the mature twigs; anthers red or tipped with red and filaments glabrous; mature leaves 4.2 to 11.5 cm in length and 10.0 to 30.0 mm in width, 2.2 to 6.5 times as long as wide, narrowly elliptic to elliptic or oblanceolate, margins entire to serrulate and then glandular, slightly revolute to flat; inflorescences coetaneous or subprecocious; floral bracts brown; male catkins 1.5 to 5.0 cm in length; female catkins 2.0 to 7.5 cm in length, ovaries glabrous; capsules 4.0 to 5.0 mm in length and glabrous. This rare montane species in New Mexico is usually a shrub or occasionally a small tree from 1.0 to 6.0 m in height. It is found from 3,600 to 4,200 ft. (1,100 to 1,280 m) in elevation, forming thickets along streams and ditches in canyons and valleys.

**Yellow Willow,** *Salix lutea* Nuttall                    Salicaceae

161.   Pedicels of mature capsules 0.5 to 2.0 mm in length; twigs dark yellow to reddish or dark brown to black, if yellowish then not developing the reddish line on the sunny side of the twigs; anthers yellow or red ........................................................................ 162.

162.   Styles of the pistils 0.7 to 1.5 mm in length; filaments hairy; anthers yellow; twigs reddish-brown to dark yellow and darkening with age; mature leaves 3.5 to 9.5 cm in length and 12.0 to 34.0 mm in width, 2.0 to 4.0 times as long as wide, lanceolate to elliptic or oblanceolate to elliptic-obovate, base acute to rounded, glaucous and reticulately veined on the lower surface and dull green, glabrous to pilose on the upper surface, especially along the midrib, stipules often present and persistent, margins serrulate to serrate, revolute to flat; inflorescences precocious to coetaneous; floral bracts brown or black and hairy;

male catkins 1.0 to 3.7 cm in length and densely flowered; female catkins 1.5 to 5.7 cm in length and densely
flowered; ovaries glabrous; capsules 4.0 to 7.0 mm in
length and glabrous. This montane to subalpine shrub or
small tree to 6.0 m in height occurs from 6,900 to 9,500
ft. (2,100 to 2,900 m) in elevation. It can be found in wet
soils forming thickets along rivers and creeks and flowers in early spring.

**Park Willow,** *Salix monticola* Bebb
Syns. *S. pseudomonticola* var. *padophylla*
(Rydberg) Ball          Salicaceae

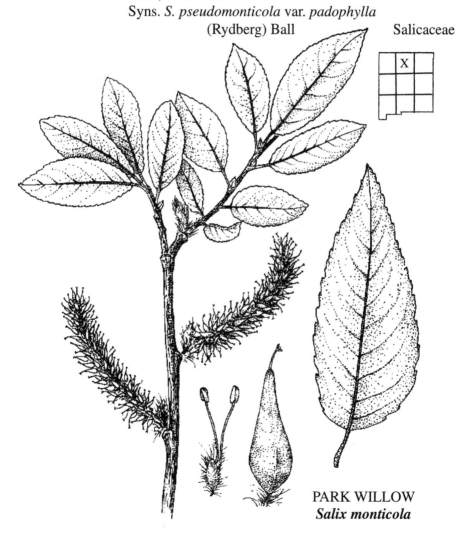

PARK WILLOW
*Salix monticola*

162.    Styles of the pistils less than 0.7 mm in length; filaments
glabrous .......................................................................... 163.

163.    Flowers precocious to subprecocious; catkins sessile or on very short flowering branchlets; stamens 2, yellow; twigs dark reddish-brown at maturity and occasionally tomentose, which can be confused with pruinose; mature leaves 4.0 to 14.0 cm in length and 1.2 to 27.0 mm in width and 3.4 to 9.0 times as long as wide, narrowly oblong to narrowly elliptic to oblanceolate and sometimes falcate, base cuneate to acute, glaucous to tomentose and gray to white on the lower surface and short-silky tomentose to glabrous on the upper surface, margins entire to widely irregular serrate and sometimes slightly revolute or glandular-dotted; floral bracts dark brown to black, persistent and white to gray woolly; stipules usually present; male catkins 1.7 to 5.6 cm in length and densely flowered; female catkins 1.5 to 7.0 cm in length and densely flowered; ovaries glabrous; capsules 3.0 to 8.0 mm in length, reddish-brown and glabrous. The **Arroyo Willow** appears to be a more western species in New Mexico. It grows as a shrub or small tree from 3.0 to 9.0 m in height and forms thickets along streams and creeks at 4,300 to 7,500 ft. (1,310 to 2,300 m) in elevation.

**Arroyo Willow**, *Salix lasiolepis* Bentham           Salicaceae

ARROYO WILLOW
*Salix lasiolepis*

163.    Flowers coetaneous; catkins on distinctly flowering branchlets;
        stamens 2, red to purple; twigs reddish-brown to dark brown at
        maturity; mature leaves 5.0 to 12.5 cm in length and 10.0 to 23.0
        mm in width, 3.5 to 6.4 times as long as wide, narrowly elliptic
        to elliptic or lanceolate or oblanceolate, base attenuate to acute to
        rounded, glaucous and glabrous on the lower surface and dull
        green and glabrous on the upper surface, margins entire to finely
        serrate to serrulate and then glandular dotted, to seldom entire;
        floral bracts tawny to brown or black and glabrous to hairy;
        stipules usually present and obvious; male catkins 1.2 to 4.0 cm
        in length and densely flowered; female catkins 1.5 to 5.0 cm in
        length and densely flowered; ovaries glabrous; capsules 4.0 to
        5.0 mm in length, reddish-brown and glabrous. This species of
        lower elevations is usually found at 3,500 to 7,500 ft. (1,070 to
        2,300 m), but the range is not clear. If one carefully compares the
        herbarium materials and descriptions of *S. ligulifolia* with *S. lutea*,
        it becomes obvious that these two species are extremely closely
        related, or are in fact a single species. We would suggest the lat-
        ter, but more study is needed.

**Strapleaf Willow,** *Salix ligulifolia* (Ball) Ball *ex* Schneider
            Syns. *S. lutea* var. *ligulifolia* Ball                    Salicaceae

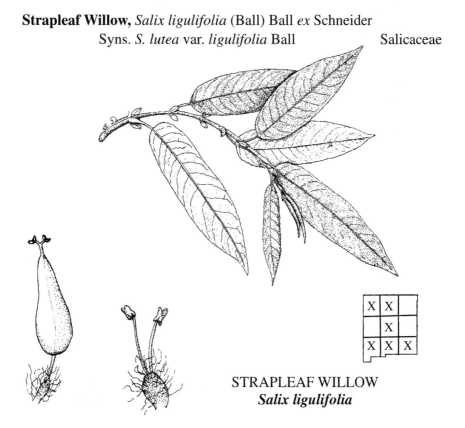

STRAPLEAF WILLOW
*Salix ligulifolia*

## Willow (*Salix*) Pistillate Characteristics

| Specific Name | Capsules glabrous (G) or pubescent (P) | Capsule length in mm | Catkin length in cm | Ovary glabrous (G) or pubescent (P) | Catkin appearing before (B), with (W) or after (A) leaves | Floral Bracts persistent (P) or deciduous (D) | Floral Bract Color |
|---|---|---|---|---|---|---|---|
| S. alba | G | 3.0-4.5 | 3.5-6.0 | G | W | D | tawny |
| S. amygdaloides | G | 3.0-8.0 | 2.5-10.0 | G | W | D | yellow to green |
| S. arctica | P | 4.0-8.0 | 2.0-7.0 | P | W | D | brown to black |
| S. babylonica | G | 1.5-2.5 | 1.8-2.2 | G | W | P | tawny to black |
| S. bebbiana | P | 5.0-9.0 | 2.5-6.0 | P | W/B | P | pale green to pale brown |
| S. bonplandiana | G | 2.0-3.0 | 1.5-5.4 | G | W/A | D | pale yellow |
| S. boothii | G | 4.0-8.0 | 1.0-7.0 | G | W/B | P | tawny to black |
| S. brachycarpa | P | 4.5-5.0 | 0.5-2.2 | P | W | - | whitish-green yellow-brown |
| S. drummondiana | P | 3.0-6.0 | 1.0-6.0 | P | B | - | black-dk. brown |
| S. exigua | G | 4.0-5.0 | 2.0-8.0 | G | W | D | tawny |
| S. fragilis | G | 4.0-6.0 | 4.0-8.0 | G | W | - | greenish-yellow |
| S. geyeriana | P | 5.0-7.0 | 0.7-2.0 | P | W | P | brown |
| S. glauca | P | 4.0-8.0 | 2.0-5.0 | G | W | P | brown to black |
| S. gooddingii | P | 3.0-8.0 | 2.2-6.5 | G/P | W | D | tawny |
| S. irrorata | G | 3.0-4.0 | 1.8-4.2 | G | B | - | black |
| S. lasiolepis | G | 3.0-8.0 | 1.5-7.0 | G | B | D/P | tawny to black |
| S. ligulifolia | G | 4.0-5.0 | 1.5-5.0 | G | W | P | tawny to black |
| S. lucida | G | 4.0-8.0 | 2.0-10.0 | G | W | D | tawny |
| S. lutea | G | 4.0-5.0 | 2.0-7.5 | G | W/B | P | tawny to black |
| S. matsudana | G | - | 1.5-3.0 | G/P | - | - | pale green |
| S. monticola | G | 4.0-7.0 | 1.5-5.7 | G | W/B | P | brown to black |
| S. myrtillifolia | G | 4.0-7.0 | 1.0-4.0 | G | W | - | brown |
| S. planifolia | P | 4.0-7.0 | 1.5-4.5 | P | B | - | brown to black |
| S. reticulata | P | 3.0-4.0 | 1.0-2.0 | P | - | - | yellow, red tinge |
| S. scouleriana | P | 7.0-10.0 | 2.5-6.5 | P | B | - | brown |
| S. taxifolia | G/P | 5.0-7.0 | 0.7-1.3 | P | W/B | - | tawny |

## Willow (*Salix*) Staminate Characteristics

| Specific Name | No. of stamens | Anther color | Filaments hairy (H) or glabrous (G) * = at base | Catkin length in cm | Catkins appearing before (B), with (W) or after (A) leaves | Floral Bract Color |
|---|---|---|---|---|---|---|
| *S. alba* | 2 | yellow | H | 3.0-3.5 | W | greenish-yellow |
| *S. amygdaloides* | 3-9 | yellow | H | 3.8-6.0 | W | yellow to green |
| *S. arctica* | 2 | red to purple | G | 1.0-2.5 | B | brown to black |
| *S. babylonica* | 3-5 | yellow | H | 2.5-3.5 | W | yellow |
| *S. bebbiana* | 2 | yellow | H/G | 0.6-2.5 | B/W | yellowish |
| *S. bonplandiana* | 3-7 | yellow | H | 1.2-6.0 | W/A | yellow |
| *S. boothii* | 2 | yellow | H/G | 2.0-6.0 | B/W | brown to black |
| *S. brachycarpa* | 2 | red, yellow | H * | 1.0-1.2 | W | yellowish |
| *S. drummondiana* | 2 | red | G | 1.5-3.0 | B | black-dk.brown |
| *S. exigua* | 2 | yellow | H | 0.9-6.0 | W | yellow |
| *S. fragilis* | 2 | yellow | H | 3.0-8.0 | W | greenish-yellow |
| *S. geyeriana* | 2 | yellow | H | 0.5-1.2 | W | yellowish |
| *S. glauca* | 2 | red, black | H */G | 1.0-5.0 | W | brown |
| *S. gooddingii* | 3-8 | yellow | H | 3.5-7.0 | W | yellow |
| *S. irrorata* | 2 | yellow | G | 1.5-3.0 | B | black |
| *S. lasiolepis* | 2 | yellow | G | 1.7-5.6 | B | black |
| *S. ligulifolia* | 2 | red to purple | G | 1.2-4.0 | W | black |
| *S. lucida* | 3-7 | yellow | H | 1.7-10.0 | W | yellow |
| *S. lutea* | 2 | red | G | 1.5-5.0 | B/W | brown, black,yellow |
| *S. matsudana* | 2 | yellow | H | 1.5-3.0 | W | greenish |
| *S. monticola* | 2 | yellow | H/G | 1.0-3.7 | B/W | brown |
| *S. myrtillifolia* | 2 | yellow | G | 1.0-4.0 | W | brown |
| *S. planifolia* | 2 | red, yellow | H/G | 1.0-3.0 | B | brown, black |
| *S. reticulata* | 2 | dark red | H*/G | 1.0-2.0 | W/A | yellow, red-tinged |
| *S. scouleriana* | 2 | yellow, red-tip | H*/G | 2.0-6.5 | B | black |
| *S. taxifolia* | 2 | yellow | H | 0.7-2.0 | W | yellowish |

## SALIX VEGETATIVE CHART

| Species Name | Tree (T) or Shrub (S) | Plant Height | Leaf length in cm | Leaf width in cm | Leaf Shape | | | | | Leaf Margin | |
|---|---|---|---|---|---|---|---|---|---|---|---|
| | | | | | Linear | Lanceolate | Oblanceolate | Elliptic | Other | Entire | Serrate-teeth per cm |
| S. alba | T | to 25 m | 6.3-11.5 | 1.0-2.0 | | √ | | √ | oblong | | 5-9 |
| S. amygdaloides | T | 12-20 m | 5.0-13.0 | 1.2-3.7 | | √ | √ | √ | | | 6-12 |
| S. arctica | S | to 20 cm | 15.0-35.0 | 0.8-1.5 | | | | √ | obovate | √ | |
| S. babylonica | T | to 20 m | 7.0-14.0 | 0.9-1.8 | | √ | | √ | | | 4-10 |
| S. bebbiana | T/S | 0.5-10 m | 2.0-8.0 | 1.0-4.0 | | | √ | √ | oblong | √ | 2-5 |
| S. bonplandiana | T | to 13 m | 5.8-15.5 | 0.7-2.7 | | √ | | √ | | | 6-12 |
| S. boothii | S | to 6 m | 2.6-10.2 | 0.8-3.0 | | √ | | √ | oblong | √ | 2-12 |
| S. brachycarpa | S | to 1 m | 2.5-3.5 | 0.6-1.3 | | | √ | √ | oblong | √ | |
| S. drummondiana* | S | to 3 m | 2.0-9.0 | 0.5-3.0 | | | √ | √ | | √ | |
| S. exigua | T/S | to 5 m | 2.0-16.0 | 0.2-1.5 | √ | √ | | | | | 1-5 |
| S. fragilis | T | to 20 m | 7.0-15.0 | 2.0-3.5 | | √ | | √ | | | 5-6 |
| S. geyeriana* | S | to 5 m | 2.0-8.9 | 0.5-1.3 | √ | | √ | √ | | √ | 1-6 |
| S. glauca | S | to 2 m | 1.0-6.0 | 0.7-2.0 | | | | √ | oblong ovate | √ | |
| S. gooddingii | T | to 30 m | 6.7-13.0 | 0.9-1.6 | | √ | | | ovate | | 5-10 |
| S. irrorata* | S | to 7 m | 4.7-11.5 | 0.8-2.2 | | √ | √ | √ | | √ | 2-7 |
| S. lasiolepis | S | to 6 m | 3.6-15.0 | 0.6-3.2 | | | | √ | oblong | √ | 2-4 |
| S. ligulifolia | S | to 8 m | 5.0-13.3 | 1.0-3.0 | | √ | | √ | | rarely | 6-13 |
| S. lucida | T/S | to 11 m | 2.4-17.0 | 0.9-4.3 | | √ | √ | √ | oblong | | 6-14 |
| S. lutea | T/S | to 7 m | 4.2-11.6 | 1.0-4.5 | | | √ | √ | | √ | 5-12 |
| S. matsudana | T | 12-18 m | 5.0-12.0 | 1.0-1.5 | √ | √ | | | | | √ |
| S. monticola | S | to 6 m | 3.5-9.5 | 1.1-3.3 | | √ | √ | | oblong | | 5-9 |
| S. myrtillifolia | S | to 1 m | 2.0-6.0 | 1.0-3.0 | | | √ | √ | obovate | | √ |
| S. planifolia | S | to 4 m | 2.0-4.8 | 0.5--1.5 | | | | √ | oblong obovate | √ | 2-8 |
| S. reticulata | S | to 10 cm | to 2.5 | to 0.2 | | | | √ | orbicular | √ | |
| S. scouleriana | T/S | to 10 m | 2.9-12.5 | 0.9-4.0 | | | √ | √ | obovate | √ | 1-4 |
| S. taxifolia | T/S | to 16 m | 0.8-4.2 | 0.1-0.4 | √ | | | √ | | √ | 1-6 |

* = branches glaucous and pruinose

## SALIX VEGETATIVE CHART

| Lower Leaf Surface | | | | | | dull(d)-shiny(s) | Upper Leaf Surface | | | | | Elevation in feet & (meters) Life Zone | Species Name |
| glaucous | pubescent | glabrous | tomentose | villous | pilose | | pubescent | glabrous | tomentose | villous | pilose | | |
|---|---|---|---|---|---|---|---|---|---|---|---|---|---|
| √ | √ | √ |  |  |  | d | √ | √ |  |  |  | --- | S. alba |
| √ |  |  |  |  |  | d |  |  |  |  |  | 4,000-7,900 (1,220-2,410) plains, montane | S. amygdaloides |
|  |  |  |  |  |  | - |  |  |  |  |  | 11,000-13,000 (3,350-3,960) alpine, tundra | S. arctica |
| √ |  | √ |  |  |  | d |  | √ |  |  |  | ------------- | S. babylonica |
| √ |  | √ | √ |  |  | d | √ | √ |  |  |  | 7,000-9,400 (2,130-2,850) montane, subalpine | S. bebbiana |
| √ |  |  |  |  |  | d/s |  | √ |  |  |  | 4,500-7,400 (1,370-2,260) forest riparian | S. bonplandiana |
|  |  | √ |  |  | √ | - |  |  |  |  |  | 9,000-10,000 (2,740-3,050) subalpine | S. boothii |
| √ |  |  | √ |  |  | d |  |  | √ |  |  | 8,500-11,500 (2,600-3,510) subalpine, alpine | S. brachycarpa |
| √ | √ |  |  |  |  | - |  |  |  |  |  | to 10,000 (to 3,050) montane, subalpine | S. drummondiana* |
| √ |  |  |  | √ |  | s |  | √ |  | √ |  | 3,500-7,500 (1,080-2,300) warm temperate | S. exigua |
| √ |  | √ |  |  |  | d |  | √ |  |  |  | ------------ | S. fragilis |
| √ |  | √ |  |  |  | s | √ |  |  |  |  | 6,500-9,500 (1,980-2,900) montane, subalpine | S. geyeriana* |
| √ |  |  |  | √ |  | - |  | √ |  | √ |  | 10,000-12,000 (3,050-3,660) subalpine, alpine | S. glauca |
|  | √ |  |  |  |  | s |  | √ |  |  |  | 4,500-7,900 (1,380-2,130) warm temperate, subtropical | S. gooddingii |
| √ |  | √ | √ |  |  | s |  | √ |  |  | √ | 5,200-8,500 (1,600-2,600) montane | S. irrorata* |
| √ |  | √ | √ |  |  | s |  | √ | √ |  |  | 4,300-7,500 (1,310-2,300) montane | S. lasiolepis |
| √ |  | √ |  |  |  | d |  | √ |  |  |  | 3,500-7,500 (1,070-2,300) plains, montane | S. ligulifolia |
| √ |  | √ |  |  | √ | s |  | √ |  |  | √ | 3,700-9,500 (1,130-2,300) montane | S. lucida |
| √ |  | √ |  |  | √ | d |  | √ |  |  | √ | 3,600-4,200 (1,100-1,280) montane | S. lutea |
| √ |  | √ |  |  |  | - |  | √ |  |  |  | --- | S. matsudana |
| √ |  | √ |  |  |  | d |  | √ |  |  | √ | 6,900-9,500 (2,100-2,900) montane-subalpine | S. monticola |
|  |  | √ |  |  |  | - |  | √ |  |  |  | above 9,000 (2,740) alpine | S. myrtillifolia |
| √ |  | √ |  |  |  | s |  | √ |  |  |  | 10,000-13,000 (3,050-3,960) subalpine, alpine, tundra | S. planifolia |
| √ |  | √ |  |  |  | - |  | √ |  |  |  | 11,000-12,500 (3,350-3,660) alpine | S. reticulata |
| √ |  |  | √ |  |  | s |  | √ |  |  | √ | 7,000-10,000 (2,130-3,050) montane, dry forests | S. scouleriana |
| √ |  | √ |  | √ |  | s |  | √ |  |  |  | 4,000-6,000 (1,220-1,830) warm temperate, subtropical | S. taxifolia |

\* = branches glaucous and pruniose

164.    Plants and stems leafless or with small, scale-like, green
        leaves or with a mixture of leafless stems and a few scale-
        like leaves throughout the growing season, never with
        obvious broad leaves ............................................................ 165.

164.    Plant and stems with obvious leaves throughout the grow-
        ing season ...................................................................... 167.

165.    Shrubs or small trees, rapidly growing to 7.0 or 8.0 m in height at
        maturity and quickly spreading over large areas, somewhat ce-
        dar-like in appearance; leaves commonly present throughout the
        growing season, green, scale-like, appressed and seldom reach-
        ing more than 1.0 to 1.5 mm in length; inflorescence a raceme,
        showy and conspicuous with pink or white flowers; flowers small,
        sepals 5, petals 4, stamens 5 or rarely more, filaments inserted
        between the lobes of the disk or arising from the disk lobes; fruit
        a capsule, 3.0 to 4.0 mm in length; seeds numerous and hairy.
        Commonly found at 3,000 to 5,500 ft. (910 to 1,680 m) in eleva-
        tion, this species is abundant in alkaline and sandy soils along
        most of the major rivers and streams throughout New Mexico.
        There is considerable confusion among authorities as to specia-
        tion in **Salt Cedar** in the western states, and there are equally
        confusing ideas as to how and when the taxon was introduced in
        the United States. One thing is certain, it is an extremely nox-
        ious, weedy species with an extensive taproot, and eliminating it
        is very expensive. As **Salt Cedar** moves into new areas, willows
        and other native riparian species are crowded out.

**Salt Cedar** or **Tamarisk**, *Tamarix ramosissima* Ledebour
                    Syns. *T. pentandra* Pallas
                          *T. chinensis* Loureiro               Tamaricaceae

165.    Shrubs remaining relatively small, to 2.0 m in height at maturity,
        often growing in isolated clumps, not cedar-like in appearance;
        leaves few to absent during the growing season, if present, scale-
        like and scattered; inflorescences small and inconspicuous ............ 166.

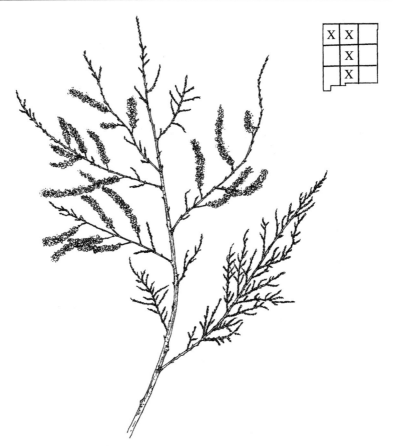

SALT CEDAR or TAMARISK
*Tamarix ramosissima*

166.    Stems distinctly jointed and swollen, not waxy, woody at
        the base, 0.3 to 1.5 m in height, succulent, glabrous and
        green; leaves scale-like and triangular; inflorescence a
        dense and cylindric spike; flowers perfect and subtended
        by peltate bracts, perianth small, sepals 4 or 5, stamens 1
        or 2, stigmas with 2 or 3 lobes; fruit an ovoid, compressed
        utricle. This perennial, branching shrub is confined to the
        margins of alkaline and salty lakes and streams at 3,000
        to 5,500 ft. (910 to 1,680 m) in elevation in New Mexico
        and throughout southwestern United States and into
        Mexico.

**Pickleweed** or **Iodine Bush**, *Allenrolfea occidentalis*
                                          (S. Watson) Kuntze
                                          Chenopodiaceae

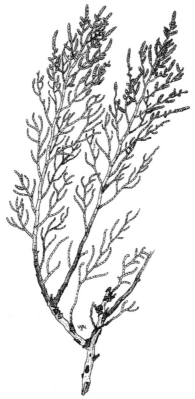

PICKLEWEED or IODINE BUSH
*Allenrolfea occidentalis*

166.     Stems not distinctly jointed, but cylindrical and waxy, shrub appearing as a clump of waxy stems, 20.0 to 80.0 cm in height, usually off-green to gray to brown in color, branching only at the base; leaves usually absent or if present, linear and quickly deciduous; inflorescence composed of a small cluster of typical *Euphorbia* flowers, borne on the upper third of the plant, in an involucre, the rim of which is lined with glands or small horns. This rare species, that has a long history of being used for candlewax and medicinal purposes, is confined to the very southeastern and southcentral counties of New Mexico at below 4,000 ft. (1,220 m) in elevation. If you are fortunate enough to locate this waxy bundle of sticks, scattered over rocky and gravel slopes, please observe and photograph only.

**Candelilla** or **Wax Spurge,** *Euphorbia antisyphilitica*
                        Zuccarin                    Euphorbiaceae

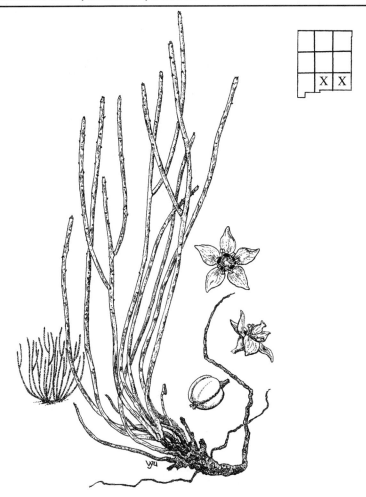

CANDELILLA or WAX SPURGE
*Euphorbia antisyphilitica*

167.    Fruit a utricle; leaves scurfy, covered with roughened scales, gray to white-mealy on both surfaces or densely stellate-pubescent in **Winterfat**, mostly entire or slightly revolute to undulate; plants dioecious or monoecious; flowers imperfect and incomplete, petals lacking; inflorescence a spike, panicle or flowers in clusters or solitary, sometimes in axillary clusters. Goosefoot Family - Chenopodiaceae ............................................................................ 168.

167.    Fruit a berry, drupe, capsule, achene, samara, legume, nutlet, follicle, pome or aggregate, but never a utricle; leaves glabrous, pubescent, tomentose or pilose, and scurfy only in several species of the Spurge Family, but never mealy on both surfaces; flowers perfect to imperfect; inflorescence variable ................................ 174.

168.  Leaves densely stellate-pubescent, commonly in fascicles
and sessile, linear to oblong with rounded and revolute
margins, 1.0 to 4.0 cm in length and 3.0 mm or less in
width; fruiting calyx or bracts covered with tufts of
straight, long, whitish hairs; suffrutescent shrub to 1.0 m
in height, erect, appearing white, especially as the fruit
develops; flowers borne in axillary clusters or terminal
spike-like clusters. This frequent and widespread low subshrub is not truly a woody plant, but because it appears as
such from a distance it is included here. It has been collected in almost every county in New Mexico at 4,800 to
6,500 ft. (1,460 to 1,980 m) in elevation, usually over dry
plains and hills.

**Winterfat** or **White Sage**, *Krascheninnikovia lanata*
(Pursh) Guldenstaedt
Syns. *Eurotia lanata* (Pursh) Moquin-Tandon
*Ceratoides lanata* (Pursh) J. Howell
Chenopodiaceae

WINTERFAT or WHITE SAGE
*Krascheninnikovia lanata*

168.   Leaves scurfy, covered with roughened scales, gray to white-mealy, but not stellate-pubescent, flattened, linear to lanceolate to elliptic or obovate, but not strongly revolute and not in fascicles; perianth on pistillate flowers absent; fruit bracts variable, but not covered with tufts of whitish hairs; plants light green to gray to glaucous and scurfy. **Saltbush** - genus *Atriplex* ........................................ 169.

169.   Plants monoecious, male and female flowers on the same plant; stems woody only at the base, prostrate or nearly so; fruiting bracts bright red; leaves 1.0 to 3.5 cm in length, oblong to obovate, sometimes slightly glabrous to scurfy on the upper surface and white-scurfy on the lower surface, entire to slightly toothed. This is a naturalized species, found in disturbed areas and sometimes cultivated, that is native to Australia and Tasmania. It is well adapted to dry, alkaline and saline soils in the desert, over the southern third of New Mexico at 3,500 to 4,500 ft. (1,070 to 1,370 m) in elevation.

**Australian Saltbush**, *Atriplex semibaccata* R. Brown
                                                            Chenopodiaceae

169.   Plants dioecious or monoecious, rarely with a few perfect and imperfect flowers on the same plant; stems erect and ascending or if prostrate then forming mats; fruiting bracts appendaged or lacking appendages, tan to yellow, but never bright red; native species ....................................................................................... 170.

170.   Plants woody throughout, large shrubs to 2.5 m in height at maturity; dioecious; bracts of the fruit producing 4 conspicuous, longitudinal wings; leaves entire, sessile, linear to elliptic to oblong, 1.0 to 5.0 cm in length and 3.0 to 12.0 mm in width. Since the staminate plants will not produce fruit they are more difficult to identify. However, if one locates the pistillate plants and walks over adjacent areas one is almost certain to spot the bright yellow to cream-colored flowers in small clusters on the spikes and panicles of the male plants. One of the most widespread

shrubs of the western states, **Four-winged Saltbush** is
common throughout New Mexico at 3,000 to 6,800 ft.
(910 to 2,070 m) in elevation. Drought resistant and found
in alkaline soils from the alkali flats to the hilly grasslands and on the plains, it identifies the sagebrush zone in
the Southwest.

**Four-winged Saltbush**, *Atriplex canescens* (Pursh)
Nuttall
Chenopodiaceae

FOUR-WINGED SALTBUSH
*Atriplex canescens*

170.    Plants woody only at or near the base or if woody throughout, then plants reaching to less than 20.0 cm in height, if
plants reach to 1.0 m or more in height, then the upper
one-half herbaceous; bracts of the fruit may develop appendages, but these not producing 4 conspicuous, longi-
tudinal wings ..................................................................... 171.

171.    Plants low, prostrate shrubs, often forming extensive mats, seldom reaching 20.0 cm in height; dioecious; leaves sessile, succulent, narrowly spatulate, entire, and less than 2.5 cm in length and less than 2.4 mm in width, alternate, or sometimes opposite on the lower stem; staminate flowers yellow to brown and in small clusters borne in spikes 1.0 to 8.0 cm in length and pistillate flowers on leafy spikes 5.0 to 15.0 cm in length and extending well above the leaves; fruiting bracts developing appendages or crested, elliptic to suborbicular, entire or undulate and united at the base, tuberculate to smooth. This is a species of very fine, saline shales and adobe soils found over rolling hills in the northwest corner of New Mexico at 5,000 to 6,500 ft. (1,520 to 1,980 m) in elevation. It may occur as a single species over large areas on the Mancos Shale.

**Mat Saltbush**, *Atriplex corrugata* S. Watson
      Syns. *A. nuttallii* var. *corrugata* (S. Watson) A. Nelson
                                     Chenopodiaceae

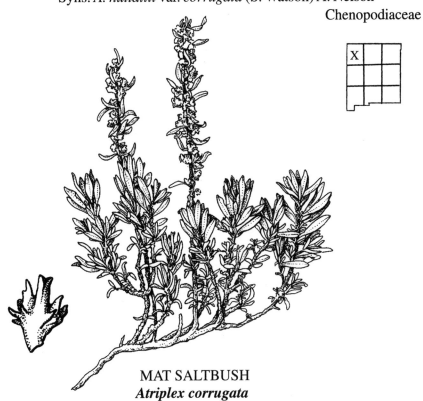

MAT SALTBUSH
*Atriplex corrugata*

171.    Plants erect and ascending, not forming mats, commonly reaching more than 25.0 cm in height, to 1.0 m or more at maturity........ 172.

172. Fruiting bracts with elongated, prominent, spine-like, flattened tubercules to 8.0 mm in length; leaf margins dentate to widely toothed or undulate to occasionally entire, the leaves lanceolate to oblong-elliptic or obovate and sometimes hastate, 1.8 to 5.0 cm in length and 10.0 to 25.0 mm in width; staminate flowers in dense panicles; pistillate flowers solitary or in small clusters; dioecious. This perennial shrub arises from a woody base to 1.0 m in height at maturity. It appears to be confined to gypsum outcrops in alkaline soils at 3,000 to 4,500 ft. (910 to 1,370 m) in elevation in the southern one-third and southwestern corner of New Mexico.

**Tubercled Saltbush**, *Atriplex acanthocarpa* (Torrey)

S. Watson

Chenopodiaceae

TUBERCLED SALTBUSH
*Atriplex acanthocarpa*

172.      Fruiting bracts lacking elongated spine-like tubercules, roughened to smooth, but not with exserted appendages; leaf margins entire to slightly undulate; flowers borne on extended spikes ................................................................. 173.

173.      Mature leaves obovate to broadly elliptic to orbicular, averaging more than 1.0 cm in width and not more than twice as long as wide, upper leaves reduced, some lower leaves opposite, 1.0 to 3.0 cm in length and 7.0 to 25.0 mm in width; plants erect and rigid from the base, older bark exfoliating; dioecious; fruiting bracts obovate to orbicular, margins entire to toothed, surface smooth or rarely tubercled; flowers borne in spikes or panicles, 6.0 to 30.0 cm in length. This common shrub, ranging in height from 20.0 to 60.0 cm in height can be found from 4,500 to 6,000 ft. (1,370 to 1,830 m) in elevation in dry, salt deserts and occasionally into lower piñon-juniper communities.

**Obovate-leafed Saltbush** or **New Mexico Saltbush**,
*Atriplex obovata* Moquin-Tandon
Syns. *A. greggii* S. Watson      Chenopodiaceae

OBOVATE-LEAFED SALTBUSH
or NEW MEXICO SALTBUSH
*Atriplex obovata*

173. Mature leaves linear to oblong-linear to narrowly obovate, averaging less than 1.0 cm in width and more than twice as long as wide, upper leaves not greatly reduced, some lower leaves opposite; plants spreading and flexible from the woody base, herbaceous above; dioecious or rarely monoecious; fruiting bracts ovate to rounded, terminating in a lanceolate or cuneate beak, surface smooth or with a few tubercles. A perennial shrub ranging in height from 20.0 to 50.0 cm, it can be found in the western one-half of New Mexico at 5,000 to 7,000 ft. (1,520 to 2,130 m) in elevation. This species is so poorly defined in the literature and in herbarium collections that it is difficult to limit its range and characteristics. As many as nine subspecies and varieties can be found in the literature. Here we have described the taxon based on personal collections and field observations.

**Gardner Saltbush,** *Atriplex gardneri* (Moquin-Tandon)

D. Dietrich

Syns. *A. nuttallii* S. Watson    Chenopodiaceae

Another rare species, **Griffith's Saltbush**, *Atriplex griffithsii* Standley (Syns. *A. lentiformis* var. *griffithsii* Hall & Clements), has been reported from southwestern New Mexico and would key to this point. It can be distinguished by tall, weak, slender and distinctly angled or ribbed stems. It is found in dry, alkaline, saline flats and depressions on the desert floor, below 4,500 ft. (1,370 m) in elevation.

fruit detail

GRIFFITH'S SALTBUSH
*Atriplex griffithsii*

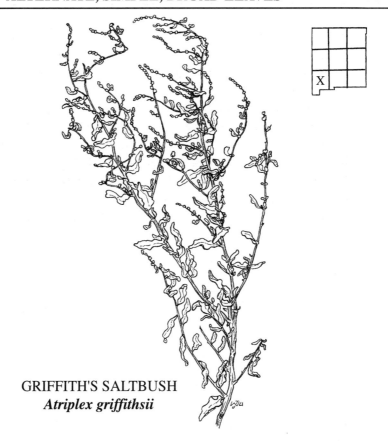

GRIFFITH'S SALTBUSH
*Atriplex griffithsii*

174. Flowers cup-shaped or urn-shaped resulting from the fusion of the 4 or 5 petals by their edges, waxy, less than 1.0 cm in length, white to pink to greenish-white in color, perfect and regular, often pendulous or in clusters of 2 or more, forming racemes or panicles, sepals and petals 4 or 5, stamens numbering twice the number of sepals and petals, 8 or 10, and opening by a distinctive pore and with horn-like appendages, ovary superior, fruit a berry, drupe or berry-like capsule; leaves thick to leathery and evergreen, glabrous or deciduous; wood usually smooth and mahogany to dark red to brown or sometimes almost yellow to pink in color and the thin bark exfoliating or remaining. These distinctive characteristics identify the attractive Heath Family, Ericaceae, which we are fortunate to have in selected habitats throughout New Mexico. Although recognized as a large family of the northern and cooler regions of the world, we have several distinctive woody species in New Mexico. ........................................... 175.

174.    Flowers never cup-shaped or urn-shaped, leaves, fruit and
        wood otherwise, never adhering to the collective charac-
        teristics of the Heath Family ................................................ 182.

175.    Trees, 7.0 to 15.0 m in height at maturity, wood dark red to brown,
        bark exfoliating; leaves leathery, evergreen and petioled; fruit a
        berry, tesselate, with a checkered surface; flowers urn-shaped,
        white to pink with 5 sepals, 5 petals and 10 stamens. Visiting the
        two opposite, southern corners of New Mexico in order to see
        these two closely related small trees is worthy of the time of any
        serious plant hunter ......................................................... 176.

175.    Shrubs, less than 3.0 m in height at maturity, wood mahogany to
        red or brown, smooth or with a roughened bark; leaves leathery
        and evergreen to thin and deciduous, fruit a berry, berry-like cap-
        sule or a drupe, smooth or somewhat lobed .................................. 177.

176.    Leaves elliptic to lanceolate, apex acute to acuminate, base
        cuneate, 3.0 to 8.0 cm in length and 1.2 to 2.5 cm in width;
        fruit globose, reddish-orange, tesselate-granular, 8.0 to
        10.0 mm in diameter. Limited to rocky slopes in the south-
        west corner of New Mexico at 4,500 to 8,000 ft. (1,370 to
        2,440 m) in elevation, this unique and attractive tree will
        catch the attention of all who are fortunate enough to find
        it along their path.

        **Arizona Madrone,** *Arbutus arizonica* (A. Gray) Sargent
                                                                    Ericaceae

176.    Leaves oblong to ovate, apex obtuse to acute, base
        rounded, 3.0 to 8.0 cm in length and 1.8 to 2.5 cm in
        width; fruit globose, reddish-yellow to red, tesselate-
        granular, 6.0 to 8.0 mm in diameter. Limited to wooded
        canyons, mountain slopes and foothill drainages in the
        southeast corner of New Mexico at 4,000 to 6,500 ft.
        (1,220 to 1,980 m) in elevation, this sometimes large shrub
        or small tree occurs in a plant association that is unique
        for the State.

        **Texas Madrone,** *Arbutus xalapensis* Kunth
                        Syns. *A. texana* Buckley              Ericaceae

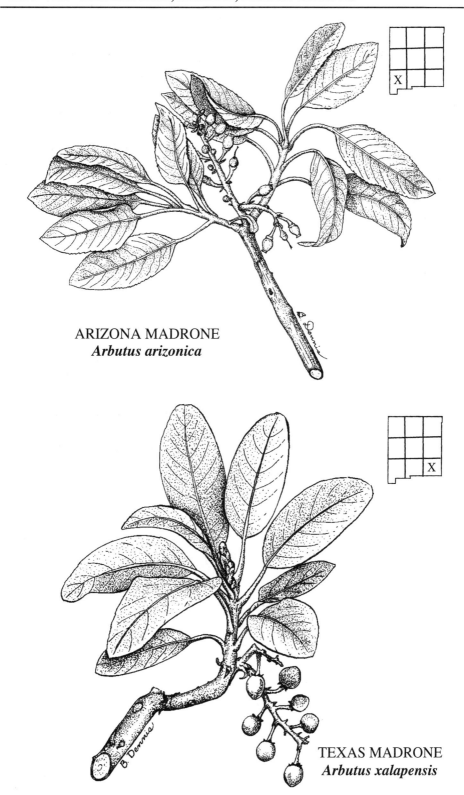

ARIZONA MADRONE
*Arbutus arizonica*

TEXAS MADRONE
*Arbutus xalapensis*

177.    Plants low, prostrate, procumbent, trailing and creeping, forming mats, less than 15.0 to 20.0 cm in height at maturity; flower ovary superior, sepals and petals 5 in number, stamens 10 in number ...... 178.

177.    Plants erect shrubs, not prostrate, trailing or creeping, not forming mats but commonly reaching 15.0 cm to 3.0 m in height at maturity; flower ovary superior or inferior, sepals and petals 4 or 5 in number, stamens 8 or 10 in number ......................................... 179.

      178.    Sepals united at the base, the calyx tube becoming fleshy in fruit and enclosing the berry-like capsule, red and 5.0 to 6.0 mm in diameter; flowers solitary in the axils of the leaves, corolla white to greenish-white; leaf blades evergreen, orbicular to oval, margins crenulate to serrulate to nearly entire, flat and not revolute. Flowering in July and August, this rare subshrub occurs in the high, northcentral mountains above 10,000 ft. (3,050 m) in elevation. Found on the mossy forest floor on wooded slopes, it is often overlooked.

**Creeping Wintergreen,** *Gaultheria humifusa*
                 (R. Graham) Rydberg      Ericaceae

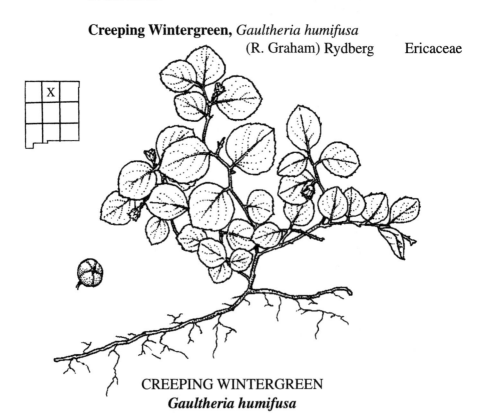

CREEPING WINTERGREEN
*Gaultheria humifusa*

178.    Sepals distinct or nearly so, not becoming fleshy and the ovary developing into a berry, red and 6.0 to 8.0 mm in diameter; flowers in short, few-flowered racemes or occasionally solitary, corolla white or pink; leaf blades obovate to oblanceolate to oblong-spatulate, margins entire and often somewhat revolute. Flowering from May through July, this low, creeping shrub can be locally abundant at 6,500 to 10,000 ft. (1,980 to 3,050 m) in elevation. It is found on shaded to partially shaded, often semi-dry, mountain slopes throughout the subalpine coniferous and montane coniferous forests of northern and westcentral New Mexico.

**Kinnikinnick,** *Arctostaphylos uva-ursi* (L.) Sprengel

Ericaceae

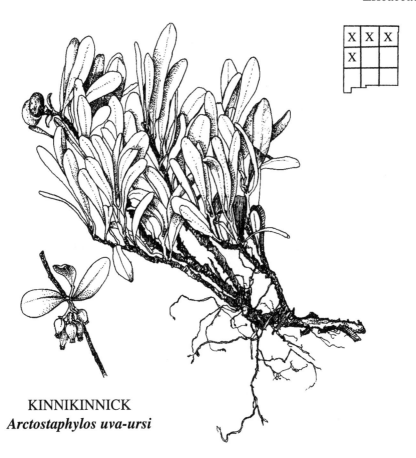

KINNIKINNICK
*Arctostaphylos uva-ursi*

179.  Mature shrubs reaching from 1.0 to 3.0 m in height, erect and
      often spreading to 1.0 m or more in diameter; found below 8,000
      ft. (2,438 m) in the mixed woodland and juniper savanna vegeta-
      tion types; stems a beautiful mahogany to reddish-brown and
      flaky; leaves elliptic to lanceolate and sharp pointed at the apex,
      12.0 to 30.0 mm in length and 10.0 to 20.0 mm in width; flowers
      small, nodding, urn-shaped, white to pink, less than 1.0 cm in
      length; inflorescence a terminal and often congested raceme; fruit
      is a smooth, globose, reddish to dark brown, several seeded, berry-
      like drupe, 5.0 to 8.0 mm in diameter. Locally abundant, but not
      common, this attractive shrub is found in western and southwest-
      ern New Mexico at 4,500 to 8,000 ft. (1,370 to 2,440 m) in eleva-
      tion. It survives and may flourish on limited water on well drained,
      dry, rocky slopes.

**Point-leaf Manzanita,** *Arctostaphylos pungens* Humboldt,
                                    Bonpland, Kunth              Ericaceae

POINT-LEAF MANZANITA
*Arctostaphylos pungens*

179. Mature shrubs reaching 15.0 to 40.0 cm in height, found above 8,000 ft. (2,440 m), in the subalpine coniferous and upper montane coniferous vegetation types ........................................................ 180.

  180. Leaves broadest above the middle, crenate to serrate above the middle to slightly below the middle, obovate to oblanceolate, glabrous, 0.7 to 3.7 cm in length and 3.0 to 20.0 mm in width; branches round to slightly angled in cross-section and brown in color at maturity, plants reaching 10.0 to 30.0 cm in height; fruit dark blue or purple at maturity, with a distinctive bloom, the berries subglobose, 5.0 to 8.0 mm in diameter, edible and, in fact, tasty; flowers solitary and axillary, white to pink, corolla 5.0 to 6.0 mm in length. Confined to the spruce-fir and lower alpine tundra zones, at 8,500 to 12,000 ft. (2,600 to 3,660 m) in elevation, this rare species may be found adjacent to ponds and on wet mossy slopes in the forest. It flowers from mid-July into August.

  **Dwarf Huckleberry,** *Vaccinium cespitosum* Michaux
  Ericaceae

  180. Leaves broadest at or below the middle, serrate to serrulate from the base to the apex; branches strongly angled in cross-section and green in color at maturity; fruit red or blue-black at maturity, devoid of a distinctive bloom. The following two species appear to hybridize and can sometimes be difficult to distinguish .................................. 181.

181. Fruit blue-black to black at maturity, 5.0 to 8.0 mm in diameter; branches less numerous, thick in diameter, seldom broom-like and less sharply angled; grooves of the branches usually puberulent; leaves 11.0 to 30.0 mm in length and 0.6 to 1.6 mm in width, lanceolate to elliptic and serrulate from the base to the apex; flowers solitary and axillary, pink, corolla 4.0 to 5.0 mm in length. This common understory species occurs in the montane to subalpine lifezones at 8,000 to 11,500 ft. (2,440 to 3,510 m) in elevation. Flowering in June and July this widely scattered shrub, from 10.0 to 40.0 cm in height at maturity, is found in the mountains of northcentral and western New Mexico.

  **Myrtle Blueberry** or **Bilberry,** *Vaccinium myrtillus* L.     Ericaceae

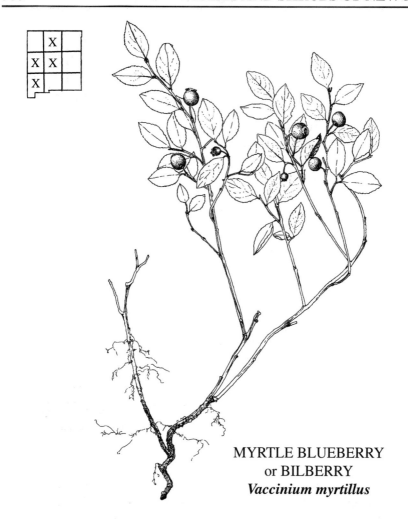

MYRTLE BLUEBERRY
or BILBERRY
*Vaccinium myrtillus*

181.  Fruit bright red at maturity, but drying to purple-red, 3.5 to 5.5 mm in diameter; branches numerous, broom-like, slender in diameter, sharply angled and glabrous; grooves of the branches usually glabrous; leaves 6.0 to 13.0 mm in length and 3.0 to 7.0 mm in width, ovate and completely serrulate along both margins; flowers solitary and axillary, pink to white, corolla 2.0 to 4.0 mm in length. Occurring in habitats similar to the previous species, the leaves of shorter length, the broom-like shape of the plant and the fact that this species more commonly ranges into the tundra, at 8,500 to 12,500 ft. (2,600 to 3,810 m) in elevation, will help separate the two species.

**Whortleberry** or **Broom Huckleberry,** *Vaccinium scoparium*
                              Leiberg                    Ericaceae

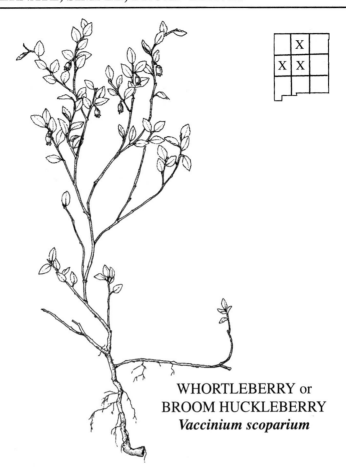

WHORTLEBERRY or
BROOM HUCKLEBERRY
*Vaccinium scoparium*

182.    Individual clusters of flowers subtended by a bell-shaped
        involucre of bracts; plants scapose to cauline, the leaves
        basal, or the leaves continue up the stems to where the
        long and exserted inflorescence begins, the inflorescence
        often forming one-forth to one-half or more of the total
        length of the plant; petal-like sepals in 2 whorls of 3 each,
        stamens 9; fruit a distinctly 3-angled achene, often winged,
        but not in the woody species included here. The 3 and
        multiples of 3 flower and fruit characteristics will some-
        times result in students assuming they have collected a
        Monocot, which the **Wild Buckwheats** (genus -
        *Eriogonum*) certainly are not. We here include the sev-
        eral species of the genus that range from suffrutescent to
        subshrubs to shrubs, recognizing that these distinctions
        can be difficult. It is also important to note that the tax-
        onomy and geography of the **Wild Buckwheats** is not
        well understood ................................................................. 183.

182.    Individual clusters of flowers not subtended by a bell-
        shaped involucre of bracts; plants not strongly scapose or
        with a long and exserted inflorescence making up a large
        portion of the total plant; sepals, petals, stamens and fruits
        variable, but not as described above ................................... 188.

183.  Perianth densely pubescent to silky-villous, yellow to cream col-
      ored, not strongly ribbed; stems woody and branched at the base,
      commonly only slightly woody above the soil level; plants pe-
      rennial and often matted; flowering stems subscapose to 30.0 cm
      in height and arising from a basal rosette of branches; leaves el-
      liptic to obovate or ovate, tomentose on one or both surfaces,
      entire to slightly undulate, flat, 1.0 to 9.0 cm in length and 4.0 to
      20.0 mm in width, petioles 1.0 to 6.0 cm in length; inflorescence
      of several umbels and/or capitate and an open cyme. This low,
      common, highly variable perennial is widely scattered over New
      Mexico at 5,000 to 10,500 ft. (1,520 to 3,200 m) in elevation,
      from the dry plains to the mountains. We could have omitted this
      plant from this publication, but the degree of variation in this
      species provides an interesting problem for those interested in
      plant diversity.

      **James Eriogonum** or **James Buckwheat,** *Eriogonum jamesii*
                                    Bentham        Polygonaceae

183.  Perianth glabrous, rarely pubescent, white or pink, midrib may
      be greenish to reddish or brown; stems woody above the soil
      level ........................................................................................ 184.

184.    Inflorescence not conspicuously cymose or corymbose,
        elongate, flowers paniculate or racemose in general ar-
        rangement, borne down the stem ........................................ 185.

184.    Inflorescence conspicuously cymose or corymbose,
        simple or compound, inflorescence flat-topped or rounded.... 186.

185.    Involucres divergent from the branches; inflorescence usually with
        the flowers arranged on only one side of the axis, much longer
        than the vegetative stems; perennial; shrubs woody at the base,
        dichotomously and trichotomously branched from the lower
        nodes, densely woolly, 2.0 to 10.0 dm in height or more, forming
        clumps; leaves often early deciduous, linear to narrowly lanceolate
        or oblanceolate, flat to revolute, 1.0 to 4.5 cm in length and 3.0 to
        8.0 mm in width, tomentose on one or both surfaces; flowers
        mostly white and glabrous. Usually associated with the sandy
        plains of the northwest corner of New Mexico at 4,500 to 6,000
        ft. (1,370 to 1,830 m) in elevation, this rare species appears to be
        closely related to the following species, **Wright's Buckwheat**.

**Sand Eriogonum** or **Sand Buckwheat,** *Eriogonum leptocladon*
                                                        Torrey & A. Gray
                                                        Polygonaceae

185.    Involucres appressed to the branches; inflorescence erect and
        ascending, the flowers arranged around the axis, and not limited
        to one side of the axis; perennial; shrubs woody at the base, pro-
        fusely branched, but not dichotomously and trichotomously
        branched, tomentose, 2.0 to 5.0 dm in height; leaves caulescent,
        not early deciduous, elliptic to oblanceolate, 0.5 to 2.5 cm in length
        and 3.0 to 10.0 mm in width, flat to slightly revolute; flowers
        white to pink and glabrous. This abundant species appears to be
        widespread throughout the western states. At the same time it is
        not well defined in the literature. Flowering throughout the sum-
        mer in New Mexico, it is found over dry hills and canyons at
        5,000 to 8,000 ft. (1,520 to 2,440 m) in elevation.

**Wright's Eriogonum** or **Wright's Buckwheat,**
                                        *Eriogonum wrightii* Torrey
                                        Polygonaceae

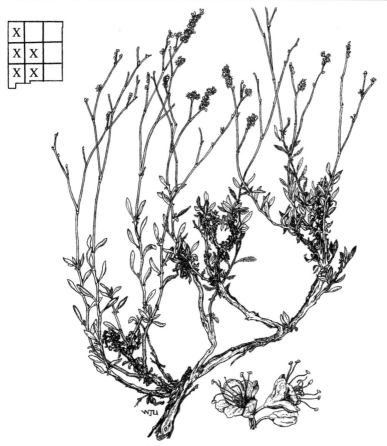

WRIGHT'S ERIOGONUM or WRIGHT'S BUCKWHEAT
*Eriogonum wrightii*

186.     Leaves oblong to oval, orbicular or elliptic to obtuse, 10.0
         mm or more in width, tomentose to floccose, 1.5 to 7.0
         cm in length, the petioles often including more than one-
         half of the total leaf length, margins flat to revolute; in-
         florescence cymose, the branches spreading and
         divaricate; flowers white with some areas of pink or red,
         glabrous. Occurring from the central to the northwestern
         quarter of New Mexico at 5,000 to 6,500 ft. (1,520 to
         1,980 m) in elevation, this species is associated with dry,
         sandy and clay soils. It has been described by some au-
         thorities to include several varieties that are not here in-
         cluded because the available herbarium materials and our
         field collections do not allow for these distinctions.


**Corymb Buckwheat,** *Eriogonum corymbosum* Bentham
                                          Polygonaceae

CORYMB BUCKWHEAT
*Eriogonum corymbosum*

186.   Leaves linear to narrowly oblong to spatulate, acute, 7.0 mm or less in width ................................................................................. 187.

187.   Leaves flat, not revolute, linear to narrowly oblong, margins entire to undulate, 2.0 to 4.0 cm in length; inflorescence an open, but widely branched cyme; perennial, woody at the base, older stems becoming woody with age, tomentose, 20.0 to 60.0 cm in height; flowers white to pink, glabrous. This widely scattered and common species of the Great Plains appears to reach its western limit in central and northwestern New Mexico. It is found on the dry plains, slopes and mesas at 5,000 to 6,500 ft. (1,520 to 1,980 m) in elevation, and we should perhaps include the following taxon as a variety of this species.

**Spreading Eriogonum,** *Eriogonum effusum* Nuttall      Polygonaceae

187.  Leaves strongly revolute, linear, margins entire, 2.0 to 4.0 cm in length; inflorescence a densely branched cyme; perennial, woody at the base, glabrous, 15.0 to 60.0 cm in height; flowers white to pink or just the midvein pink, glabrous. The few records for this species are limited to the northwest quarter of New Mexico at 5,000 to 6,500 ft. (1,520 to 1,980 m) in elevation.

**Narrow Leafed Eriogonum,** *Eriogonum leptophyllum* (Torrey)
Wooton & Standley
Syns. *E. effusum* var. *leptophyllum* Torrey
Polygonaceae

188.  Plants covered with stellate or forked hairs or small scurfy, peltate scales; flowers unisexual, borne on short lateral spurs, solitary, spikes or racemes, petals absent, rarely present or vestigial, ovary 2- or 3-celled; plants monoecious or dioecious; fruit a 2- or 3-celled capsule; only shrubs or subshrubs included. We describe here only three species of the large and diverse Spurge Family, the Euphorbiaceae. Due to the scurfy appearance of the woody members of the Spurge Family, they may seem similar to the Goosefoot Family, Chenopodiaceae, (see couplets 167 to 173, pages 353 to 359) but on closer examination the two families are very different............................................. 189.

188.  Plants not covered with stellate or forked hairs or small scurfy, peltate scales; flowers bisexual or unisexual; inflorescence variable; fruit variable; plants never adhering to the collective characteristics of the Spurge Family.... 191.

189.  Plants densely covered with forked, branched or stellate hairs; true much-branched shrubs, 20.0 cm to 2.5 m in height, the branches of two types, either elongate to 25.0 cm or short lateral spurs usually bearing the inflorescences; flowers in small clusters or solitary, stamens commonly 10, sepals 3 in staminate flowers and 4 or 5 in pistillate flowers; petals absent or reduced in size; monoecious or dioecious; capsules predominantly 3-celled with 1 seed in each cell. This shrub is uncommon on dry south-facing slopes in the southern tier of counties at 3,500 to 4,500 ft. (1,060 to 1,370 m) in elevation. Another closely related species, *Bernardia obovata* I. M. Johnston, may occur in southern New Mexico and should be expected in similar habitats.

**Southwest Bernardia,** *Bernardia myricifolia* (Scheele)
S. Watson        Euphorbiaceae

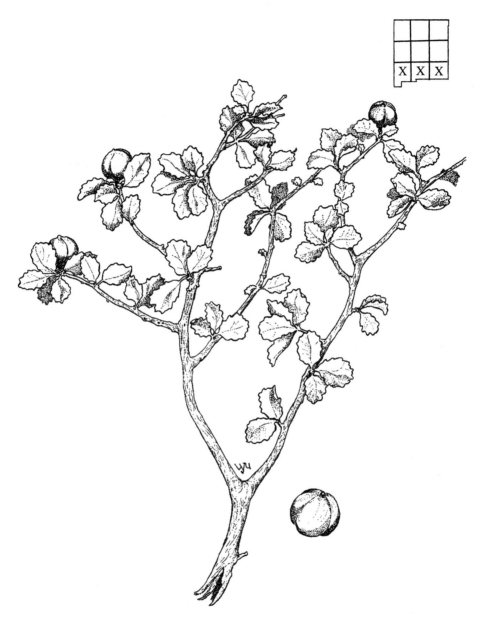

SOUTHWEST BERNARDIA
*Bernardia myricifolia*

189.    Plants densely covered with stellate hairs or stalked, flat scales,
        appearing scurfy; subshrubs or shrubs, 10.0 to 100.0 cm in height;
        flowers in terminal spikes or racemes; calyx of staminate flow-
        ers with 4 to 6 lobes and calyx of pistillate flowers with 5 to 9
        lobes; fruit a 3-celled capsule with 1 seed in each cell.................... 190.

190.    Styles in female flowers branching to form 10 to 12 stigmas; dioecious; suffrutescent perennial or herb, 15.0 to 50.0 cm in height; leaves linear-lanceolate to ovate-oblong to rarely broadly ovate, 2.0 to 4.0 cm in length, lower surface covered with scurfy scales, margins entire, petioles present, 0.3 to more than 1.0 cm in length; staminate flowers in racemes, 4.0 to 9.0 cm long; pistillate flowers in racemes, 2.0 to 3.0 cm long. This relatively abundant species is widely scattered over the plains and mesas in southern and eastern New Mexico at 4,000 to 5,000 ft. (1,220 to 1,520 m) in elevation. Identification is not easy because this species may be easily confused with several other closely related herbaceous crotons.

**New Mexico Croton** or **Hierba del gato**, *Croton dioicus*
Cavanilles
Syns. *C. neomexicanus* Mueller
Euphorbiaceae

190.    Styles in female flowers branching to form 4 to 6 stigmas; plants monoecious, androgynous, with male and female flowers in the same inflorescence; woody throughout, to 1.5 m in height at maturity; leaves ovate-lanceolate and tapering to the apex, 2.5 to 8.0 cm in length and 20.0 to 35.0 mm in width, sparsely stellate-pubescent on the upper surface and tomentose to stellate-pubescent on the lower surface, margins entire to slightly toothed, petioles present; staminate flowers in racemes with 5 sepals and 5 petals; pistillate flowers in small clusters with 5 sepals and the petals absent or vestigial. This is the most common and widespread of the truly woody crotons in southern New Mexico. Flowering in early spring, it ranges over dry rocky hillsides and canyons at 4,000 to 6,000 ft. (1,220 to 1,830 m) in elevation.

**Bush Croton** or **Hierba Loca**, *Croton fruticulosus*
Engelmann                        Euphorbiaceae

BUSH CROTON or HIERBA LOCA
*Croton fruticulosus*

191.    Leaf bases oblique or distinctly asymmetrical or unequal on all or most leaves; fruit a drupe, samara or multiple; inflorescences pendulous catkins, spikes, cymes, small clusters or solitary ........... 192.

191.    Leaf bases evenly cordate, rounded, attenuate, cuneate or symmetrical, but not obviously oblique or unequal on all or most leaves; fruits variable; inflorescences variable ................................ 197.

    192.    Leaves with 1 main midvein from the base, leaf margins double dentate; fruit a 1-seeded samara with the wing surrounding the seed; plants introduced, cultivated as shade trees and escaping cultivation .................................... 193.

    192.    Leaves with 3 to 5 veins from the base; fruit a drupe or multiple .......................................................................... 194.

193.    Leaves 4.0 to 8.0 cm in length, leaf bases oblique to symmetrical; samaras glabrous with a single notch, but the sinus closed; mature leaf buds ovoid, 2.0 to 3.0 mm in length, dark brown to black, usually ciliate; flowering in early spring, before the leaves appear, the flowers borne in clusters from the previous year's buds; small trees or shrubs to 15.0 m in height, commonly with many branches from the base. This small tree can become an intrusive weed, and once introduced, it is difficult to control.

**Siberian Elm** or **Chinese Elm**, *Ulmus pumila* L.          Ulmaceae

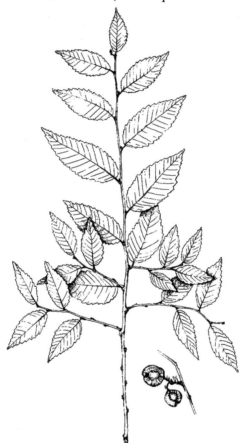

SIBERIAN ELM or CHINESE ELM
*Ulmus pumila*

Another closely related, cultivated species observed in eastern New Mexico, **Chinese Elm**, *Ulmus parvifolia* Jacquin, is similar to *Ulmus pumila*. However, this is a fall flowering species and the flowers are borne in racemes.

193.  Leaves 7.0 to 12.0 cm in length, oblique at the base; samaras slightly pubescent with a notch, the sinus usually open; mature leaf buds acute to elongate, 2.0 to 3.0 mm in length, gray to light brown, glabrous to ciliate; large trees at maturity to 25.0 m in height with one large trunk; commonly cultivated, especially in lawns and along city streets. Although long recognized as a fine shade tree, it is this species that has been attacked over the past 40 years by Dutch Elm Disease, a disease caused by the fungus *Ceratocystis ulmi.*

**American Elm** or **White Elm**, *Ulmus americana* L.          Ulmaceae

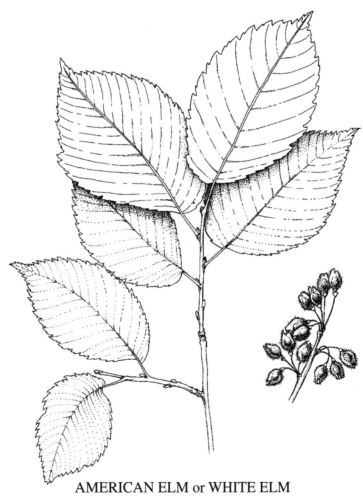

AMERICAN ELM or WHITE ELM
*Ulmus americana*

194.  Fruit a succulent, cylindric multiple, consisting of many small fleshy nutlets, 1.5 to 2.5 cm in length, bright red when immature, becoming black to purple or white when mature, sweet, juicy and edible; leaves 6.0 to 10.0 cm in length and 3.0 to 6.0 cm in width, ranging from an oblique to a cordate base and from not lobed to deeply lobed on the same tree, margins serrate to crenate, petioles 2.5 to 5.0 cm long, exudes a milky juice when broken; plants monoecious or dioecious; flowers in catkins 1.5 to 4.0 cm in length, axillary and densely flowered; a spreading tree to 8.0 m in height at maturity. Introduced from Asia, this tree is transplanted and commonly dispersed by *Homo sapiens* and other animals.

**Red Mulberry** or **White Mulberry**, *Morus alba* L.

Moraceae

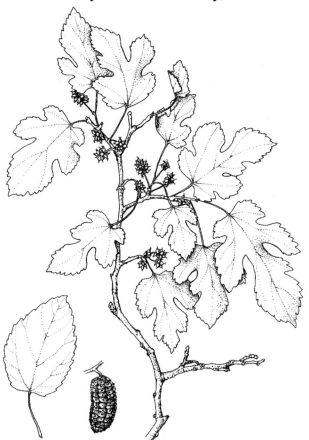

RED MULBERRY or WHITE MULBERRY
*Morus alba*

The **Texas Mulberry** or **Littleleaf Mulberry**, *Morus microphylla* Buckley, may also key to this point if there are few or no palmately lobed leaves on the plant, which is seldom true. If the petioles average less than 1.2 cm in length and the mature leaves average less than 7.5 cm in length, and the leaves are scabrous on both surfaces you probably should return to couplet 39, page 221 in this key and read the full description.

194.  Fruit a globose drupe or a nutlet suspended from a winged bract, never in a fleshy multiple or catkin; leaves never lobed; petioles never exuding a milky juice when broken

................................................................................. 195.

195.  Petioles 3.0 to 7.0 cm in length; fruit two or more small nutlets suspended by pedicels from a narrow, wing-like, foliaceous bract, 7.0 to 15.0 cm in length; leaves commonly with 5 to 7 veins from near the base, vein axils often with tufts of hair, 10.0 to 18.0 cm in length and 9.0 to 13.0 cm in width, margins sharply serrate; flowers perfect, sweet scented, calyx lobes 5, petals 5, stamens many, pistil compound, style 5 lobed. This attractive, eastern United States species, to 20.0 m in height at maturity, has been and continues to be planted in lawns and gardens and lines the streets in many eastern cities. Because of its high water requirements, it should not continue to be planted in New Mexico and the arid Southwest.

**Basswood** or **Linden**, *Tilia americana* L.          Tiliaceae

195.  Petioles 0.4 to 1.2 cm in length; fruit a globose drupe, 5.0 to 9.0 mm in diameter, borne singly in the axils of the leaves, and not supported by a wing-like bract; leaves commonly with 3 veins from near the base; plants polygamous to monoecious, trees or shrubs, the bark gray, often furrowed with corky ridges ................ 196.

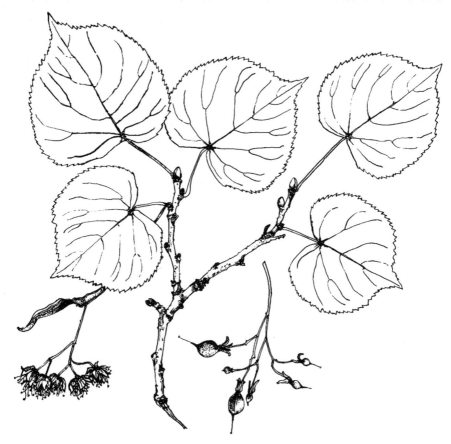

BASSWOOD or LINDEN
*Tilia americana*

196.    Mature leaves 3.0 to 6.5 cm in length and 2.0 to 4.5 cm in
width, typically averaging less than 5.5 cm in length,
margins mostly entire or occasionally somewhat serrate
above the middle, ovate to ovate-lanceolate, prominently
reticulate veined on the lower surface; fruit globose, red
to reddish-brown, 8.0 to 9.0 mm in diameter. This widespread and relatively abundant native shrub or small tree,
to 8.0 m in height, is found on dry rocky hillsides and
ravine banks at 3,500 to 6,000 ft. (1,070 to 1,830 m) in
elevation.

**Netleaf Hackberry** or **Palo Blanco**, *Celtis reticulata*
                                                        Torrey
              Syns. *C. laevigata* var. *reticulata* L. Benson
                                                    Ulmaceae

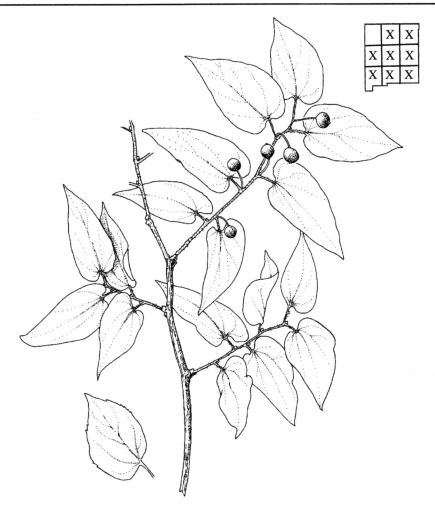

NETLEAF HACKBERRY or PALO BLANCO
*Celtis reticulata*

196.   Mature leaves 6.0 to 10.0 cm in length and 3.0 to 5.5 cm
       in width, typically averaging more than 6.0 cm in length,
       long-acuminate, ovate-lanceolate to ovate, margins more
       or less coarsely serrate, with a few leaves sometimes en-
       tire; fruit globose, orange-red, on pedicels, to 15.0 mm
       long, 8.0 to 11.0 mm in diameter. Not always easy to dis-
       tinguish from the previous species, this introduced tree to
       20.0 m in height, is infrequently found growing in moist
       soil or along stream banks, around old home sites and in
       pastures over the eastern one-third of New Mexico.

**Eastern Hackberry,** *Celtis occidentalis* L.            Ulmaceae

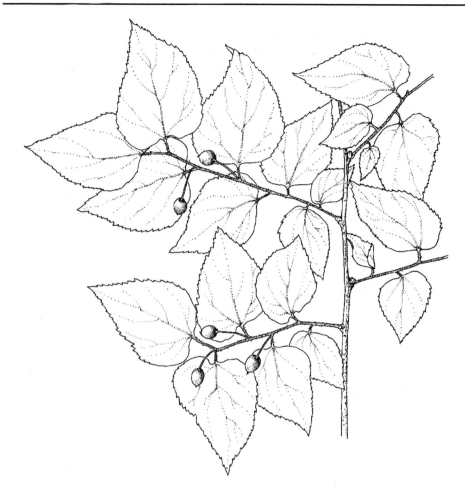

EASTERN HACKBERRY
*Celtis occidentalis*

197.  Margins of mature leaves entire, not toothed, lobed or divided,
      only rarely some leaves slightly undulate or with a few teeth ...........198.

197.  Margins of mature leaves toothed, serrate, dentate, crenate, but
      not distinctly cleft or lobed .............................................................. 212.

    198.  Mature leaves averaging more than 1.0 cm in width. (Some
      of the more recently introduced cultivars of the **Russian
      Olive** may have leaves averaging slightly less than 1.0
      cm in width) ........................................................................ 199.

    198.  Mature leaves averaging less than 1.0 cm in width ............. 202.

199. Fruit a legume, 5.0 to 11.0 cm in length and 10.0 to 15.0 cm in width; leaves broadly cordate to reniform, base cordate, palmately veined, 5.0 to 15.0 cm in length and 5.0 to 15.0 cm in width, petioles more than 3.0 cm in length; flowers appearing before the leaves, papilionaceous, and bright rose-purple; small trees to 4.0 m in height at maturity, appearing as large shrubs when young. One rare variety of this species, *C. canadensis* var. *mexicana* (Rose) M. Hopkins, is considered native to New Mexico and has been reported to occur in the southeastern corner of the State at 4,500 to 6,000 ft. (1,370 to 1,830 m) in elevation. At the same time the attractive and showy, spring flowering **Redbud Tree** is commonly introduced into lawns and gardens throughout much of New Mexico.

**Redbud Tree**, *Cercis canadensis* L. Fabaceae

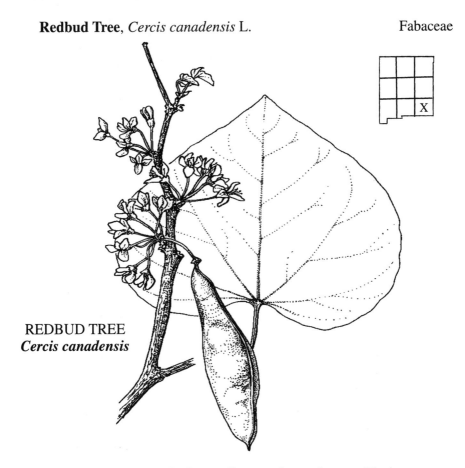

REDBUD TREE
*Cercis canadensis*

199. Fruit a drupe or capsule; leaves linear to lanceolate to elliptic or ovate, base rounded to cuneate to attenuate, but not cordate, pinnately veined, petioles less than 2.5 cm in length ......................... 200.

200.     Leaf surfaces silver-scurfy to scurfy-pubescent, leaves linear to lanceolate, base narrowed to attenuate or cuneate, 3.0 to 8.0 cm in length and 0.9 to 2.5 cm in width; flowers perfect, borne solitary and axillary, sepals 4, silvery scaly on the outside and yellow with stellate pubescence on the inside, petals none; fruit a drupe, 8.0 to 11.0 mm in diameter, covered with silver scales. This introduced, Asian shrub or small tree to 8.0 m in height appears to have found a new home in the arid regions of the Southwest. Because it can withstand drought and cold winters, forms excellent windbreaks and provides food for birds and other animals it is probably here to stay. At the same time, once planted it spreads rapidly and is difficult to control, so be certain it is what you want.

**Russian Olive,** *Elaeagnus angustifolia* L.       Elaeagnaceae

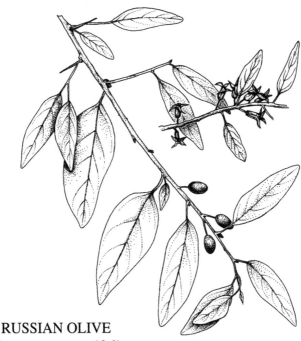

RUSSIAN OLIVE
*Elaeagnus angustifolia*

200.     Leaf surfaces glabrous to pubescent, but not silver-scurfy, leaves elliptic to ovate to obovate, base rounded to cuneate, 2.5 to 7.5 cm in length and 1.0 to 3.8 cm in width; flowers borne in terminal panicles or cymes, sepals 5, petals 4 or 5 ....................................................................... 201.

201.  Inflorescence a many flowered cyme; fruit a fleshy, berry-like drupe, red to black at maturity; leaves gray to white-tomentose on the lower surface, evergreen to partially deciduous, elliptic to oblong, 3.0 to 7.5 cm in length and 1.5 to 2.5 cm in width, margins entire, rarely minutely toothed; flowers small, bisexual or occasionally unisexual, light green, calyx free from the ovary, stamens 4 or 5. This shrub to 3.0 m or more in height is confined to the southwest corner of New Mexico at 4,500 ft. (1,370 m) in elevation. It is uncommon, but flourishes on dry south-facing slopes. (Please see couplet 226, page 408 for further description.)

**California Buckthorn,** *Frangula californica* (Eschscholtz)

A. Gray

Syns. *Rhamnus californica* Eschscholtz

Rhamnaceae

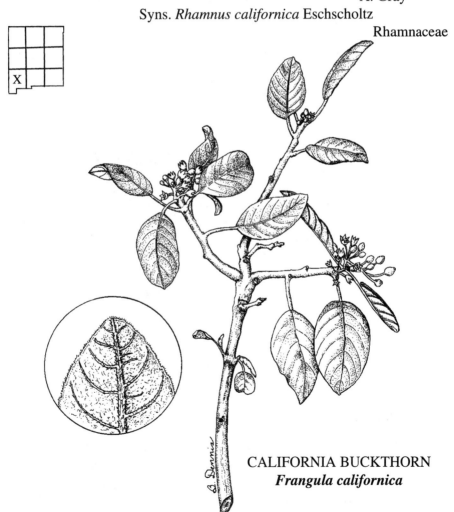

CALIFORNIA BUCKTHORN
*Frangula californica*

201. Inflorescence a terminal, often leafless, panicle; fruit a 3-lobed capsule, often splitting into 3 parts; leaves glabrous or slightly pilose, darker green above and paler green on the lower surface, elliptic to ovate to oblong-ovate, 2.5 to 7.0 cm in length and 1.0 to 3.8 cm in width, with 3 main veins, margins entire; flowers small, petals commonly white or sometimes tinged with light pink or blue, calyx fused to the base of the ovary, stamens 5. This rare yet distinctive species has been collected only a few times in southwestern New Mexico at 4,500 to 7,000 ft. (1,370 to 2,130 m) in elevation. More common in southeastern Arizona, it occurs in rocky canyons, on rocky slopes and in gravelly soils in the pine-oak woodlands.

**Deer Bush** or **Mogollon Ceanothus**, *Ceanothus integerrimus*
Hooker & Arnott
Rhamnaceae

202. Leaves 7.0 to 17.0 cm in length and 5.0 to 10.0 mm in width at maturity, linear to linear-lanceolate; flowers fragrant and showy, corolla funnelform to campanulate, bilaterally symmetrical, usually white to pale blue or purplish-red to pink, 2.0 to 3.5 cm in length; fruit a long, slender, bivalved capsule to 30.0 cm in length and filled with winged seeds, often incorrectly identified as a legume; plants trees to 10.0 m or large shrubs at maturity. This unique and attractive small tree of the Southwest is often found growing adjacent to arroyos, in gravelly soils, at 4,000 to 5,500 ft. (1,220 to 1,740 m) in elevation. It is common over the southern two-thirds of New Mexico, especially along the Rio Grande. Often cultivated as an ornamental, it may flower from spring into the early fall, and does not require excessive water.

**Desert Willow,** *Chilopsis linearis* (Cavanilles ) Sweet
Bignoniaceae

202. Leaves 0.3 to 5.0 cm in length and 1.0 to 9.0 mm in width at maturity; plants shrubs or subshrubs, seldom reaching 3.0 m at maturity ................................................................ 203.

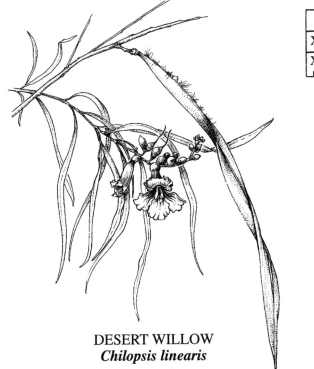

### DESERT WILLOW
### *Chilopsis linearis*

203.  Plants true shrubs, erect, from 50.0 cm to 3.0 m in height at maturity ........................................................................................ 204.

203.  Plants perennial subshrubs, prostrate to erect, from 10.0 to 40.0 cm in height at maturity, seldom reaching 50.0 cm ........................ 207.

204.  Mature leaves averaging 1.0 mm in width, never more than 2.0 mm in width and 0.5 to 1.9 cm in length, linear to linear-spatulate, rarely trifoliate, glandular-dotted; fruit a legume, obliquely obovate, pubescent and glandular-dotted; peduncles exserted 2.0 to 7.0 cm above the vegetative portion of the plant, with few or no leaves; flowers borne in dense spikes or weak heads, few flowered, calyx strongly ribbed and white-villous, corolla dark blue. This common shrub, to 1.5 m or more in height, occurs in sandy soils from the hills and dunes of southwestern New Mexico at 5,300 ft. (1,620 m) in elevation to the margins of the Rio Grande at 3,500 ft. (1,070 m).

**Broom Dalea**, *Psorothamnus scoparius* (A. Gray) Rydberg
Syns. *Dalea scoparia* A. Gray

Fabaceae

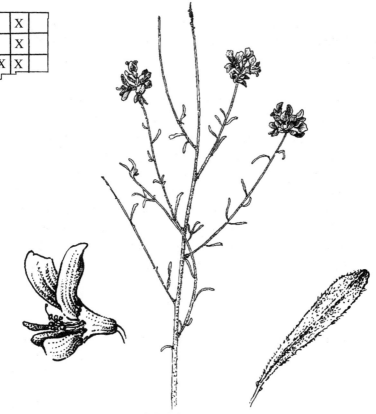

BROOM DALEA
*Psorothamnus scoparius*

204.    Mature leaves averaging 4.0 mm in width or more, al-
        ways more than 2.0 mm in width; fruit a capsule or a
        pome; flowers not borne in dense spikes ............................ 205.

205.    Leaves 2.0 to 4.0 cm in length and 4.0 to 9.0 mm in width, fas-
        cicles at the ends of the branches, sessile or nearly so, narrowly
        oblanceolate to oblong and cuneate at the base, margins com-
        monly entire or with a few gland-tipped teeth; fruit a 2-celled
        pome with persistent calyx lobes; carpels united, enclosed by and
        adnate to the hypanthium; flowers in clusters of 2 or 3 or solitary,
        calyx adnate to the ovary, petals 5 and pink to rose col-
        ored, stamens 20, ovary inferior. This uncommon shrub
        occurs in the alkaline soils of northwestern New Mexico
        at 5,500 to 7,000 ft. (1,680 to 2,130 m) in elevation. Of-
        ten found growing with oaks, it flowers in early spring.

**Squaw-Apple,** *Peraphyllum ramosissimum* Nuttall                    Rosaceae

205.    Leaves 0.3 to 1.8 cm in length; scattered along the stem or a few
        in small clusters, but not in fascicles, oval to elliptic to obovate;
        fruit a capsule ................................................................................. 206.

    206.    Flowers borne towards the ends of the branches in small
            clusters, 2.0 to 4.0 cm long, regular and perfect, white in
            color, 2.0 to 4.0 mm in length; leaves small, scabrous to
            sparsely hispid, thickened on the margins and revolute,
            elliptic to oblong or oval, sessile, 6.0 to 10.0 mm in length
            and 3.0 to 6.0 mm in width; fruit a capsule, oblong and
            glabrous, 4.0 to 5.0 mm in length. This erect shrub, to 1.0
            m in height, is not common, but is sometimes locally abun-
            dant on dry limestone hills in the southwest corner of New
            Mexico. Occurring at 3,500 to 5,500 ft. (1,070 to 1,680
            m) in elevation, the white stems and oval, yellowish-green
            leaves make this species easy to recognize.

**Rough Mortonia**, *Mortonia sempervirens* ssp. *scabrella*
(A. Gray) Prigge
Celastraceae

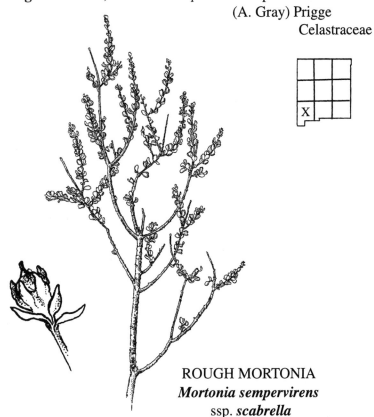

ROUGH MORTONIA
*Mortonia sempervirens*
ssp. *scabrella*

206. Flowers axillary along the stem, slightly campanulate to funnelform and perfect, usually solitary, occasionally in pairs, pale violet to purple to pink, seldom white in color, 10.0 to 20.0 mm in length, sepals 5, corolla 2-lipped and 5-lobed, stamens 4, rarely 5; leaves silvery-canescent, ovate-spatulate to obovate, sessile or with short petioles, 0.8 to 1.8 cm in length and 0.5 to 10.0 mm in width; fruit a capsule, 2-valved, with many rugose seeds. This low spreading shrub, to 1.0 m in height, is confined to south-eastern New Mexico and the Guadalupe Mountains at 4,500 to 6,000 ft. (1,370 to 1,830 m) in elevation. It is usually found growing on limestone outcrops in rocky areas, and it flowers in late summer.

**Lesser Texas Silverleaf**, *Leucophyllum minus* A. Gray

Scrophulariaceae

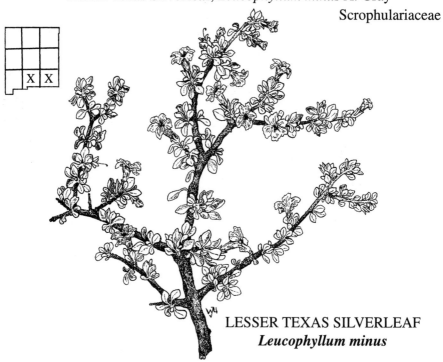

LESSER TEXAS SILVERLEAF
*Leucophyllum minus*

207. Leaves linear, 1.0 mm or less in width, strikingly glandular hispid and revolute .......................................................................... 208.

207. Leaves lanceolate, oblanceolate, spatulate, elliptic, ovate, obovate, more than 2.0 mm in width at the widest point, glabrous to pubescent to tomentose, but not hispid ............................................ 209.

208.    Plants prostrate, forming mats, spreading from a heavy woody taproot, may reach to 40.0 cm in diameter, seldom reaching 10.0 cm above the soil level; leaves narrowly linear, 0.3 to 1.0 cm in length and clustered on short branches, hispid, hairs arising from a bulbous base; flowers small, axillary and solitary, corolla funnelform and pink, ovary 4-lobed, the style borne in the center between the lobes; fruit of 4 separate nutlets. This low growing perennial can only be considered woody on close examination. As it spreads from the central taproot the lateral stems are usually woody throughout. A species of dry hills and plains, it is usually found in gypsum soils in the southwestern and southern counties at 3,000 to 5,000 ft. (910 to 1,520 m) in elevation.

**Matted Tiquilia**, *Tiquilia hispidissima* (Torrey)

A. Richardson

Syns. *Coldenia hispidissima* (Torrey) A. Gray

Boraginaceae

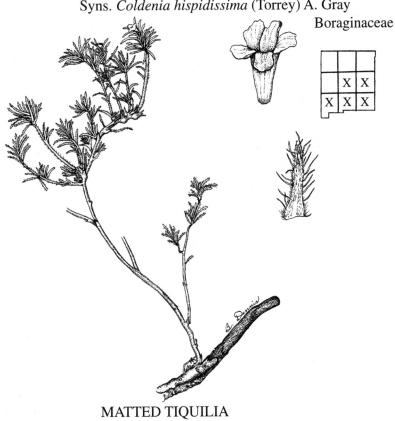

MATTED TIQUILIA
*Tiquilia hispidissima*

208.    Plants erect, suffrutescent, obscurely woody, commonly reaching 20.0 to 35.0 cm above the soil; leaves 0.4 to 3.0 cm in length, linear, strongly revolute, hispid; flowers white to purplish and in terminal cymes; calyx deeply 5-lobed, corolla 5-lobed and bell-shaped to tubular, stamens borne on the corolla and alternate with the corolla lobes, ovary half inferior and 2-celled; fruit an ovoid capsule. Confined to gypsum soils in the southern tier of counties at 3,500 to 4,500 ft. (1,070 to 1,370 m) in elevation, this uncommon, perennial member of the Waterleaf Family flowers in April through June.

**Gypnama**, *Nama carnosum* (Wooton) C. L. Hitchcock

Hydrophyllaceae

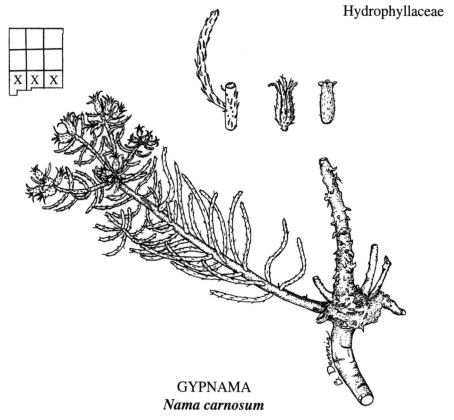

GYPNAMA
*Nama carnosum*

209.    Leaves ovate to elliptic to elliptic-lanceolate to oval, short petiolate, 0.5 to 1.4 cm in length and 2.5 to 8.0 mm in width, densely tomentose, margins entire and revolute; fruit a nutlet .................... 210.

209.    Leaves lanceolate to obovate to oblanceolate to spatulate to ob-
        long, sessile, 0.7 to 3.2 cm in length and 2.0 to 8.0 mm in width,
        glabrous to pubescent or with appressed silky hairs, margins en-
        tire and flat; fruit a capsule or follicle ........................................... 211.

    210.    Plant a small, erect, much branched shrub to 35.0 cm in
            height; flowers and fruit in dense, globose clusters, 1.0 to
            2.0 cm in diameter, terminating the leafy branches; leaves
            ovate to elliptic, 5.0 to 9.0 mm in length and 2.5 to 6.0
            mm in width; sepals 5, corolla white to pink or magenta
            and campanulate and 5-lobed, stamens 5, ovary 4-lobed
            and 4-celled with 3 ovules aborting, fruit consequently
            producing only a single mature ovule. This infrequent
            shrub of Chihuahuan Desert scrub habitats appears to be
            confined to dry limestone outcrops in southern New
            Mexico at 3,500 to 5,000 ft. (1,070 to 1,520 m) in eleva-
            tion. Flowering is closely associated with summer rains.

            **Plume Tiquilia**, *Tiquilia greggii* (Torrey & A. Gray)
                                                    A. Richardson
                    Syns. *Coldenia greggii* Torrey & A. Gray
                                                    Boraginaceae

    210.    Plants low, spreading and prostrate from a woody tap-
            root, suffrutescent, to 10.0 cm in height; flowers and fruit
            borne in the leaf axils; leaves ovate to elliptic or elliptic-
            lanceolate, 7.0 to 15.0 mm in length and 2.5 to 9.0 mm in
            width; sepals 5, corolla white to pale pink, funnelform,
            stamens 5, ovary slightly 4-lobed, usually producing a
            fruit with 4 smooth nutlets. This species, like the **Matted
            Tiquilia**, could have been omitted from this publication,
            but closer examination reveals a relatively common, low,
            prostrate and woody plant. It occurs over dry hills and on
            the plains in the southern one-half of New Mexico at 4,000
            to 5,500 ft. (1,220 to 1,680 m) in elevation.

            **Oreja De Perro**, *Tiquilia canescens* (DeCandolle)
                                                    A. Richardson
                    Syns. *Coldenia canescens* DeCandolle
                                                    Boraginaceae

OREJA DE PERRO
*Tiquilia canescens*

211.    Plants erect, small, clumped perennials to 35.0 cm in height,
        woody below, but herbaceous above; flowering peduncles less
        than 3.0 cm in length and not extending well above the plant;
        leaves generally alternate, but with a few leaves opposite, lan-
        ceolate to obovate or oblong, occasionally ovate, 0.9 to 3.2 cm in
        length and 5.0 to 9.0 mm in width, scabrous to glabrous; inflo-
        rescence a cyme; flowers perfect, calyx campanulate, 4.0 to 9.0
        mm long, corolla of 5 petals, yellow, the tube 2.5 to 7.0 mm long,
        stamens 2 or 3, exserted, 6.0 to 8.0 mm long; fruit a capsule with
        4 seeds in each cell. This common species is widely scattered
        over New Mexico at 3,000 to 7,000 ft. (910 to 2,130 m) in eleva-
        tion, in sandy and gravelly soils from rocky hills to mesas. There
        are several poorly defined varieties recognized in other treatments
        that we have included in this description. (Please see couplet 45,
        Key VI, pages 127 and 128 for further description and illustra-
        tion.)

**Rough Menodora**, *Menodora scabra* A. Gray                    Oleaceae

211. Plants low, densely caespitose, subshrubs, forming mats, often appressed over rock faces; flowering peduncles 3.0 to 10.0 cm above the plant with bract-like leaves; leaves alternate, but with some leaves appearing fascicled, spatulate to lanceolate or oblanceolate, 0.7 to 2.4 cm in length and 2.0 to 5.0 mm in width, densely covered with appressed silky hairs; inflorescence a raceme; flowers perfect and small, hypanthium well developed, sepals 5, petals 5, white and imbricate, stamens 20, pistils 3 to 5; fruit 3 to 5 follicles that are dehiscent along both sutures. This often overlooked, low shrub appears to be limited to crevices on limestone cliffs, canyon walls and ledges at 6,500 to 8,000 ft. (1,980 to 2,440 m) in elevation. Although the distribution records are more southern in New Mexico, the species has a wide range throughout the western states.

**Tufted Rockmat**, *Petrophyton caespitosum* (Nuttall) Rydberg
      Syns. *Spiraea caespitosa* Nuttall            Rosaceae

212. Plants low shrubs or suffrutescent perennials from a woody base, less than 45.0 cm in height or prostrate .......... 213.

212. Plants tall shrubs or trees 1.0 m or more in height, woody throughout, never prostrate ................................................. 214.

213. Plants suffrutescent, woody only at the base and herbaceous above; ovary and fruit borne on an obvious stipe; stems and lower surfaces of leaves with straight or few-branched hairs, seldom stellate; blades of petals notched at apex with a small appendage; leaves orbicular to ovate-elliptic to lanceolate, dentate to crenate, 0.8 to 2.0 cm in length; fruit a capsule, 3.0 to 3.5 mm at maturity. This rare species has only been collected a few times on limestone and igneous soils in the southern tier of counties at 3,000 to 4,000 ft. (910 to 1,220 m) in elevation.

**Dwarf Ayenia**, *Ayenia pilosa* Cristobal            Sterculiaceae

213.  Plants small, but woody throughout and much branched; ovary and fruit borne on a very reduced stipe, often difficult to distinguish; stems and lower surfaces of leaves with a felt-like covering of short, stellate hairs; blades of petals not notched at apex and lacking a small appendage; leaves orbicular to ovate, crenate to dentate, 0.8 to 2.4 cm in length; fruit a capsule, 4.7 to 5.3 mm at maturity. Infrequent, but more common than the **Dwarf Ayenia** on rocky slopes and mesas, this species may be found in the southern one-third of New Mexico at 3,000 to 4,000 ft. (910 to 1,220 m) in elevation. It flowers from May through August.

**Littleleaf Ayenia**, *Ayenia microphylla* A. Gray          Sterculiaceae

DWARF AYENIA                LITTLELEAF AYENIA
*Ayenia pilosa*              *Ayenia microphylla*

214.   Inflorescence a catkin; plants monoecious or dioecious; flowers imperfect and incomplete, lacking obvious and showy petals; fruit a nutlet or capsule ................................. 215.

214.   Inflorescence a corymb, cyme, panicle, raceme, umbel or flowers solitary, but never a catkin; flowers perfect. (*Rhamnus smithii,* which is dioecious with unisexual flowers, may be confusing at this point, but the inflorescence in this case is a drupe, not a catkin, and the flowers are borne in the leaf axils.) ....................................................... 223.

215.  Plants monoecious trees or large shrubs; buds not distinctly resinous and sticky to the touch; staminate catkins elongated and pendulous, pistillate catkins pine cone-like, not usually drooping, or in a flattened, papery bladder-like husk; sepals or petals present, not both; leaves commonly double serrate to slightly lobed; fruit a 1-seeded nutlet. Birch Family - Betulaceae ............... 216.

215.  Plants dioecious trees or large shrubs; buds of several species resinous and sticky to the touch; catkins, both staminate and pistillate, elongated and pendulous, never pine cone-like; sepals and petals none; leaves serrate to crenate, never double serrate; fruit a 2- or 4-valved dehiscent capsule. Cottonwoods & Aspen, genus *Populus* - Salicaceae ................................................................. 219.

216. Pistillate catkins a flattened bladder-like, papery husk; nutlets not winged, each enclosed in the papery bractlets; perianth absent in the staminate flowers, present in the pistillate flowers; staminate catkins 2.0 to 3.0 cm in length and pistillate catkins 2.0 to 4.5 cm in length at maturity; staminate flowers solitary in the axil of each bract; leaves suborbicular-ovate to ovate-elliptic, rounded to slightly cordate at base, double-serrate, 3.5 to 6.0 cm in length and 3.0 to 5.0 cm in width. This small, rare tree, to 9.0 m at maturity, has only been collected in southwestern New Mexico at 5,000 to 7,000 ft. (1,520 to 2,130 m) in elevation. It flowers in early spring, May and June, and is known for its extremely hard wood.

**Hophornbean** or **Ironwood**, *Ostrya knowltonii* Coville

Betulaceae

HOPHORNBEAN or IRONWOOD
*Ostrya knowltonii*

216.    Pistillate catkins not bladder-like or papery, but hard and woody, several nutlets in a pine cone-like catkin; nutlets narrowly or widely winged; perianth present in staminate flowers, absent in the pistillate flowers; staminate flowers 2 or more in the axil of each bract ................................. 217.

217.    Pistillate catkins solitary, 2.0 to 3.0 cm in length at maturity, their bracts remaining thin, deciduous with or soon after the nutlets and deeply 3-lobed, the midlobe longer; leaves flat, 2.5 to 5.5 cm in length, ovate to rhombic-ovate and sharply serrate, petioles 5.0 to 15.0 mm in length; pith round in cross-section; bark dark brown to reddish-brown, lenticels horizontal. This large shrub or small tree to 10.0 m in height commonly grows in clumps along streams, sometimes forming thickets at 5,500 to 9,000 ft. (1,680 to 2,740 m) in elevation. It is a more northern species in New Mexico, flowering in April and May.

**Water Birch**, *Betula occidentalis* Hooker
            Syns. *B. fontinalis* Sargent                    Betulaceae

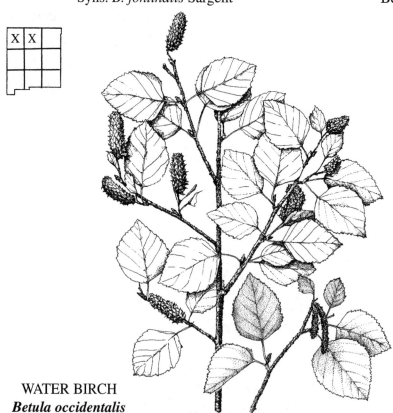

WATER BIRCH
*Betula occidentalis*

217. Pistillate catkins commonly several in a raceme-like cluster, their bracts becoming thick and woody, persistent on the branches long after the nutlets have fallen, shallowly 3- to 5-lobed; leaves wrinkled; pith triangular in cross-section ....................................... 218.

218. Leaves ovate to oblong-ovate, rounded to cordate or sub-cordate at the base, deeply and doubly serrate-dentate, almost lobed, 3.0 to 11.0 cm in length and 3.0 to 6.5 cm in width; bark smooth, gray to brown or reddish-brown; stamens 4; pistillate catkins ellipsoid, 1.0 to 2.0 cm in length. This large shrub or small tree, to 8.0 m in height, is found in canyons and along streams at 6,500 to 8,500 ft. (1,980 to 2,590 m) in elevation in the mountains of northern New Mexico. It is widely distributed in western North America and throughout western Canada and into Alaska.

**Thinleaf Alder** or **Aliso**, *Alnus incana* ssp. *tenuifolia*
(Nuttall) Breitung
Syns. *A. tenuifolia* Nuttall        Betulaceae

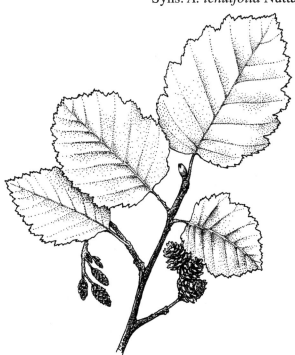

THINLEAF ALDER or ALISO
*Alnus incana* ssp. *tenuifolia*

218.	Leaves elliptic or ovate-oblong, acute or short-cuneate at the base, shallowly and doubly serrate-dentate, appearing less lobed, 5.0 to 7.8 cm in length and 1.9 to 5.8 cm in width; bark smooth, thin, gray to brown, large trunks fissured; stamens 1 to 3, usually 2. This large, straight tree to 20.0 m or more in height is found along canyons and streams in the mountains and ponderosa pine forests at 5,500 to 7,500 ft. (1,680 to 2,300 m) in elevation in southwestern New Mexico. It also occurs in adjacent Arizona and Mexico.

**New Mexico** or **Arizona Alder,** *Alnus oblongifolia* Torrey
Betulaceae

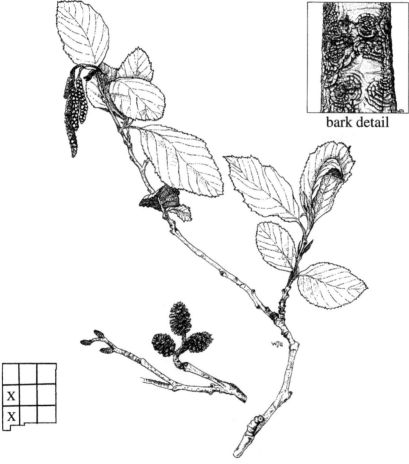

bark detail

NEW MEXICO or ARIZONA ALDER
*Alnus oblongifolia*

219.    Petiole flattened perpendicular to the plane of the leaf; leaves about as long as wide ........................................................................ 220.

219.    Petiole not flattened perpendicular to the plant of the leaf, but terete or channeled; leaves longer than broad ................................. 222.

        220.    Leaves broadly ovate to suborbicular, base rounded, 3.0 to 8.0 cm in diameter, finely serrate, bright green on the upper surface and dull green on the lower surface; bark gray or greenish-white, marked with dark, raised, eye-shaped branch scars; buds conical; stigmas filiform, 2; capsules 5.0 to 8.0 mm in length. These often small, rapidly growing trees are usually under 12.0 m in height, but may reach to more than 20.0 m in height under ideal growing conditions. They occur throughout New Mexico, in the mountains, on slopes and in valleys at 6,500 to 10,500 ft. (1,980 to 3,200 m) in elevation. The **Quaking Aspen** takes its name from the trembling of the leaves in the slightest breeze. The species is a pioneer tree in burned areas where it rapidly forms thickets.

**Quaking Aspen**, *Populus tremuloides* Michaux

Salicaceae

| X | X | X |
|---|---|---|
| X | X |  |
| X | X |  |

QUAKING ASPEN
*Populus tremuloides*

220.  Leaves deltoid or deltoid-cordate, 5.0 to 10.0 cm in length, coarsely serrate; bark rough, thick and furrowed. The following two species are not well defined in the literature and field collections are often difficult to distinguish ......... 221.

221.  Leaves mostly with more than 10 teeth on each side, blade 5.0 to 10.0 cm in length, coarsely serrate, glabrous, abruptly acuminate at the apex, petiole laterally flattened, 7.0 to 8.0 cm in length, usually bearing a pair of glands at the summit; stigmas broad, 3- or 4-lobed; capsules oblong-ovoid, 8.0 to 10.0 mm in length, pedicels shorter than the capsules. A large tree to 35.0 m in height, it is commonly found below 6,500 ft. (1,980 m) in elevation. It flowers and produces fruit from March through May. This appears to be a more eastern and northeastern species of the plains and river bottoms in New Mexico.

**Plains Cottonwood**, *Populus deltoides* ssp. *monilifera* (Aiton)
Eckenwalder
Syns. *P. deltoides* var. *occidentalis* Rydberg
*P. sargentii* Dode        Salicaceae

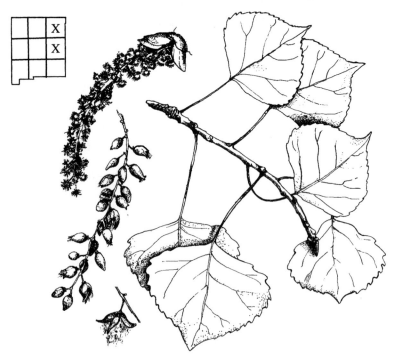

PLAINS COTTONWOOD
*Populus deltoides* ssp. *monilifera*

221.    Leaves mostly with fewer than 10 teeth on each side, blade 5.0 to
        9.0 cm in length, coarsely crenate-serrate, glabrous, abruptly
        acuminate at the apex, petiole laterally flattened, 3.0 to 5.0 cm in
        length, usually lacking a pair of glands at the summit; stigmas
        broad, 3- or 4-lobed; capsules ovoid to ellipsoid, 4.0 to 6.0 mm
        in length, pedicels as long or longer than the capsules. A large
        tree to 30.0 m in height, it is commonly found up to 7,000 ft.
        (2,130 m) in elevation. It flowers and produces fruit from March
        through May. This appears to be a more southern and western
        species of the valleys and river banks in New Mexico.

**Wislizenus, Alamo** or **Fremont Cottonwood**, *Populus deltoides*
ssp. *wislizeni* (S. Watson) Eckenwalder
Syns. *P. fremontii* S. Watson
*P. wislizeni* (S. Watson) Sargent
Salicaceae

222.    Leaves lanceolate to ovate-lanceolate to elliptic, averag-
        ing 3.5 cm or less in width and 5.0 to 10.0 cm in length,
        finely crenate-serrate with 7 to 9 teeth per cm, apex acumi-
        nate with a fine clear gland at the tip, lower surface pale
        green, upper surface darker or bright green to yellow-
        green, petiole one-third the length of the blade or less;
        bud scales 5, somewhat sticky and aromatic; capsules are
        borne in catkins to 10.0 cm in length. This common, me-
        dium sized tree to 17.0 m in height occurs along streams,
        in marshy, sandy and gravelly areas, and occasionally in
        roadside ditches at 5,000 to 8,000 ft. (1,520 to 2,440 m)
        in elevation. Widespread over most of New Mexico, it
        produces flowers and fruits from March through May.

**Narrowleaf Cottonwood**, *Populus angustifolia* James
Salicaceae

222.    Leaves ovate-lanceolate to rhombic-lanceolate, averag-
        ing 4.5 cm or more in width and 6.0 to 9.0 cm in length,
        coarsely crenate-serrate, apex acute, green on both sur-
        faces, lighter below, petiole one-half the length of the blade
        or more; bud scales 6 or 7, not sticky or only slightly
        resinous, not aromatic. This uncommon, but locally abun-
        dant and rapidly growing tree may reach 17.0 to 20.0 m

in height. It occurs in moist or dry soils, on hillsides or in valleys, and often in poor soils at 4,500 to 8,000 ft. (1,370 to 2,440 m) in elevation. It is frequently cultivated as a shade tree. Most authorities define this species as a hybrid between *P. angustifolia* and *P. deltoides.*

**Smooth-barked Cottonwood,** *Populus* x *acuminata*
Rydberg      Salicaceae

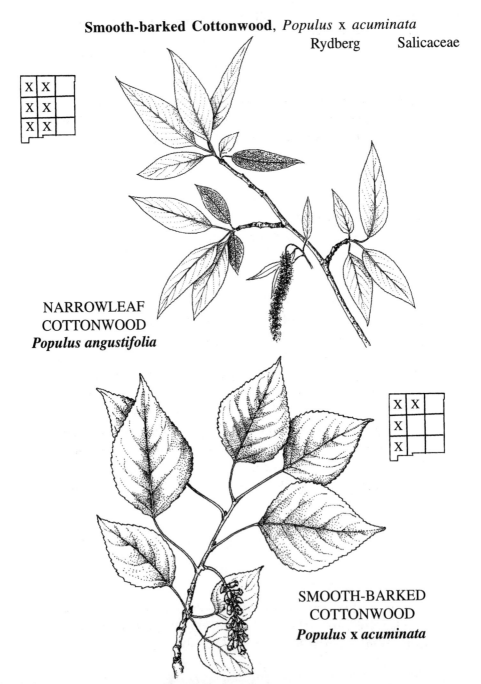

NARROWLEAF
COTTONWOOD
*Populus angustifolia*

SMOOTH-BARKED
COTTONWOOD
*Populus* x *acuminata*

223. Fruit a drupe, 1-seeded or a berry-like drupe with 2 to 4 seeds; flowers white to pink or greenish; inflorescence a cyme, umbel, corymb or raceme ........................................................................ 224.

223. Fruit a capsule, achene, follicle or pome; flower color variable; inflorescence variable ................................................................. 232.

    224. Flowers small, greenish, not showy, perfect or unisexual, sepals and petals in 4s or 5s or absent, stamens 4 or 5; fruit a berry-like drupe with 2 to 4 seeds ........................... 225.

    224. Flowers white or pink, rarely greenish, attractive and showy, perfect, sepals and petals in 5s, stamens 10 or more; fruit a 1-seeded drupe ........................................................ 227.

225. Flowers, unisexual, solitary or in 2- or 3-flowered clusters or umbels, usually 4-merous, sepals 4, petals 4 or absent; bud scales present; leaves alternate to fascicled to almost opposite, 1.5 to 4.5 cm in length and 0.8 to 2.0 cm in width, oblong-ovate to elliptic, serrulate to crenulate, glabrous to somewhat pubescent on the upper and lower surfaces, the lower surface yellowish; fruit a globose, black drupe, usually with 2 seeds. The range and variation within this uncommon species has not been well established over New Mexico. A bushy shrub to 3.0 m in height, it can be found in mountain canyons, in open hill country and along stream margins from 6,000 to 7,500 ft. (1,830 to 2300 m) in elevation.

**Smith's Buckthorn**, *Rhamnus smithii* Greene        Rhamnaceae

225. Flowers perfect, in cymes or axillary umbels, mostly 5-merous or seldom 4, sepals 5, petals 4 or 5; bud scales lacking; leaves 3.0 to 15.0 cm in length ........................................................................ 226.

SMITH'S BUCKTHORN
*Rhamnus smithii*

226.   Leaves gray or densely white-tomentose on the lower
surface and green to light green above, 3.0 to 7.5 cm in
length and 1.3 to 2.5 cm in width, predominantly alternate to almost opposite, elliptic to oblong, margins
serrulate to entire and sometimes slightly revolute; fruit a
berry-like, green to red to black drupe with 2 or 3 seeds.
This western shrub has been reported to reach 3.0 to 5.0
m in height at maturity in southwestern New Mexico, but
personal sightings have seldom been 3.0 m in height.
(Please see description and illustration at couplet 201, page
387.)

**California Buckthorn**, *Frangula californica*
(Eschscholtz) A. Gray
Syns. *Rhamnus californica* Eschscholtz
Rhamnaceae

226. Leaves green to dark green on both surfaces, the upper surface glabrous to lustrous, 5.0 to 15.0 cm in length and 2.5 to 4.0 cm in width, elliptic to ovate or oblong, margins serrate to crenate, rarely entire; flowers small and greenish, sepals 5, petals 4 or 5 or sometimes absent, stamens 4 or 5; fruit a subglobose, black to dark purple drupe and commonly 3-seeded. This attractive, upright shrub has been reported to reach more than 5.0 m in height, but we have never seen it above 3.0 m within its range in southwestern New Mexico. Occurring in moist canyons and along streams at 4,500 to 7,500 ft. (1,370 to 2,300 m) in elevation, it is today being cultivated in lawns and gardens.

**Birch-leaf Buckthorn**, *Frangula betulifolia* (Greene)

V. Grub

Syns. *Rhamnus betulifolia* Greene

Rhamnaceae

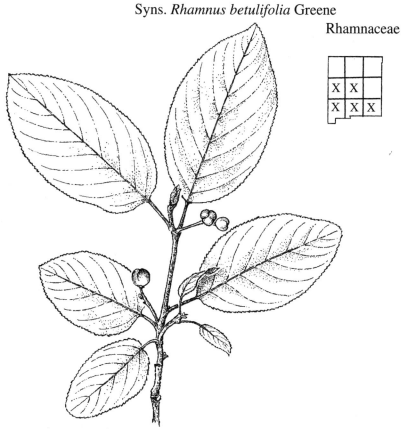

BIRCH-LEAF BUCKTHORN
*Frangula betulifolia*

227.    Flowers and fruit borne in elongate racemes, with the leaves of
        the current year ............................................................ 228.

227.    Flowers and fruit borne in corymbs, umbels or small clusters,
        before the leaves on the branches of the previous year ................. 229.

    228.    Calyx lobes deciduous long before the fruit matures; leaf
        margins finely toothed and sharply serrulate, triangular
        or slender ascending without callous teeth, ovate to
        broadly elliptic or obovate, 4.0 to 12.0 cm in length, base
        rounded to somewhat cordate, dark green and somewhat
        lustrous on the upper surface and glaucescent to grayish-
        green on the lower surface; flowers white, in dense gla-
        brous racemes, 7.0 to 15.0 cm in length; fruit a fleshy,
        dark purple, globose 1-seeded drupe. This widespread and
        common shrub or small tree, to 8.0 m in height, is found
        in moist canyons and along streams throughout New
        Mexico at 5,500 to 8,000 ft. (1,680 to 2,440 m) in eleva-
        tion. Used in erosion control and commonly escaping
        cultivation, the **Chokecherry** often forms attractive road-
        side thickets. It flowers in April through June, is eaten by
        birds and other wildlife and the fruit is widely used in
        jams and jellies.

        **Common** or **Western Chokecherry,** *Prunus virginiana* L.
        Syns. *P. melanocarpa* (A. Nelson) Rydberg
        *Padus calophylla* Wooton & Standley
        Rosaceae

    228.    Calyx lobes persistent under the fruit until the fruit ma-
        tures; leaf margins mostly finely serrate-crenate with blunt,
        appressed or incurved callous teeth, ovate to oblong-lan-
        ceolate to obovate-oblong, 3.5 to 15.0 cm in length, base
        acute, dark green and lustrous on the upper surface and
        pale green on the lower surface; flowers white, in long,
        slender racemes, 6.0 to 15.0 cm in length; fruit a fleshy,
        dark red to purple or black, globose 1-seeded drupe, the
        stone relatively large. Less common, especially over the
        northern counties, the **Southwestern Chokecherry** oc-
        curs at 4,500 to 7,500 ft. (1,370 to 2,300 m) in elevation

in oak-woodland mountains, along streams and in canyons. Both species may form shrubs or small trees and distinguishing the two species is not always an easy task.

**Southwestern Chokecherry**, *Prunus serotina* Ehrhart

Syns. *Prunus virens* Wooton & Standley

*Padus serotina* (Ehrhart) Agardt

Rosaceae

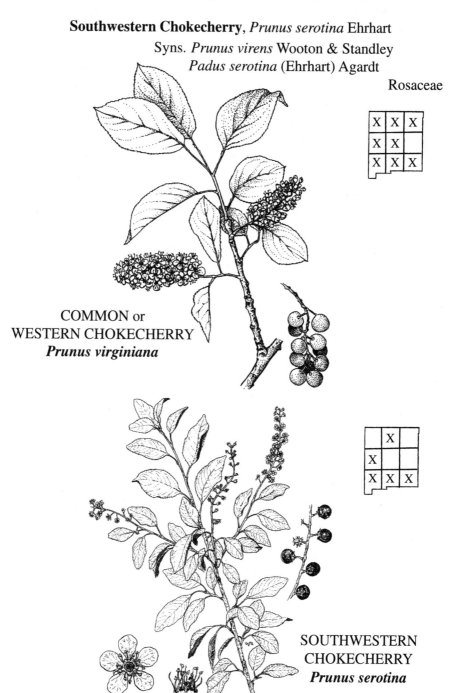

COMMON or
WESTERN CHOKECHERRY
*Prunus virginiana*

SOUTHWESTERN
CHOKECHERRY
*Prunus serotina*

229.    Calyx tube, pedicels and often the younger branches densely short-
        pubescent, calyx lobes glandular-toothed, pedicels 5.0 to 15.0
        mm long; leaves ovate to oval or elliptic, rounded to cuneate at
        the base, obtuse to acute at the apex, 2.5 to 5.0 cm in length and
        1.5 to 2.5 cm in width, densely pubescent on the lower surface
        and finely pubescent to glabrous on the upper surface, margins
        finely serrate, flat (not folded); flowers axillary in clusters of 2 to
        8 on wood of the previous year or on short spurs, sepals 5, petals
        white and 5, stamens 20; fruit a globular drupe, 17.0 to 18.0 mm
        in length. This low spreading shrub, to 1.5 m in height, is ex-
        tremely rare over the eastern, sandy plains of New Mexico at
        3,000 to 5,000 ft. (910 to1,520 m) in elevation. It may be con-
        fused with *P. angustifolia*, another species of the sandy plains,
        that is less pubescent and on which the leaves tend to fold.

        **Oklahoma** or **Sand Plum**, *Prunus gracilis* Engelmann & A. Gray
                        Syns. *P. normalis* (Torrey & A. Gray) Small
                                                              Rosaceae

229.    Calyx tube, pedicels and the younger branches glabrous or nearly
        so .................................................................................................... 230.

        230.    Bark and twigs purplish-brown or reddish-brown, twigs
                seldom, if ever, becoming thorny or spiny lateral branches;
                leaves crenate to crenulate with conspicuously gland-
                tipped teeth on the margin, oblong to elliptic to obovate
                or oblanceolate, the base acute to cuneate, the apex ob-
                tuse to rounded or emarginate, upper surface glabrous and
                lower surface glabrous to pubescent, 2.0 to 6.0 cm in
                length and 0.8 to 3.7 cm in width; flowers 3 to 12 in
                corymbs or seldom in short racemes, dull white or green-
                ish, sepals 5, petals 5, stamens many; fruit globose or oval,
                6.0 to 12.0 mm in length, red to black at maturity, seed of
                fruit flattened. Based on herbarium collections and field
                data the **Bitter Cherry** is more common in western and
                southwestern New Mexico at elevations of 5,000 to 9,000
                ft. (1,520 to 2,740 m). Flowering in April and May it oc-
                curs in moist canyons and on stream banks. Some au-
                thorities identify two varieties of the taxon that we have
                omitted from this coverage.

                **Bitter Cherry**, *Prunus emarginata* (Douglas) D. Dietrich
                                                              Rosaceae

BITTER CHERRY
*Prunus emarginata*

230. Bark gray; leaves sharply serrate or serrulate, the teeth appressed or incurved, not conspicuously gland-tipped; seed of fruit round to oval, not flattened; twigs occasionally becoming thorny or spiny lateral branches or spurs ..... 231.

231. Flowers less than 13.0 mm across, sepals 5, petals 5, white, 4.0 to 6.0 mm in length, stamens 15 to 20; inflorescence 2- to 4-flowered umbels; leaves elliptic to lanceolate to oblong, 2.5 to 5.0 cm in length and 0.9 to 1.8 cm in width, serrate with glandular teeth, glabrous on the upper surface and pubescent on the lower; fruit a globose drupe, 2.0 to 2.2 cm in length, red to yellowish with a slight bloom. Infrequent in pastures, along fence rows, prairie stream banks and in sandy areas on the plains, this shrub or small tree may reach 2.0 to 5.0 m in height. It occurs in the eastern and northeastern counties at 4,000 to 6,000 ft. (1,220 to 1,830 m) in elevation and flowers in May and June.

**Sand Plum**, *Prunus angustifolia* Marshall
      Syns. *P. watsonii* Sargent            Rosaceae

231.    Flowers more than 13.0 mm across, sepals 5, petals 5, white, 8.0
        to 15.0 mm in length, stamens 20; inflorescence 2- to 5-flowered
        umbels or solitary; leaves elliptic to oblanceolate to oblong, 6.0
        to 10.0 cm in length and 3.8 to 5.0 cm in width, margin serrate or
        doubly serrate and lacking glandular teeth, glabrous on both sur-
        faces, some pubescence on the lower midrib; fruit a globose to
        oval drupe, 2.0 to 2.5 cm in diameter, purple to red with a slight
        bloom. Widespread throughout North America, this common,
        small, native tree reaching 7.0 to 8.0 m, also occurs as a thicket
        forming shrub, and is found along stream banks, in woodlands
        and in upland prairies at 4,000 to 7,500 ft. (1,220 to 2,300 m) in
        elevation. Often a locally abundant species, it is cultivated and
        often escapes cultivation. (Please see couplet 70, page 249 for
        further description and illustration, page 250.)

        **Wild** or **American Plum**, *Prunus americana* Marshall       Rosaceae


232.    Fruit a capsule or somewhat woody follicle; species of
        the most southern and southwestern counties...................... 233.


232.    Fruit a pome or an achene; species widely scattered over
        New Mexico ................................................................. 234.


233.    Leaves narrowly lanceolate, 3.8 to 8.0 cm in length and 0.6 to 1.4
        cm in width, margins serrate, glabrous to puberulent on the up-
        per surface and puberulent to tomentose on the lower surface;
        calyx persistent and 5 lobed, petals 5 and white, stamens 15 to
        25, pistils 5; inflorescence a corymb or cyme; fruit an ovoid cap-
        sule, however it opens by 1 suture as a follicle, seeds winged.
        First reported by Wooton & Standley in 1915, this rare species
        has only been collected in the Guadalupe Canyon in Hidalgo
        County at 4,000 to 5,000 ft. (1,220 to 1,520 m) in elevation. This
        evergreen shrub or small tree to 6.0 m in height should be ex-
        pected on dry, rocky, limestone hillsides and in canyons.

        **Arizona Rosewood**, *Vauquelinia californica* (Torrey) Sargent
                                                             Rosaceae

233. Leaves ovate to ovate-cordate, 1.5 to 4.0 cm in length and 0.7 to 1.5 cm in width, margins serrate to crenate, densely pubescent with stellate or simple hairs on the upper and lower surface; petals white (or yellow) to pink, sometimes with a spot at the base; inflorescence a panicle or raceme or flowers solitary; stems to 1.0 m in height, woody well above the soil line. (This description is from a single collection in Luna County, and we have found nothing similar in the major state herbaria.)

**Woody Indian-Mallow**, *Abutilon incanum* ssp. *pringlei*
(Hochreutiner) Felger & Lowe
Syns. *A. pringlei* Hochreutiner

Malvaceae

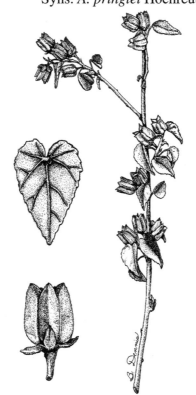
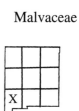

WOODY INDIAN-MALLOW
*Abutilon incanum* ssp. *pringlei*

234. Fruit an achene; pistils superior, carpels separate, not connate, free from the hypanthium ............................................ 235.

234. Fruit a pome; pistils inferior or half inferior, the carpels united, enclosed by and adnate to the hypanthium ............. 238.

235.  Petals present, 5, small but visible, white, cream or pink, sepals
      5, stamens 20, pistils 5 and distinct, ovary superior; inflorescence
      a loose and feathery panicle; leaves distinctly toothed, pinnately
      veined, sometimes appearing slightly lobed and almost palmately
      veined, but not lobed, obovate-cuneate, 1.5 to 5.0 cm in length
      and 1.0 to 3.5 cm in width, gray hairy-pubescent on the lower
      surface; achenes somewhat flattened and villous-hirsute. An at-
      tractive shrub to 2.5 m in height, **Mountain Spray** is common
      and widely scattered over the mountainous regions of New
      Mexico at 6,500 to 10,000 ft. (1,980 to 3,050 m) in elevation.
      Flowering over much of the growing season, it is found on rock
      outcrops, on high plateaus and at the bases of cliffs.

**Mountain** or **Ocean Spray**, *Holodiscus dumosus* (Nuttall) Heller

Rosaceae

MOUNTAIN or
OCEAN SPRAY
*Holodiscus dumosus*

A somewhat related, commonly cultivated species may key to this point. This is the well known **Bridal Wreath** or **Spiraea**, *Spiraea x vanhoutei* (Briot) Carriere. This shrub to 2.0 m in height, with rhombic-ovate to obovate leaves, 2.0 to 4.0 cm in length, produces white to pink flowers in round-topped umbels at the ends of short leafy branches. The leaves are coarsely serrate towards the apex and entire below. The fruit is a follicle. Confined to lawns and gardens, it seldom escapes cultivation, but may be found near old home sites.

**Bridal Wreath** or **Spiraea**, *Spiraea* x *vanhoutei* (Briot) Carriere

Rosaceae

BRIDAL WREATH or SPIRAEA
*Spiraea* x *vanhoutei*

235. Petals lacking, flowers inconspicuous, borne solitary or in small clusters, stamens in 2 or 3 whorls; leaves entire or entire on the lower half of the leaf and toothed at the apex, often appearing fascicled; fruit an achene with an elongate plumose style that persists and is very attractive in the fall and winter months. **Mountain Mahogany,** genus *Cercocarpus*................................................. 236.

236.  Leaves linear to linear-elliptic or narrowly oblong, entire and revolute, coriaceous (leathery), often resinous, evergreen, 0.3 to 1.8 cm in length and less than 2.0 mm in width; stamens 10 to 20, anthers glabrous, sepals 5, pistil 1; achene with persistent style, 1.0 to 3.0 cm in length. This extremely rare, much branched shrub, from 0.5 to 2.5 m in height, is confined to the northwest corner of the State in San Juan County. It is found on cliffs and rocky slopes, in desert shrub, piñon-juniper and mountain brush communities at 4,500 to 7,000 ft. (1,370 to 2,130 m) in elevation.

**Dwarf Mountain Mahogany**, *Cercocarpus intricatus*

S. Watson

Rosaceae

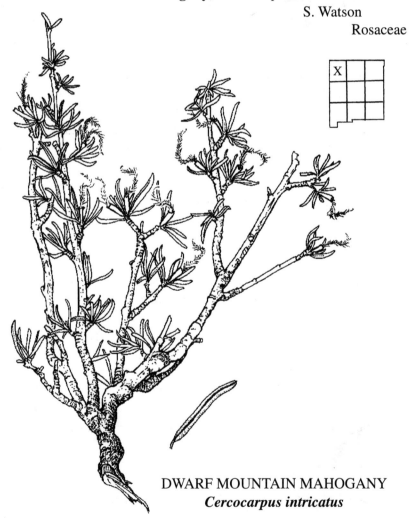

DWARF MOUNTAIN MAHOGANY
*Cercocarpus intricatus*

236.  Leaves obovate-orbicular to oblanceolate to ovate or spatulate, margin entire below and crenate to crenate-dentate toward the apex, but not coriaceous, revolute or strongly resinous, deciduous or evergreen; anthers hirsute. Several varieties have been described for the following two species, but they are not included in this treatment ............................................................................ 237.

237.  Leaves winter deciduous and thin, crenate to serrate-dentate well below the apex to one-half of the leaf, obovate-orbicular to ovate to oval, 2.2 to 4.0 cm in length and 1.5 to 3.0 cm in width; flowers solitary or in clusters of 2 or 3, sepals 5, petals lacking, stamens 20 or more, pistil 1; achene fruit style 4.0 to 8.0 cm in length. This more northern species is common from Wyoming, Nebraska, and Utah south into northern Arizona, the northern half and the southern mountains of New Mexico and northwest Texas. A shrub to 2.0 m or small tree to 4.0 m in height, this widespread species is found over sunny slopes and dry hillsides in piñon-juniper and mixed coniferous forests, and even into aspen communities at 5,500 to 8,500 ft. (1,680 to 2,600 m) in elevation. Based on location and elevation it flowers from May through July.

**Alder-leaf Mountain Mahogany** or **Palo Duro,**
*Cercocarpus montanus* Rafinesque
Rosaceae

237.  Leaves evergreen and thick, toothed only at or very near the apex, lanceolate to oblanceolate or spatulate, 0.9 to 2.5 cm in length and 0.5 to 1.4 cm in width; flowers solitary or in clusters of 2 or 3, sepals 5, petals lacking, stamens 15 or more, pistil 1; achene fruit style 2.0 to 4.0 cm in length. This more southern species occurs in southern and eastern Arizona, the southern and eastern two-thirds of New Mexico, the Trans-Pecos of Texas and the mountainous northern regions of Mexico. Commonly a shrub, it may become tree-like to 4.5 m in height. It is found in chaparral on dry slopes and mesas at 5,000 to 7,500 ft. (1,520 to 7,500 m) in elevation.

**Southern Mountain Mahogany**, *Cercocarpus breviflorus* A. Gray
Rosaceae

ALDER-LEAF MOUNTAIN
MAHOGANY or PALO DURO
*Cercocarpus montanus*

238.    Leaves sessile or short petiolate, petiole less than 5.0 mm
        in length, fascicled at the ends of the branches, 2.0 to 4.0
        cm in length and 4.0 to 9.0 mm in width, narrowly oblan-
        ceolate to oblong and cuneate at the base, margins com-
        monly entire or with gland-tipped teeth; flowers in clus-
        ters of 2 or 3 or solitary, calyx adnate to the ovary, petals
        5 and pink or rose colored, stamens 20, ovary inferior;
        fruit a 2-celled pome with persistent calyx lobes; carpels
        united, enclosed by and adnate to the hypanthium. (Please
        see couplet 205, page 390 for further description.)

**Squaw-Apple**, *Peraphyllum ramosissimum* Nuttall

Rosaceae

238.    Leaves petiolate, petiole more than 5.0 mm in length, not
        fascicled, but scattered along the stems; flowers in um-
        bels, umbel-like racemes or corymbs, usually with more
        than 2 or 3 flowers, if few flowered, then borne on spurs.... 239.

239.    Inflorescence an umbel; leaves toothed along both margins; plants cultivated or escaping cultivation; flowers large and showy, white to occasionally pink, petals 5, more than 20.0 mm in length, ovary completely inferior; leaves densely white tomentose on the lower surface, oblong-ovate, 8.0 to 12.0 cm in length, margins serrate-crenate. This is the common apple tree of commerce. The common **Pear**, *Pyrus communis* L., in which the flowers are borne in a corymb, may also key to this point.

**Apple**, *Malus pumila* Miller                                    Rosaceae

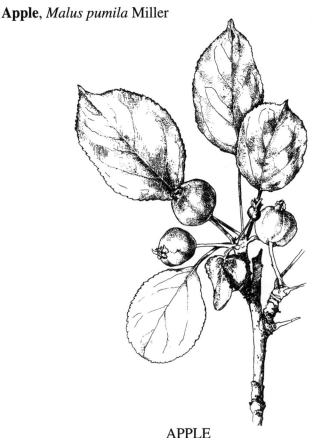

APPLE
*Malus pumila*

239.    Inflorescence a short raceme; leaves prominently toothed toward the apex and entire below; plants native; flowers small and attractive, petals 5, white, less than 15.0 mm in length. As the large number of synonyms indicate, there has been and continues to be considerable confusion in describing this taxon, the **Serviceberries**, genus *Amelanchier* ................................................................. 240.

240.  Mature leaves finely and permanently pubescent on the lower surface, 0.8 to 3.0 cm in length and 0.5 to 2.7 cm in width, commonly averaging less than 2.5 cm in length; petals oval to round, 5.0 to 10.0 mm long and less than 3 times as long as wide; pome purple to pink, 5.0 to 12.0 mm in length. This more western species is found from dry rocky slopes in piñon-juniper, grassland and sagebrush communities to wet stream margins among aspens and in ponderosa pine communities at 6,000 to 8,000 ft. (1,830 to 2,440 m) in elevation. A thicket forming shrub, or seldom a small tree, from 2.0 to 5.0 m in height, this species produces many small white flowers that are extremely fragrant in the early spring.

**Utah Serviceberry**, *Amelanchier utahensis* Koehne
Syns. *A. bakeri* Greene
*A. australis* Standley
*A. goldmanii* Wooton & Standley
*A. mormonica* Schneider
*A. oreophilla* A. Nelson          Rosaceae

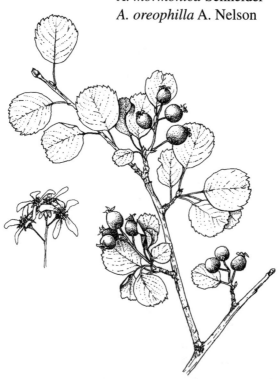

UTAH SERVICEBERRY
*Amelanchier utahensis*

240. Mature leaves glabrous and not permanently pubescent on the lower surface, 2.0 to 5.0 cm in length and 1.5 to 4.2 cm in width, commonly averaging more than 2.5 cm in length; petals oblong, 9.0 to 15.0 mm long and more than 3 times as long as wide; pome purple to dark purple, 5.0 to 15.0 mm in length. This is the more northern of the two species here included, and is found well into Canada and Alaska. It occurs at higher elevations of 7,000 to 9,000 ft. (2,130 to 2,740 m), in wet meadows, along stream margins and on forested mountain slopes.

**Shadbush** or **Cluster Serviceberry**, *Amelanchier pumila*
(Torrey & A. Gray) Nuttall *ex* M. Roemer
Syns. *A. alnifolia* var. *pumila*
(Torrey & A. Gray) Schneider
*A. polycarpa* Greene

Rosaceae

## ALTERNATE AND COMPOUND LEAVES

1.    Leaves palmately compound or trifoliate ........................................... 2.

1.    Leaves pinnately compound ............................................................. 14.

   2.        Plants with spines or thorns on leaves or stems ...................... 3.

   2.        Plants without spines or thorns on leaves or stems ................. 8.

3.    Leaflets spine tipped, leathery and sessile, with 3 to 7 lobes on a
      trifoliate, holly-like leaf; young stems are often red or green, with
      older twigs becoming dark reddish-brown or gray; flowers ap-
      pear in March through May, are perfect and borne in racemes,
      the corolla has 6 petals in two whorls, sepals 6, stamens 6; the
      fruit is a bright red, somewhat flattened, berry with 1 to several
      seeds; these are evergreen, aromatic shrubs with distinctly yel-
      low internal wood, growing to 2.0 m in height. This species oc-
      curs infrequently in the southern tier of counties at 3,300 to 6,000
      ft. (1,010 to 1,830 m) in elevation. The acidic berries attract birds
      and are sometimes used for jellies, while the yellow wood has
      been used as a dye.

**Algerita** or **Palo Amarillo**, *Mahonia trifoliata* (Moricand)  Fedde
Berberidaceae

ALGERITA or
PALO AMARILLO
*Mahonia trifoliata*

3.     Leaflets not spine tipped, spines and thorns confined to the stems of the plant ........................................................................................ 4.

    4.     Leaves consistently trifoliate with strongly exserted petioles, the three leaflets entire, commonly triangular in shape, with a truncate base and the margins entire, the terminal petiolule several times longer than the 2 lateral petiolules; the fruit is a long legume to 30.0 cm in length and producing 8 to 15 obvious seeds; the zygomorphic flowers develop before the leaves, the inflorescence is a raceme, the petals are a beautiful scarlet red to 6.0 cm in length; scattered separate or paired hooked prickles occur on the stems and petioles. This attractive shrub, reaching 3.0 to 5.0 m in height and sometimes becoming a small tree, is confined to the very southwest corner of New Mexico at 4,500 to 5,500 ft. (1,370 to 1,680 m) in elevation. It usually flowers in the spring, but may flower again in late summer if adequate moisture is available.

**Western Coral Bean** or **Chiliote**, *Erythrina flabelliformis*
Kearney
Fabaceae

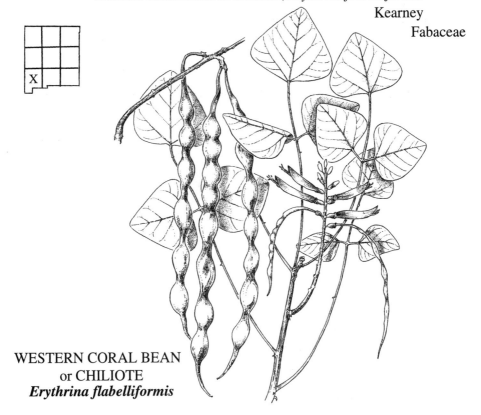

WESTERN CORAL BEAN
or CHILIOTE
*Erythrina flabelliformis*

4.    Leaves predominantly trifoliate with some leaves occa-
      sionally palmately or pinnately compound, the leaflets
      serrate or biserrate, ovate to lanceolate or slightly cordate
      but not triangular in shape, the terminal petiolule longer
      but not several times longer than the lateral petiolules;
      the fruit a hip, a drupe, a cluster of drupelets or an aggre-
      gate; the flowers developing with the leaves or slightly
      after the leaves and radial, in clusters or actinomorphic .......... 5.

5.    Flowers borne solitary at the tips of the branches, with 5 pink to
      red petals, 5 sepals and numerous stamens; the fruit is a hip, (a
      large globose and densely prickled hypanthium surrounding nu-
      merous achenes), that turns red at maturity; the base of the leaves
      characterized by large exserted and conspicuous stipules. This
      spiny and infrequent shrub, growing to 60.0 cm in height at 4,700
      to 7,500 ft. (1,430 to 2,300 m) in elevation over the southern half
      of New Mexico, is characterized by small, wedge-shaped leaf-
      lets measuring 0.5 to 1.0 cm in length.

**Desert Rose** or **Star Rose**, *Rosa stellata* Wooton          Rosaceae

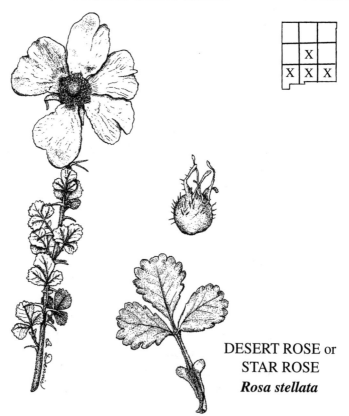

DESERT ROSE or
STAR ROSE
*Rosa stellata*

5. Flowers borne in corymbs or racemes, with 5 white petals and 5 sepals, numerous stamens and many carpels, the hypanthium is open and saucer-shaped; the fruit is an aggregate (raspberry), which is a cluster of small fleshy red to black drupelets formed from many separate pistils in a single flower; stipules present but not conspicuous ................................................................................. 6.

6. Plants strigose or bristly with straight, stiff hairs and glandular hairs over the stems and petioles; the aggregate fruit is red to white in color, separating easily from the receptacle with the drupelets again separating at maturity; shrubs usually slender and weak, less than 1.5 m in height at maturity; compound leaves with 3 to 5 leaflets, the terminal leaflet ovate to oblong-ovate, 5.0 to 7.0 cm in length and the lower surface of the leaves densely white tomentose; flowering occurs from May to July, producing perfect flowers with 5 white petals and 5 sepals and many stamens and pistils. This wide ranging species with several varieties occurs at 6,500 to 10,000 ft. (1,980 to 3,050 m) in elevation and is more common over northern New Mexico. Locating this shrub in fruit in late July or August can be a real treat. Native Americans used the inner bark of the roots of *Rubus idaeus* in combination with *Rosa arkansana* to treat cataracts. The two remedies were used successively, the first for removing inflammation, and the second for healing the eye. (Although shown here with 5 leaflets, this species may commonly be found with 3 leaflets. Please see couplet 24, page 441 for further description.)

**Red Raspberry**, *Rubus idaeus* L.
Syns. *R. strigosus* Michaux          Rosaceae

6. Plants not or only slightly strigose, but with well developed, flattened and often curved, stout prickles or sometimes with limited armature; the aggregate fruit is black or purple in color, not easily separating, with drupelets remaining fused at maturity; primocanes often rooting at the tips; leaflets white-canescent to white-tomentose beneath; shrubs usually robust, more than 2.0 m in height at maturity ........................................................................................ 7.

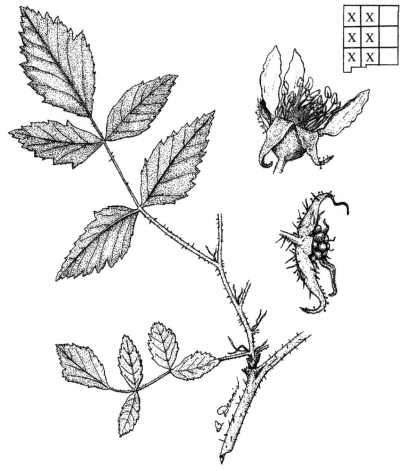

RED RASPBERRY
*Rubus idaeus*

7.   Aggregate fruits purple in color, maturing in July through September; leaves commonly 3-foliate, with some leaves 5- to 7-foliate and either palmate or pinnate; mature bark gray to white; prickles flatbased, stout, ranging from straight to hooked; canes may reach 3.0 m in height. This is a native and more northern and western species of questionable distribution. It is thought to be a more western species in New Mexico, occurring at 5,000 to 7,000 ft. (1,530 to 2,130 m) in elevation. It can be separated from the **Black Raspberry** by its geographic range, however, the **Black Raspberry** is cultivated.

**Whitebark Raspberry**, *Rubus leucodermis* Douglas            Rosaceae

WHITEBARK RASPBERRY
*Rubus leucodermis*

7.  Aggregate fruits black in color, maturing in June through August; leaves commonly 3-foliate, the lower leaves sometimes 5-foliate, with a few simple leaves formed on the flowering stems; mature bark red to purple to tan; prickles broadbased, stout, recurved and sharp; canes may reach 2.5 m in length. This commonly cultivated species readily escapes cultivation and is widely scattered over New Mexico. It may be found along fence rows and the borders of woods at a wide range of elevations above 4,500 ft. (1,370 m). (Please see couplet 24, page 442, for further description.)

**Black Raspberry**, *Rubus occidentalis* L.

Rosaceae

8.  Plants becoming heavy woody vines <u>with</u> <u>tendrils</u>; leaflets commonly 5 to 7 in number ............................................. 9.

8.  Plants shrubs, occasionally becoming small trees to 5.0 m, or woody vines, but if a vine then not producing tendrils; leaflets commonly 3 to 5, seldom 6 or 7 in number ...... 10.

9.    Tendrils with few if any adhesive disks, branching several times, without flattened tips; leaves shiny above, the leaflets oblong-lanceolate and coarsely serrate but thin; flowers small and green in cymes; mature fruit a black globose berry; native to wooded canyons at 4,500 to 7,500 ft. (1,370 to 2,300 m) in elevation throughout New Mexico.

**Western Five-Leaved Ivy**, *Parthenocissus inserta* (Kerner)
Fritsch
Syns. *P. vitacea* (Knerr) Hitchcock     Vitaceae

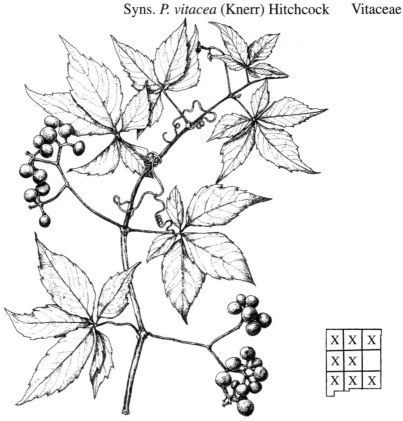

WESTERN FIVE-LEAVED IVY
***Parthenocissus inserta***

9.    Tendrils ending in adhesive somewhat circular disks, branching several times with flattened tips; leaves dull green, the leaflets oblong-lanceolate and coarsely serrate but thick; flowers and fruit similar to the native ivy; cultivated and adventive species, commonly climbing on stone or brick structures.

**Virginia Creeper**, *Parthenocissus quinquefolia* (L.) Planchon
Vitaceae

10. Plants producing both small compound and small simple
leaves over a skeleton-like shrub to 1.5 m in height, the
leaves and leaflets linear to filiform and less than 1.5 cm
in total length; the blue flowers are borne in small ovoid,
globose to oblong spikes throughout the growing season;
the fruit a small legume measuring less than 0.5 cm in
length. This abundant and attractive shrub is common to
the sandy soils of the Rio Grande Valley and southwestern New Mexico at 3,500 to 5,300 ft. (1,070 to 1,620 m)
in elevation. (Please see couplet 204, Key VIII, page 389.)

**Broom Dalea**, *Psorothamnus scoparius* (A. Gray)
Rydberg

Syns. *Dalea scoparia* A. Gray

Fabaceae

BROOM DALEA
*Psorothamnus scoparius*

10.     Plants producing all compound leaves, leaflets variable, but never linear or filiform, 1.0 cm or more in length, the leaves more than 2.0 cm in length; the flowers white, cream colored, light green or yellow ..................................... 11.

11.     Leaflets 3 to 7 per leaf, obovate to lanceolate, silky white on the lower surface, somewhat revolute and entire, appearing trioliate to palmate when in fact, under closer examination, the leaves are more often pinnate; flowers are 5-merous with bright yellow petals and 20 to 25 stamens; many separate achenes are produced in each pistil. This shrub, growing to 1.0 m in height, produces brown shredding bark and occurs from 6,500 ft. (1,980 m) in elevation to the subalpine. This attractive shrub is today commonly planted in lawns and gardens. A concoction made from the leaves of **Cinquefoil** was considered a deadly arrow poison by the Cheyenne and administered only by holy people. (Please see couplet 45, page 460 for further description.)

**Shrubby Cinquefoil**, *Pentaphylloides floribunda* (Pursh) A. Löve
Syns. *Potentilla fruticosa* L.
*P. floribunda* Pursh                              Rosaceae

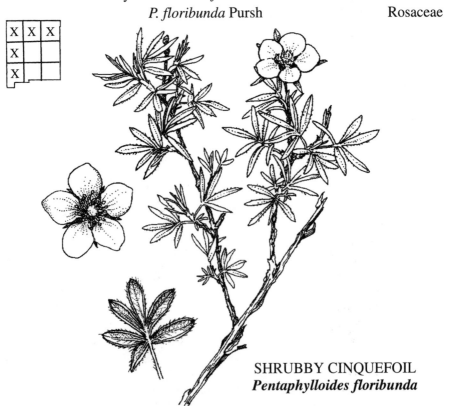

SHRUBBY CINQUEFOIL
*Pentaphylloides floribunda*

11. Leaflets 3 per leaf, ovate, deltoid, elliptic, obovate or lobed in shape, the leaves truly trifoliate; the fruit a samara or drupe. (If the fruit is a drupe you may be working with **Poison-Ivy**. Handle with care.) ................................................................................ 12.

    12. Fruit at maturity a dry, straw-colored, orbicular samara; 1.0 to 2.0 cm in length; the inflorescence is a compound cyme, often becoming corymbose; leaves 9.0 to 15.0 cm in length, usually alternate but occasionally opposite; twigs pubescent when young, becoming smooth with age, with raised lenticels; flowers are polygamous, with uni- sexual and bisexual flowers on the same plant, perianth and stamens are in 4s or 5s, and the petals green to white. This taxon is not well understood and is variable in its morphology, with several possible varieties or subspecies. It is widely scattered over the western states and in New Mexico from 4,000 to 8,000 ft. (1,220 to 2,440 m) in el- evation and mostly confined to canyons and rocky areas. By crumbling the leaves the strong odor of citric acid (Rutaceae) is forthcoming which some folks enjoy and others find too pungent.

**Hop Tree**, *Ptelea trifoliata* L.
    Syns. *P. angustifolia* Bentham
        *P. pallida* Greene            Rutaceae

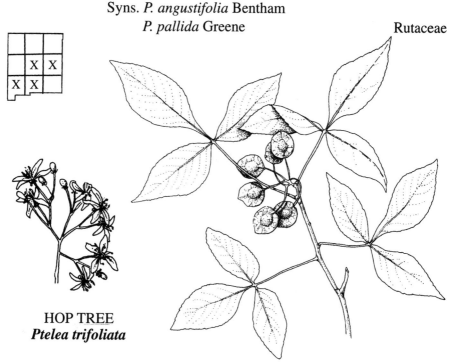

HOP TREE
*Ptelea trifoliata*

12.    Fruit at maturity a dry, one-seeded globular, white, cream
       colored, red or orange drupe; the inflorescence is a panicle...... 13.

13.    Leaflets 1.0 to 3.5 cm in length, the margins round lobed to shal-
       low crenate, the terminal leaflet sessile; the fruit is a red to or-
       ange, extremely pubescent drupe, arranged in dense panicles; the
       yellow flowers are borne in small tight clusters in early spring,
       from April through June and are 5-merous, but difficult to dis-
       sect. This widely scattered and common shrub with several vari-
       eties occurs at 5,000 to 7,500 ft. (1,520 to 2,300 m) in elevation.
       The pungent odor of the plant is offensive, thus the common name
       **Skunkbrush.**

       **Skunkbrush** or **Squawbush,** *Rhus aromatica* Aiton ssp.
                               *pilosissima* (Engelmann) W. A. Weber
                        Syns. *R. trilobata* Nuttall
                                                    Anacardiaceae

SKUNKBRUSH or SQUAWBUSH
*Rhus aromatica* ssp. *pilosissima*

13.    Leaflets 3.0 to 15.0 cm in length, shiny green above, the margins broadly serrate, especially above the middle of the leaflet, the terminal leaflet petiolate; the fruit is a white to cream colored, glabrous drupe, these arranged in loose, axillary panicles; the flowers are 5-merous and greenish white in color. Found in woods and thickets and especially common in disturbed areas at 4,500 to 8,500 ft. (1,370 to 2,600 m) in elevation, **Poison-Ivy** is today one of the most widely scattered and obnoxious shrubs in North America. Because it contains the chemical toxicodendrol, coming in contact with any part of the plant, including the wind blown pollen, is all that is required for sensitive individuals to be affected. Since many people do not know their level of sensitivity to the plant, the best policy is to leave it alone.

**Poison-Ivy** or **Poison-Oak**, *Toxicodendron rydbergii*
(Small *ex* Rydberg) Greene
Syns. *Rhus radicans* L.
*T. radicans* (L.) Kuntze

Anacardiaceae

| X | X | X |
|---|---|---|
| X | X | X |
| X | X |   |

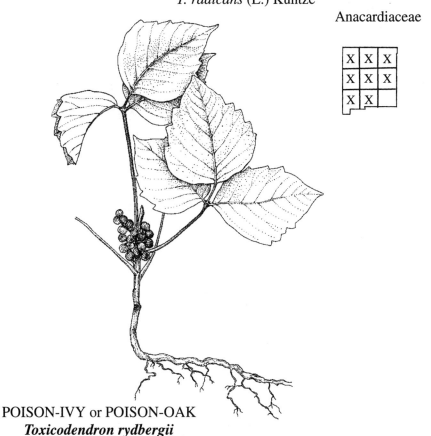

POISON-IVY or POISON-OAK
*Toxicodendron rydbergii*

14.     Leaves odd pinnately compound ............................................ 15.

14.     Leaves even pinnately compound.......................................... 59.

15.     Plants with spines or thorns on leaves or stems ................................ 16.

15.     Plants without spines or thorns on leaves or stems .......................... 29.

16.     Leaflets spine-tipped, leathery and sessile, on a pinately
        compound holly like leaf; the wood and inner bark yel-
        low; the inflorescence a raceme or a subcorymbose
        raceme; flowers yellow, sepals 6 in 2 whorls, petals 6,
        stamens 6 and the fruit a 1 to several seeded berry be-
        coming red to dark purple at maturity. genus *Mahonia* ......... 17.

16.     Leaflets not spine-tipped, spines and thorns confined to
        the stems of the plant ................................................................ 21.

17.     Leaflets with a total of 12 to 40 marginal teeth ................................ 18.

17.     Leaflets with a total of fewer than 12 marginal teeth, commonly
        5 to 10 ......................................................................................... 19.

18.     Plants trailing and spreading close to the ground, less than
        0.5 m in height at maturity; leaflets 3 to 7 per leaf, leaves
        blue to dull green above, glaucous to gray-green below;
        racemes densely many flowered; berries blue to blue-black
        and glaucous. This is a common species of dry, shady
        pine forests at 6,200 to 10,000 ft. (1,890 to 3,050 m) in
        elevation. With abundant water it tends to grow taller and
        take on the appearance of *M. aquifolium*. It has been used
        in reclamation projects in recent years.

        **Creeping Mahonia** or **Oregon Grape**, *Mahonia repens*
                        (Lindley) G. Don                    Berberidaceae

18.     Plants erect, 0.5 to 3.0 m in height at maturity; leaflets 5
        to 9 per leaf, leaves bright glossy above, light green be-
        neath; the berries are blue and glaucous. This is a culti-
        vated ornamental that is more commonly introduced in
        the northern part of New Mexico. This species can truly
        be called the **Oregon Grape** because it is indigenous to
        the Northwest and Oregon.

        **Oregon Grape**, *Mahonia aquifolium* (Pursh) Nuttall
                                        Berberidaceae

CREEPING MAHONIA or OREGON GRAPE
*Mahonia repens*

19.   Berries blood-red and juicy at maturity; terminal leaflet 2.5 to
6.0 cm in length, attenuate, tapering gradually to a narrow tip or
acuminate, the base acute to cuneate, leaflets commonly 2 or more
times longer than wide; apical and lateral inflorescences producing small clusters of 3 to 5 flowers. This frequent species of central and southern New Mexico occurs at 4,500 to 6,800 ft. (1,370
to 2,070 m) in elevation on dry and sunny slopes and on the plains.
Gambel's Quail and other ground feeding birds are attracted to
the fruit. **Red Mahonia,** as well as other species of this genus are
attractive plants for cultivation in lawns and gardens of the Southwest.

**Red Mahonia**, *Mahonia haematocarpa* (Wooton) Fedde
Syns. *Berberis haematocarpa* Wooton          Berberidaceae

RED MAHONIA
*Mahonia haematocarpa*

19.    Berries purple to blue-black and dry at maturity, some appearing
       yellow to reddish-purple when immature; terminal leaflet ovate,
       oblong or rounded, some lateral leaflets obliquely truncate at the
       base, leaflets commonly less than 2 times longer than wide ............ 20.

       20.    Leaves mostly 5-foliate, ranging from 3 to 7 leaflets per
              leaf, the veins not obviously reticulate, leaflets ovate,
              oblong to lanceolate, averaging 1.3 to 4.5 cm in length;
              inflorescence a raceme of short branches with 3 to 10 flow-
              ers; fruit turning from yellow to reddish-purple or purple
              at maturity. This species is infrequent on well-drained
              sunny slopes at 4,500 to 7,500 ft. (1,370 to 2,300 m) in
              elevation, but it is more common in the southern coun-
              ties. The specific name honors General Charles Fremont,
              distinguished soldier and explorer of the western United
              States.

       **Fremont Mahonia,** *Mahonia fremontii* (Torrey) Fedde
                                              Berberidaceae

### FREMONT MAHONIA
### *Mahonia fremontii*

20.  Leaves mostly 7-foliate, ranging from 5 to 9 leaflets per leaf, the veins on the lower surface obviously reticulate, leaflets glabrous and ovate, oblong to rounded, averaging 3.0 to 5.5 cm in length; inflorescence an elongate raceme of more than 10 flowers; fruit turning from blue to purple at maturity. Our collections of this species are confined to the canyons of Coronado National Forest and the southwestern corner of New Mexico at 5,500 to 7,000 ft. (1,680 to 2,130 m) in elevation.

**Wilcox Mahonia**, *Mahonia wilcoxii* Kearney

Berberidaceae

21.     Leaflet margins entire, 9 to 23 per leaf; fruit a legume, 5.0 to 10.0 cm in length; flowers zygomorphic or bilaterally symmetrical, borne in many-flowered, pendulous racemes, petals yellow to white or rose to bluish-purple ............................................................. 22.

21.     Leaflet margins serrate, dentate, and never entire, 3 to 11 per leaf; fruit a hip or a drupelet; flowers actinomorphic or radially symmetrical, borne solitary, few to a cluster or simple raceme, but not pendulous, petals pink to rose or white .................................. 23.

    22.     Young branches, inflorescences and fruit pubescent with glandular hispid hairs; petals rose to bluish-purple in color; plants shrubs becoming small trees to 8.0 m in height at maturity; 2 sharp, stout, paired, red to brown spines develop at the nodes at the base of each leaf. This relatively common, native species is found in river bottoms, along stream banks and in canyons at 4,500 to 9,000 ft. (1,370 to 2,740 m) in elevation. Flowering normally occurs from May through July in this attractive and often cultivated species.

**New Mexico Locust**, *Robinia neomexicana* A. Gray

Fabaceae

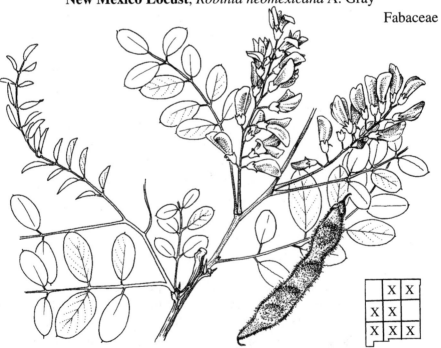

NEW MEXICO LOCUST
*Robinia neomexicana*

22. Young branches, inflorescences and fruit glabrous or with only weak pubescence; petals yellow to white; plants shrubs becoming large trees to 20.0 m in height at maturity; 2 sharp, stout, paired spines develop at the nodes at the base of each leaf. This cultivated plant, native to eastern North America escapes cultivation and occurs in large clones along roadsides and near old farm sites. It is commonly planted in lawns and gardens.

**Black Locust**, *Robinia pseudoacacia* L.　　　Fabaceae

23. Fruit a cluster of drupelets forming an aggregate fruit or raspberry; leaves glaucous or strongly whitened beneath, leaflets commonly 3 to 5 in number; petals white; the raspberry. genus *Rubus* ..... 24.

23. Fruit a hip or a berry-like structure formed from a hypanthium enclosing several seeds; leaves green to pale green beneath but not strongly glaucous beneath, leaflets ranging from 3 to 11 in number, commonly 5 to 9; petals pink to rose, seldom white; the rose, genus *Rosa* ........................................................................... 25.

24. Plants strigose or bristly with straight stiff hairs and glandular hairs over the stems and petioles; the aggregate fruit red to white in color, separating easily from the receptacle, with the drupelets again separating at maturity; shrubs usually slender and weak, less than 1.5 m in height at maturity; leaves 3- to 5-foliate, the terminal leaflet ovate to oblong-ovate, 4.0 to 7.0 cm in length. This wide ranging species with several varieties occurs at 6,500 to 10,000 ft. (1,980 to 3,050 m) in elevation and is more common over northern New Mexico. (Please see couplet 6, page 427 for further description, and illustration, page 428.)

**Red Raspberry**, *Rubus idaeus* L.
　　　　　Syns. *R. strigosus* Michaux　　　Rosaceae

An isolated taxon, the **Alice Raspberry**, *Rubus aliceae* L. H. Bailey, may key to this point. Identified only from Santa Fe Canyon in Santa Fe County this species, with short leaves and small leaflets, and armed with prickles and some bristles, is poorly defined and appears to be an isolated hybrid.

24.     Plants not or only slightly strigose, but with well developed broadbased, stout, recurved and sharp prickles; the aggregate fruits black in color, not easily separating, with the drupelets remaining fused at maturity; shrubs robust, from 1.5 to 2.5 m in height at maturity, with primocanes rooting at the tips; leaves commonly 3-foliate, occasionally 5-foliate. This cultivated species readily escapes cultivation and is widely scattered over New Mexico. It may be found along fence rows and the borders of woods at a wide range of elevations above 4,500 ft. (1,370 m). (Please see couplet 7, page 429, for further description.)

**Black Raspberry**, *Rubus occidentalis* L.            Rosaceae

## BEFORE YOU TACKLE THE WILD ROSES

Considerable hybridization is known to occur in the genus *Rosa*, thus one should not become too discouraged if field collections do not specifically fit the species here described. Plants, like people, are a product of their genetics and environment, consequently they do not all turn out exactly as we would like.

25.     Infrastipular prickles present (these are 1 to 2, usually 2, prickles situated on the twig just below the node) .......................................... 26.

25.     Infrastipular prickles absent................................................................ 27.

26.     Shrubs to 2.0 m in height at maturity; stems not bristly or with scattered weak prickles, often dying back in winter; leaflets 5 to 9, the margins double serrate with glandular teeth; flowers solitary, rarely 2 to 4 in corymbs, sepals 1.5 to 4.0 cm in length, pedicels 1.9 to 2.3 cm in length, petals 2.0 to 3.8 cm in length, usually pink or occasionally white in color; hips 1.2 to 2.2 cm in length at maturity. Occurring on the high plains, mesas and foothills, this infrequent species is generally confined to the northern part of New Mexico at 5,500 to 10,000 ft. (1,680 to 3,050 m) in elevation.

**Nootka Rose**, *Rosa nutkana* Presl                Rosaceae

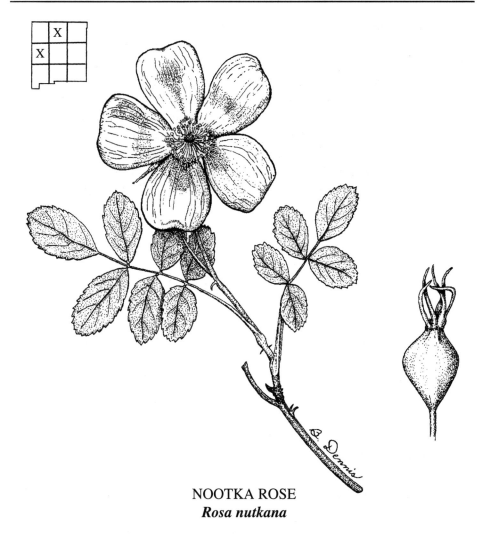

NOOTKA ROSE
*Rosa nutkana*

26.    Shrubs to 1.5 m in height at maturity; stems with numerous bristles, not dying back in winter; leaflets  5 to 9,
commonly 7, the margins serrate to entire near the base;
flowers 3 or more in corymbs, less often solitary, sepals
1.0 to 2.2 cm in length, pedicels 1.0 to 1.9 cm in length,
petals 1.0 to 2.5 cm in length, pink in color; hips 0.6 to
1.5 cm in length at maturity. This common and widely
scattered species occurs in sandy soils, rocky ravines,
stream banks, open prairies or near the margins of woods
at 4,500 to 9,500 ft. (1,370 to 2,900 m) in elevation.

**Wood's Rose**, *Rosa woodsii* Lindley
       Syns. *R. neomexicana* Cockerell                    Rosaceae

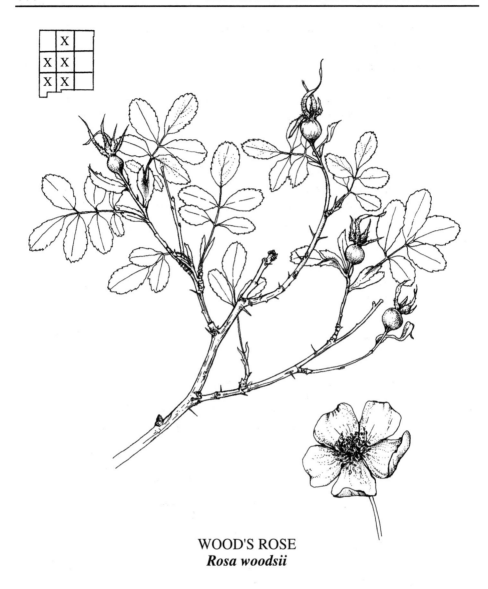

WOOD'S ROSE
*Rosa woodsii*

27.    Shrubs to 1.5 m in height at maturity; stems with few to no prickles, with bristles only near the base; leaflets 1.0 to 3.0 cm in length,
margins with some glandular teeth; petals with notched apices;
occurring on sandy or clay soils, in rocky ravines, stream banks,
open prairies or near margins of woods at higher elevations. This
description appears to fit a potential hybrid between *R. woodsii*
and *R. nutkana*. (See descriptions, pages 442-43.)

**Wood's Rose**, *Rosa woodsii* Lindley
Syns. *R. arizonica* Rydberg
*R. fendleri* Crepin                         Rosaceae

27.     Stems with bristles and/or prickles to the apex; leaflets 1.0 to 5.0 cm in length, margins lacking glandular teeth; petals lacking notched apices ............................................................................. 28.

28.     Shrubs less than 0.5 m in height at maturity; stems often dying back in winter; leaflets 9 to 11 per leaf; flowers few to several in corymbs, on basal shoots or on lateral shoots from old wood, petals 1.5 to 2.5 cm in length, calyx lobes lanceolate, 0.6 to 1.3 cm in length; hip subglobose, not tapering to the apex. This species occurs frequently on dry rocky slopes and prairies, often in thickets at 3,500 to 8,000 ft. (1,070 to 2,440 m) in elevation. Scientific research has found that fresh rose hips (*Rosa* sp.) contain up to 1,750 milligrams of vitamin C per 100 grams, and that three fresh rose hips may contain as much vitamin C as a whole orange.

**Arkansas Rose**, *Rosa arkansana* Porter          Rosaceae

ARKANSAS ROSE
*Rosa arkansana*

28.      Shrubs to 1.0 m in height at maturity; stems not dying back in winter; leaflets 5 to 9 per leaf; flowers in small clusters of 1 to 3 and always on lateral shoots from old wood, petals 2.5 to 3.0 cm in length, calyx lobes lanceolate, 2.0 to 2.5 cm in length; hip pear-shaped, tapering to the apex, species occurring on wooded hillsides, stream banks and rocky ledges at 4,500 to 9,000 ft. (1,370 to 2,740 m) in elevation.

**Prickly Rose** or **Wild Rose**, *Rosa acicularis* Lindley

Syns. *R. sayi* Schweinitz      Rosaceae

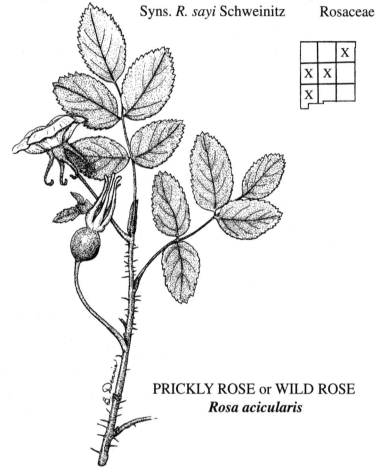

PRICKLY ROSE or WILD ROSE
*Rosa acicularis*

29.      Mature fruit a legume, these sometimes small, ranging in size from less than 1.0 to 10.0 cm in length and 1 to several seeded (Fabaceae) ................................................................ 30.

29.      Mature fruit a drupe, nut, achene, pome, berry, capsule or samara, but never a legume ................................................ 43.

30. Leaves twice pinnately compound with many leaflets on 2 to 7 pairs of pinnae, with a small orbicular gland located between the lower pair of pinnae, commonly more than 75 leaflets per leaf; plants only slightly shrubby, suffrutescent to 50.0 cm in height, frequently decumbent, and often overlooked as a woody plant; inflorescences arranged terminally in heads of white to pale green flowers; fruit flattened and 7.0 cm in length, producing several seeds, dehiscent very early. (This species may appear odd pinnately compound, but more commonly even pinnately compound. For the full description, map and illustration please see couplet 64, page 478.) This locally common species occurs over the plains and mesas of New Mexico at 3,500 to 6,000 ft. (1,070 to 1,830 m) in elevation.

**Bundle Flower,** *Desmanthus cooleyi* (Eaton) Trelease

Fabaceae

30. Leaves once pinnately compound with 5 to 45 leaflets per leaf ................................................................................ 31.

31. Leaflets averaging less than 1.0 cm in length .................................... 32.

31. Leaflets averaging more than 1.0 cm in length ................................. 37.

32. Petals absent, filaments of stamens separate and not united, 9 or 10 in number, flowers small, yellow or yellow-green and borne in terminal, spikelike racemes; plants low, shrubby, much branched perennials, usually less than 1.0 m in height at maturity; leaflets narrow, linear and glandular-punctate; the fruit is 1-seeded, small and also glandular-dotted. This uncommon species of sandy soils occurs more widely over the western half of New Mexico at 4,000 to 6,000 ft. (1,220 to 1,830 m) in elevation. Flowering through the growing season, it has been used in recent years to hold sandy soils and reduce erosion.

**Dune Broom**, *Parryella filifolia* Torrey & A. Gray

Fabaceae

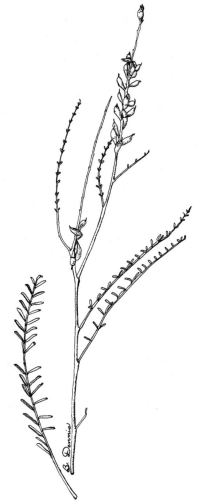

**DUNE BROOM**
*Parryella filifolia*

32.　　Petals 5 in number, corolla purple, rose to pink to purple,
　　　　sometimes tinged with white or yellow, or with a yellow
　　　　spot, filaments of stamens united, 9 or 10 in number and
　　　　monodelphous; the fruit is 1 to 3 seeded and indehiscent.
　　　　genus *Dalea* ........................................................................ 33.

33.　　Leaves and younger branches green and glabrous; plants com-
　　　　monly to 1.0 m in height at maturity ................................. 34.

33.　　Leaves and younger branches gray to gray-green with dense, silky
　　　　hairs; plants commonly 80.0 cm or less in height at maturity........... 35.

34. Calyx lobes narrow at the base and as long or longer than the tube of the calyx, corolla purple to rose colored often with some yellow on the banner; leaves with 5 to 11 leaflets, leaflets 1.0 to 3.0 mm in length; the fruit is pilose and glandular dotted. This plant is a true woody shrub with stems diversely branching to 70.0 cm in height. Widely scattered over New Mexico on dry hills, mesas and in southern canyons at 3,500 to 7,000 ft. (1,070 to 2,130 m) in elevation. Flowering occurs in early spring or with the coming of the rains in July. Pueblo Indians dried the flowering branches to use for a sweet, delicate tea to relieve aches and growing pains. Hopi used this remedy for influenza and virus infections; it was thought to be a "cold" herb for fever conditions.

**Feather Dalea** or **Feather Indigo**, *Dalea formosa* Torrey

Fabaceae

FEATHER DALEA or
FEATHER INDIGO
*Dalea formosa*

34.     Calyx lobes with a broad base and much shorter than the
        tube of the calyx, corolla purple, yellow on the banner
        absent; leaves with 13 to 17 leaflets, leaflets 2.0 to 5.0
        mm in length; the fruit is glabrous and glandular dotted.
        This plant is a woody perennial of erect, slender stems to
        1.0 m in height that sometimes remains herbaceous. It
        appears to be confined to southeastern New Mexico in
        dry soils and over rocky hills at 4,500 to 6,800 ft. (1,370
        to 2,070 m) in elevation.

**Black Dalea** or **Black Indigo**, *Dalea frutescens* A. Gray

Fabaceae

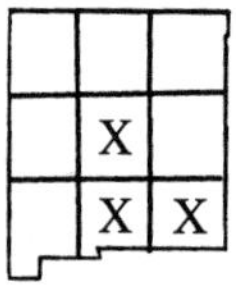

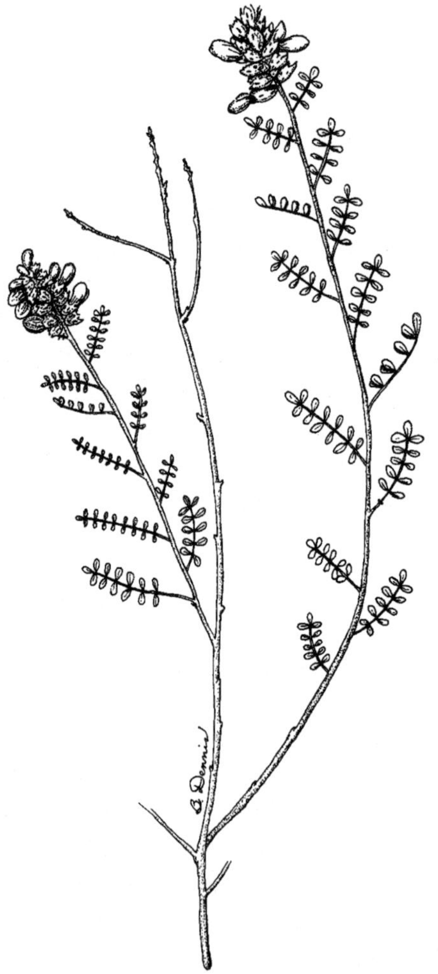

BLACK DALEA or
BLACK INDIGO
*Dalea frutescens*

35.  Plants subshrubs from a woody base, decumbent to prostrate, the gray, tomentose, glandular-dotted stems spreading over the ground at less than 30.0 cm in height, and often rooting at the nodes; leaves with 5 to 11 leaflets, commonly 7 to 9, the leaflets 3.0 to 6.0 mm in length; flowers in terminal, erect heads, purple in color; the fruit villous and glandular-dotted on the upper surface, with glands few or absent below. This uncommon and practically unknown subshrub, occurring only in southern counties is usually found on limestone outcrops at 2,500 to 5,500 ft. (760 to 1,680 m) in elevation. This species along with other members of the genus *Dalea* needs further study in New Mexico and the Southwest.

**Gregg Dalea**, *Dalea greggii* A. Gray                    Fabaceae

35.  Plants erect shrubs, not decumbent and spreading, but growing upright, commonly more than 30.0 cm in height but seldom reaching 1.0 m ...................................................................................... 36.

36.  Calyx lobes 3.0 to 4.0 mm in length, flowers borne in cylindric or subcapitate spikes, flowers purple to reddish-purple, the banner tinged with yellow or cream colored; leaflets 3.0 to 6.0 mm in length, linear to spatulate in shape, with 9 to 23 leaflets per leaf. This species, of dry rocky hills and canyons, has only been collected in southwestern New Mexico at 4,500 to 6,000 ft. (1,370 to 1,830 m) in elevation. Flowering appears to be determined by available moisture.

**Wislizenus Dalea**, *Dalea versicolor* var. *sessilis* (A. Gray)
                                                  Barneby
          Syns. *D. wislizeni* A. Gray                    Fabaceae

36.  Calyx lobes 0.5 to 1.0 mm in length; flowers borne in spheroid to oblong spikes, flowers purple, the banner yellow; leaflets 5.0 to 8.0 mm in length, obovate to oblong-obovate in shape, with 7 to 13 leaflets per leaf. This silver colored species, of limestone bluffs and hills, occurs in southeastern New Mexico at 3,500 to 5,500 ft. (1,070 to 1,680 m) in elevation.

**Silver Dalea**, *Dalea bicolor* var. *argyrea* (A. Gray)
                                                  Barneby
          Syns. *D. argyrea* A. Gray                    Fabaceae

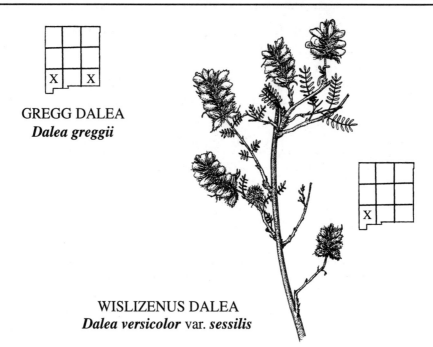

GREGG DALEA
*Dalea greggii*

WISLIZENUS DALEA
*Dalea versicolor* var. *sessilis*

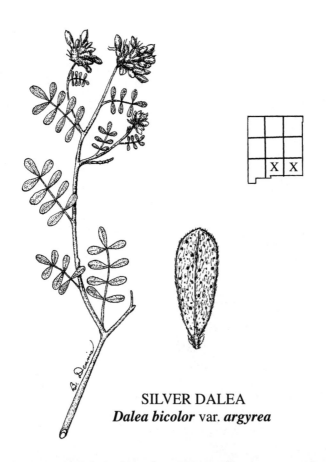

SILVER DALEA
*Dalea bicolor* var. *argyrea*

37.    Mature legume 0.4 to 2.0 cm in length; leaves glandular-dotted
       with the use of a handlens ................................................................. 38.

37.    Mature legume 5.0 to 12.0 cm in length; leaves not glandular-
       dotted with the use of a handlens. *Sophora* or *Colutea* ..................... 42.

   38.    Corolla of 5 white petals, slightly zygomorphic, calyx 5
          lobed and glandular punctate, stamens 10 and diadelp-
          hous, inflorescence a raceme of many small flowers; leaf-
          lets 1.0 to 5.0 mm in width; fruit an indehiscent pod 1.0
          to 1.5 cm in length. Confined to the southwest corner of
          New Mexico, this attractive species occurs in rocky can-
          yons and ravines at 4,500 to 6,000 ft. (1,370 to 1,830 m)
          in elevation. Flowering dates vary over the growing sea-
          son in close association with available moisture.

**Kidneywood**, *Eysenhardtia polystachya* (Ortega) Sargent

Fabaceae

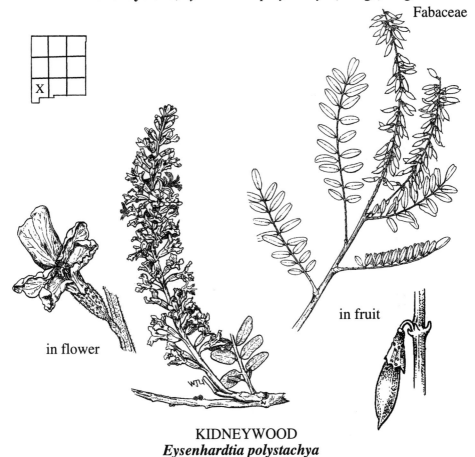

in flower

in fruit

KIDNEYWOOD
*Eysenhardtia polystachya*

38.     Corolla of 1 petal, the banner, which may range in color
        from deep red to blue to purple; leaflets 6.0 to 30.0 mm in
        width. False Indigo, genus *Amorpha* .................................... 39.

39.     Stems and petioles bearing prickle-like glands, appearing strongly
        pubescent, but not bearing true prickles; calyx lobes 5, pubes-
        cent and lanceolate, inflorescence an extended spikelike raceme,
        6.0 to 20.0 cm in length, single petal (banner) solitary and deep
        red to purple in color; fruit 1 seeded and indehiscent; leaflets 11
        to 23 in number; shrubs 1.0 to 3.0 m in height at maturity. This
        relatively uncommon shrub is confined to moist wooded can-
        yons in the southern and western portions of New Mexico at 5,000
        to 7,000 ft. (1,520 to 2,130 m) in elevation. It has been collected
        in flower from May through July.

**California Amorpha**, *Amorpha californica* Nuttall          Fabaceae

39.     Stems and petioles not bearing prickle-like glands or true prick-
        les; shrubs 30.0 cm to 3.0 m in height at maturity ............................. 40.

40.     Calyx lobes dimorphic, the upper 4 lobes about equal,
        wider than long, not more than one-fourth as long as the
        calyx tube, the lower lobe longer and narrower; the single
        petal on each flower purple; fruit usually producing 2
        seeds; leaves 7.0 to 20.0 cm in length, petioled, (the peti-
        ole longer than the width of the lowest leaflet), producing
        9 to 25 leaflets, the leaflets 2.0 to 4.0 cm in length; inflo-
        rescence of one to several spikes in a cluster; shrubs tall,
        seldom less than 2.0 m in height at maturity. Two rela-
        tively well established varieties have been described based
        on the number of spikes in the inflorescence. The ranges
        of the two varieties overlap, as do the flowering dates
        (May through July), and the habitats in which they occur.
        This species requires moist soils commonly in canyons
        and the margins of streams.

**Indigo Bush** or **False Indigo**, *Amorpha fruticosa* L.
                                                        Fabaceae

**INDIGO BUSH or FALSE INDIGO**
*Amorpha fruticosa*

*Amorpha fruticosa* var. *angustifolia* Pursh is characterized by producing several, usually 4 or more spikes in
the inflorescence.

*Amorpha fruticosa* var. *occidentalis* (Abrams) Kearney
& Peebles is characterized by producing 1 or possibly 2
or 3 spikes in the inflorescence.

40.  Calyx lobes all the same length or nearly so, lanceolate,
     acute to acuminate, at least half as long as the calyx tube;
     fruit usually producing 1 seed; leaflets 0.9 to 1.7 cm in
     length; shrubs low, rarely over 1.0 m in height at maturity.......41.

41.    Plants densely white-canescent, woody only at the base; petioles
       not longer than the width of the lowest pair of leaflets; calyx
       lobes about as long as the tube; banner blue to purple in color;
       spikes several to many; leaflets numbering 11 to 47. This villous
       shrub to 1.0 m in height at maturity occurs infrequently over the
       northeastern and eastern plains and hills of New Mexico. Flow-
       ering throughout the warm summer months of June through Au-
       gust, it grows at 4,000 to 6,000 ft. (1,220 to 1,830 m) in eleva-
       tion. Native Americans burned the stem of *Amorpha canescens*
       on top of an injury as a moxa. This was believed to counteract the
       injury beneath it. Moxa is used in Asia today to stimulate an acu-
       puncture point or serve as a counterirritant.

**Lead-plant**, *Amorpha canescens* Pursh                    Fabaceae

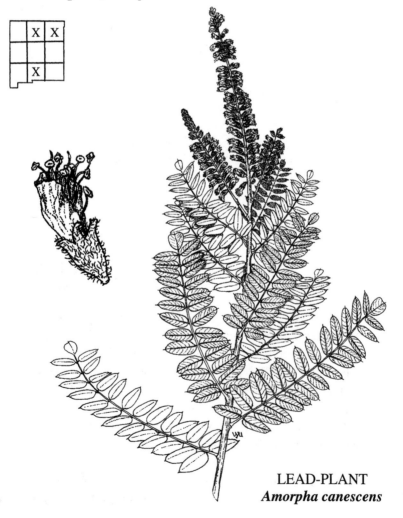

LEAD-PLANT
*Amorpha canescens*

41.  Plants glabrous or only sparsely pilose, woody throughout; petioles much longer than the width of the lowest pair of leaflets; calyx lobes about half as long as the tube; banner purple in color; spikes solitary, rarely 2 or 3; leaflets numbering 13 to 19. This low, erect shrub seldom reaches 80.0 cm in height. Flowering in June and July, it is widely scattered over New Mexico at 5,300 to 7,000 ft. (1,620 to 2,130 m) in elevation.

**Dwarf Indigo** or **Fragrant False Indigo**, *Amorpha nana* Nuttall

Fabaceae

DWARF INDIGO or
FRAGRANT FALSE INDIGO
***Amorpha nana***

42.  Legume woody, hard, terete, densely brown pubescent and commonly constricted between the seeds, 5.0 to 12.0 cm in length and 1.0 to 1.5 cm in width, indehiscent, seeds 1 to 8 and red; flowers in terminal or axillary racemes, corolla purple to violet. Confined to limestone bluffs and rocky washes in southeastern New Mexico at 4,000 to 5,000 ft. (1,220 to 1,520 m) in elevation, this attractive shrub is commonly cultivated.

**Mescal-bean Sophora**, *Sophora secundiflora* (Ortega)
DeCandolle          Fabaceae

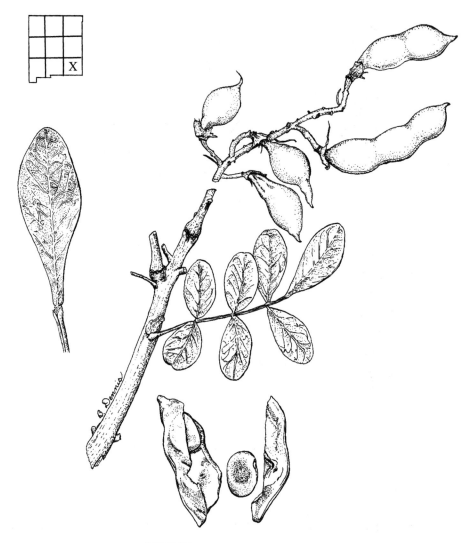

MESCAL-BEAN SOPHORA
*Sophora secundiflora*

42. Legume inflated, membranous, flexible, partially trans-
    lucent and not constricted between the seeds, but blad-
    der-like, 6.0 to 8.0 cm in length and approximately 3.0
    cm in thickness, indehiscent or dehiscent at the summit
    only, containing many brown or black seeds; flowers in
    axillary racemes, corolla yellow and often marked with
    red. This introduced species is cultivated in various parts
    of our range.

**Bladder Senna**, *Colutea arborescens* L.                    Fabaceae

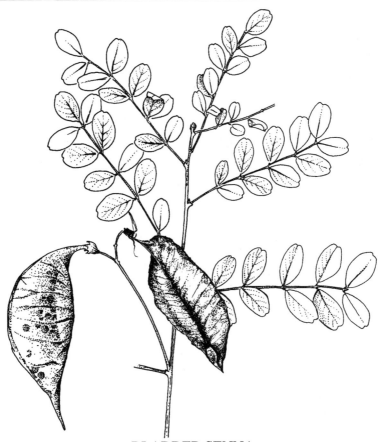

BLADDER SENNA
*Colutea arborescens*

43.   Mature leaflets averaging less than 1.0 cm in width ........................ 44.

43.   Mature leaflets averaging more than 1.0 cm in width ..................... 46.

44.   Leaflets filiform, averaging more than 3.0 cm in length; flowers several in heads, the ray flowers numbering 10 to 16 and yellow, each cluster of flowers surrounded or sub-tended by an involucre of bracts in 3 series. This common shrub of rocky and gypsum soils may reach more than 1.0 m in height. It occurs over southern and south-eastern New Mexico at 3,200 to 6,200 ft. (1,000 to 1,900 m) in elevation. (Please see couplet 50, Key VI, pg. 132, couplet 117, Key VIII, page 199 for further description and illustration.)

**Skeletonleaf Goldeneye,** *Viguiera stenoloba* Blake Asteraceae

44.     Leaflets not filiform, but oblong, oblanceolate, lanceolate,
        elliptic or ovate averaging less than 3.0 cm in length; flow-
        ers not in heads, individual flowers borne in a corymb or
        a spike ................................................................................ 45.

45.   Rachis of the leaf not winged; the fruit an achene; leaflets 3 to 7,
      silky white on the lower surface, somewhat revolute and entire,
      appearing trifoliate to palmate when in fact under closer exami-
      nation the leaves are more often pinnate; twigs never spinescent;
      flowers are 5-merous with bright yellow petals and 20 to 25 sta-
      mens; many separate achenes are produced in each pistil. This
      shrub, growing to 1.0 m in height, produces brown shredding
      bark and occurs from 6,500 ft. (1,980 m) in elevation to the sub-
      alpine. This attractive shrub is commonly cultivated. (Please see
      couplet 11, page 432 for further description and illustration.)

**Shrubby Cinquefoil**, *Pentaphylloides floribunda* (Pursh) A. Löve
Syns. *Potentilla fruticosa* L.
*P. floribunda* Pursh          Rosaceae

45.   Rachis of the leaf winged; the fruit is a red to orange drupe cov-
      ered with glandular hairs; leaflets 5 to 9, oblong, elliptic to obo-
      vate, sessile and entire, the margin may be slightly revolute; some
      branches appearing spinescent; flowers small, greenish-white, 5-
      merous with 5 stamens and appearing before the leaves. This shrub
      of the rocky hillsides and mesas of southern New Mexico may
      grow to 4.0 m in height. It occurs at 4,000 to 6,000 ft. (1,220 to
      1,830 m) in elevation and flowers from March through May.

**Little-Leaf Sumac**, *Rhus microphyllum* Engelmann
Syns. *Rhoeidium microphylla* (Engelmann) Greene
Anacardiaceae

46.     Fruit a drupe or a nut ............................................................ 47.

46.     Fruit a pome, capsule, berry or samara ................................ 54.

47.   Fruit a drupe; pith continuous; inflorescence a thryse or panicle,
      flowers perfect or polygamous ........................................................ 48.

LITTLE-LEAF SUMAC
*Rhus microphyllum*

47. Fruit a nut surrounded by a green, indehiscent husk that becomes brittle and papery with age; pith chambered; inflorescences of 2 types of catkins, either staminate or pistillate on the same tree, thus the plants monoecious ............................................................ 52.

48. Leaves large, bipinnate or twice compound, to 60.0 cm in length, with up to 45 leaflets per leaf; flowers borne in long pendulous panicles, purple to blue and fragrant, sepals and petals numbering 5 or 6 per flower; the berry-like, drooping, smooth, yellow, fleshy fruit is borne in large clusters. This large tree, growing to over 15 m in height at maturity, is introduced from Asia, but has today escaped cultivation. We have observed it growing only in the southeastern corner of New Mexico, but it could be expected over the southern part of the State where water is adequate.

**China-berry**, *Melia azedarach* L.                    Meliaceae

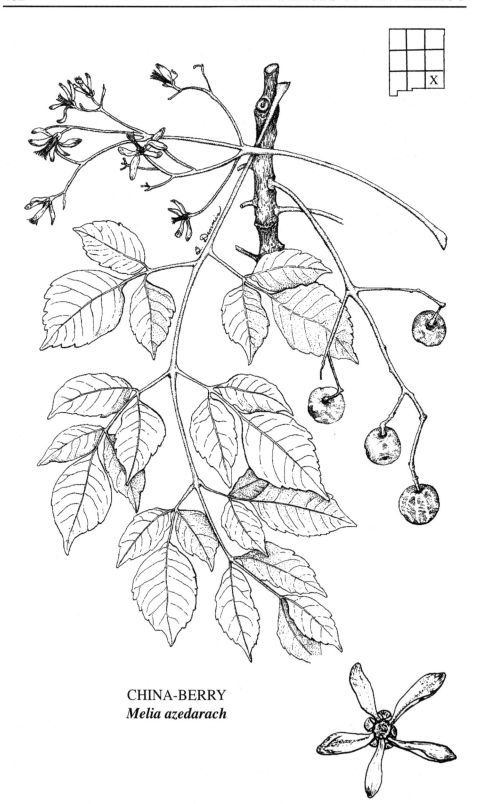

CHINA-BERRY
*Melia azedarach*

48. Leaves once pinnate, to 40.0 cm in length, with 25 or fewer leaflets at maturity; flowers polygamous ................... 49.

49. Rachis of the leaf winged; the leaflets mostly entire, 2.5 to 7.5 cm in length, 11 to 21 in number, the upper surface dark green and lustrous; flowers appearing after the leaves and borne in terminal panicles, the petals yellow-green to white; the fruit dark red and glandular hairy. This species is frequently found growing to 2.0 to 3.0 m in height, on limestone, on the eastern and southern plains and rocky hills of New Mexico. Flowering throughout the warm summer months, it occurs at 4,500 to 5,200 ft. (1,370 to 1,600 m) in elevation.

**Prairie Sumac** or **Wing-rib Sumac**, *Rhus copallinum* L.
Syns. *R. lanceolata* (Gray) Britton
Anacardiaceae

49. Rachis of the leaf not winged ............................................................ 50.

50. Leaflets 13 to 27, deciduous and thin, not leathery, 7.0 to 9.0 cm in length, with the longest leaflets near the middle; plant dioecious, with the staminate flowers in loose terminal panicles, and the pistillate flowers in dense, terminal panicles; fruits form a dense, pyramidal cluster, 10.0 to 15.0 cm in length, these dark red drupes persisting over the winter. This species is widespread throughout North America and is common along streams, forming borders of woods and in rocky canyons throughout New Mexico. Occurring from 5,500 to 8,000 ft. (1,680 to 2,440 m) in elevation, it flowers at different times throughout the summer months based on habitat and available moisture.

**Smooth Sumac**, *Rhus glabra* L.    Anacardiaceae

50. Leaflets 3 to 9, evergreen and leathery ................................. 51.

SMOOTH SUMAC
*Rhus glabra*

The following two closely related taxa have a different external
morphology and growth habit in New Mexico, thus the **Toughleaf
Sumac** is retained as a variety of *Rhus virens*. Both forms are
limited to the southern counties at 4,000 to 6,000 ft. (1,220 to
1,830 m) in elevation. Of the two growth forms, the **Evergreen
Sumac** appears more commonly in the southeast corner of New
Mexico and the **Toughleaf Sumac** appears more commonly in
the southwest corner of New Mexico. Further study is encouraged.

51. Leaflets 5 to 9, sparsely pubescent but shining and dark above, and sparsely soft pubescent beneath; inflorescences few, usually terminating the branches; fruit red and pubescent with simple and glandular hairs.

**Evergreen Sumac**, *Rhus virens* Lindheimer *ex* A. Gray

Anacardiaceae

51. Leaflets 3 to 5, glabrous and dull green above and beneath; inflorescences more numerous, both axillary and terminal; fruit red and pubescent with simple and glandular hairs.

**Toughleaf Sumac**, *Rhus virens* var. *choriophylla* (Wooton & Standley) L. Benson          Anacardiaceae

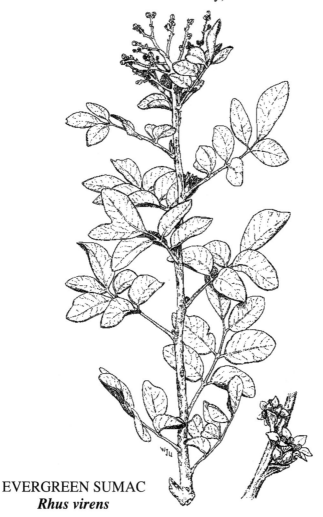

EVERGREEN SUMAC
*Rhus virens*

52.     Nut, including the husk, 35.0 mm or more in diameter at maturity; a large introduced tree, commonly reaching 30.0 to 45.0 m in height; leaves to 60.0 cm in length, leaflets numbering 11 to 23 and sessile. This attractive tree is found around farm sites and occasionally introduced in lawns and gardens. Transplanted from the eastern United States into isolated locations in the West, it is grown for the tasty fruit and beautiful wood.

**Black Walnut**, *Juglans nigra* L.                    Juglandaceae

BLACK WALNUT
*Juglans nigra*

52. Nut, including the husk, less than 35.0 mm in diameter at maturity; species native to New Mexico and relatively common over the southern half of the State; trees, 17.0 m or less in height, or shrubs ...................................................... 53.

53. Trees to 17.0 m in height usually with a single trunk; mature nut 20.0 to 25.0 mm in diameter; leaves to 35.0 cm in length, with 9 to 13 leaflets per leaf. This slow growing and attractive tree can be found at 6,000 to 7,000 ft. (1,830 to 2,130 m) in elevation. It occurs in canyons and along stream beds in the southern mountainous areas of New Mexico.

**Arizona Walnut**, *Juglans major* (Torrey) Heller          Juglandaceae

ARIZONA WALNUT
*Juglans major*

53.     Shrubs to 6.0 m in height with several branches from the base; nut 10.0 to 15.0 mm in diameter; leaves to 30.0 cm in length, with 15 to 23 leaflets per leaf. This more rapidly growing shrub can be found at 3,500 to 6,000 ft. (1,070 to 1,830 m) in elevation. It occurs in canyons and along streams as does the previous species, but it is more common to drier habitats with less moisture.

**Little Walnut**, *Juglans microcarpa* Berlandier          Juglandaceae

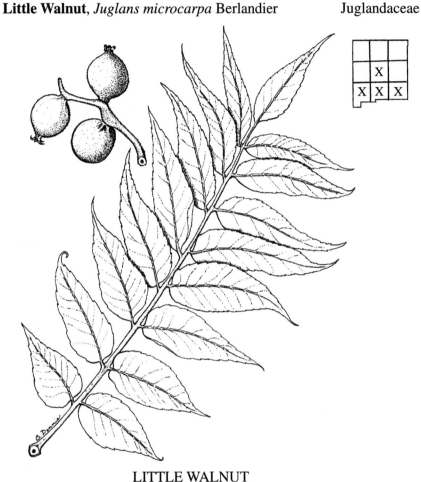

LITTLE WALNUT
*Juglans microcarpa*

54.     Fruit a pome; flowers white; the inflorescence a flat-topped cyme; species native to higher elevations, above 7,000 ft. (2,130 m) in elevation; tall shrubs or small trees to 4.0 to 5.0 m in height .......................................................... 55.

54.  Fruit a samara, berry or capsule; flowers yellow, yellow-green or bright pink; the inflorescence an extended panicle; species of lower elevations, commonly below 6,000 ft. (1,830 m) in elevation or introduced ....................... 56.

55.  Rachis densely white-hairy; winter buds densely white-hairy; leaves 7.0 to 15.0 cm in length, bearing 9 to 14 leaflets, leaflets 18.0 to 45.0 mm in length. Found only in the moist, coniferous forests of New Mexico and Arizona, this species occurs at 7,500 to 10,000 ft. (2,300 to 3,050 m) in elevation. It flowers in late May and June and appears to be limited to the western and northern counties of New Mexico.

**Arizona Mountain Ash**, *Sorbus dumosa* Greene        Rosaceae

ARIZONA MOUNTAIN ASH
*Sorbus dumosa*

55.    Rachis only slightly pilose to glabrous; winter buds sparsely hairy;
       leaves 10.0 to 25.0 cm in length, bearing 11 to 15 leaflets, leaf-
       lets 35.0 to 70.0 mm in length. This shrub or small tree, which is
       sometimes cultivated, is found in the moist, heavily vegetated,
       middle or upper montane at 7,000 to 10,000 ft. (2,130 to 3,050
       m) in elevation. A Rocky Mountain or more northern species, it
       flowers in June and July.

**Rocky Mountain Ash,** *Sorbus scopulina* Greene          Rosaceae

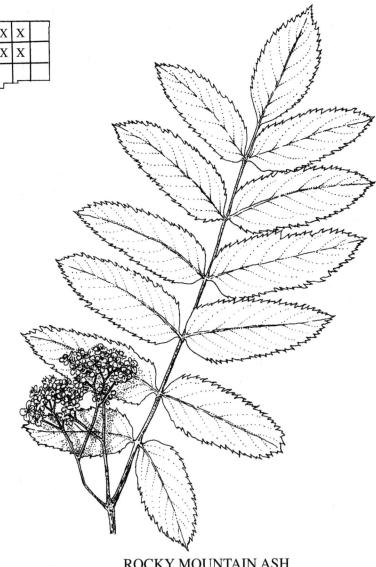

ROCKY MOUNTAIN ASH
*Sorbus scopulina*

56.    Fruit a samara, 2.5 to 5.0 cm long, produced in large panicles, and straw-colored to red at maturity; mature leaves 25.0 to 60.0 cm in length, averaging 30.0 cm or more, with 11 to 25 leaflets per leaf and each leaflet with 1 to 3 glandular teeth near the base; a dioecious species (which may produce some perfect flowers), with many yellow to green flowers borne in terminal panicles on both staminate and pistillate plants. This large, weedy, introduced species becomes a tree from 15.0 to 20.0 m in height at maturity and is almost impossible to control. The underground rhizomes spread rapidly throughout the growing season to produce a forest of young trees. The **Tree of Heaven** consumes a great deal of water and crowds out native species. It gets its name, **Smoke Tree,** from its tolerance for smoke and smog in large cities, where it is commonly planted.

**Tree of Heaven** or **Smoke Tree**, *Ailanthus altissima*
(Miller) Swingle
Simaroubaceae

TREE OF HEAVEN or SMOKE TREE
*Ailanthus altissima*

56.    Fruit a capsule or berry; mature leaves 10.0 to 30.0 cm in
       length, averaging 25.0 cm or less in length ........................... 57.

57.    Fruit a berry or modified drupe; leaflets entire, neither truly odd-
       pinnate nor even-pinnate, but opposite leaflets usually slightly
       offset up the rachis so that the apical leaflet may be absent; plant
       dioecious; inflorescence a panicle of small white flowers; fruit
       borne in terminal panicles of 10 to 30 golden, 1- or 2-seeded
       berries or drupes. This medium sized, native tree from 8.0 to 15.0
       m in height can be found in eastern and southern New Mexico at
       3,500 to 5,500 ft. (1,070 to 1,676 m) in elevation. Flowering
       throughout the growing season from May through August, this
       species occurs at the margins of wooded areas, on moist hillsides
       and along canyons and ravines. Although difficult to transplant it
       is often cultivated.

**Soapberry** or **Jaboncilla**, *Sapindus saponaria* L.
               Syns. *S. drummondii* Hooker & Arnott
                                                    Sapindaceae

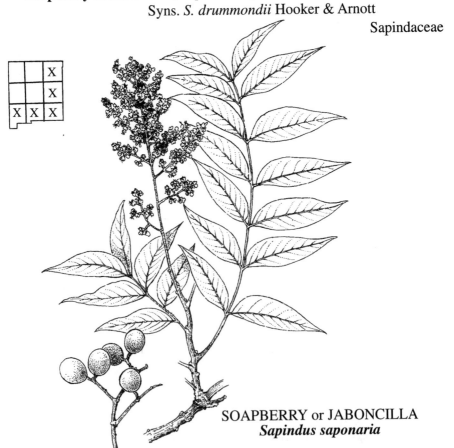

SOAPBERRY or JABONCILLA
*Sapindus saponaria*

57. Fruit a 3-celled papery or leathery capsule; leaflets serrate to crenate, truly odd-pinnate, the leaflets on each leaf opposite with one apical leaflet; flowers bright yellow or rose pink ...................... 58.

58. Leaflets numbering 3 to 7 per leaf, mature leaflets 4.0 to10.0 cm in length; flowers polygamous and irregular with 5 sepals, 4 or 5 rose-colored petals, and 5 to 10 stamens; the inflorescence is a terminal panicle; the fruit is an inflated, leathery or woody, 3-celled capsule, producing 3 brown seeds. This infrequent, attractive shrub, to 2.0 m in height, occurs in southeastern and southcentral New Mexico at 4,500 to 6,000 ft. (1,370 to 1,830 m) in elevation. Flowering in the spring, it appears to be confined to limestone outcrops.

**Mexican Buckeye**, *Ungnadia speciosa* Endlicher

Sapindaceae

MEXICAN BUCKEYE
*Ungnadia speciosa*

58.    Leaflets numbering 7 to 15 per leaf, mature leaflets 3.0 to
       6.0 cm in length; flowers with 5 sepals, 4 yellow petals
       and 8 stamens; the inflorescence is a panicle, 2.0 to 4.5
       dm in length; the fruit is an inflated, papery, 2-celled cap-
       sule producing 3 black seeds. This attractive, small, orna-
       mental tree, native to east Asia, occasionally escapes cul-
       tivation.

       **Golden Raintree**, *Koelreuteria paniculata* Laxmann
                                                    Sapindaceae


59.    Spines or thorns absent on stems or leaves........................................ 60.


59.    Spines or thorns present on stems or leaves ................................... 66.


60.    Leaflets 3.0 to 9.0 cm in length, entire, neither truly odd-
       pinnate or even-pinnate, but opposite leaflets usually
       slightly offset up the rachis so that the apical leaflet may
       be absent; fruit a berry or modified drupe with 1 or 2
       seeds; inflorescence a panicle of small white flowers.
       (Please see couplet 57, page 472 for further description
       and illustration.)

       **Soapberry** or **Jaboncilla**, *Sapindus saponaria* L.
                        Syns. *S. drummondii* Hooker & Arnott
                                                    Sapindaceae


60.    Leaflets 1.0 cm or less in length; fruit a legume; inflores-
       cence a head or raceme .......................................................... 61.


61.    Flowers large and showy, petals yellow and more than 1.0 cm in
       length, weakly bilaterally symmetrical; inflorescence a raceme
       of flowers loosely arranged ................................................. 62.


61.    Flowers small and not showy, petals yellow, creamy white, or
       pink to purple and less than 1.0 cm in length, radially symmetri-
       cal; inflorescence a head of small flowers arranged in a ball........... 63.

62. Leaves pinnately once-compound; leaf 1.2 to 4.0 cm in length; fruit a legume, less than 1.0 cm in width and 5.0 to 14.0 cm in length at maturity; flowers with 5 imbricate, slightly unequal, yellow petals that are twice as long as the sepals, stamens 10, the upper 3 abortive; shrub to 2.5 m in height. This rare shrub is limited to dry rocky soils in the southwest corner of New Mexico at less than 6,000 ft. (1,830 m) in elevation. Flowering over a large part of the growing season, this attractive and showy species should be protected.

**Wislizenus Senna** or **Shrubby Senna**, *Senna wislizeni*
(A. Gray) Irwin & Barneby
Syns. *Cassia wislizeni* A. Gray
Fabaceae

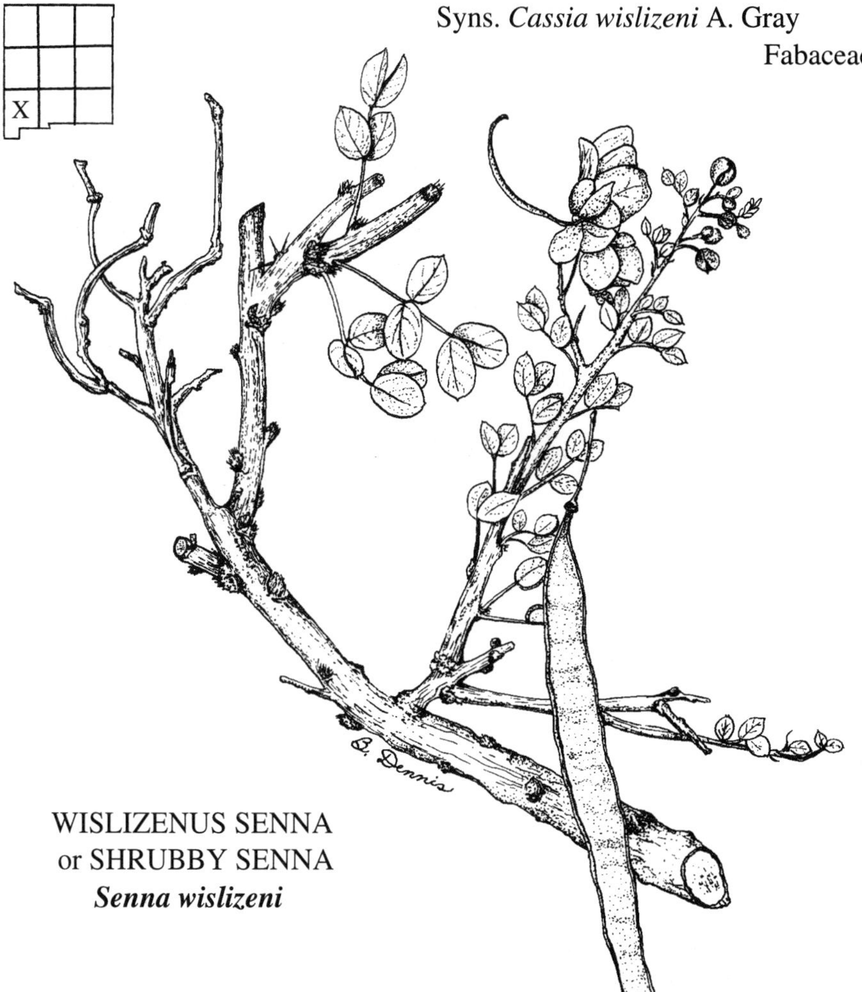

WISLIZENUS SENNA
or SHRUBBY SENNA
*Senna wislizeni*

62.    Leaves pinnately twice-compound; leaf 7.0 to 13.0 cm in length; fruit a legume, 1.5 to 2.4 cm in width and 6.0 to 12.0 cm in length at maturity; flowers with 5 yellow and densely glandular petals, sepals larger than the petals, stamens 10, red and exserted beyond the petals; shrub to 3.0 m in height. This introduced shrub, along with several other members of the genus, is widely cultivated throughout the Southwest and often escape cultivation. They survive well on limited water and are attractive plants for lawns and gardens.

**Bird-of-Paradise** or **Poinciana**, *Caesalpinia gilliesii*
(Hooker) Bentham
Fabaceae

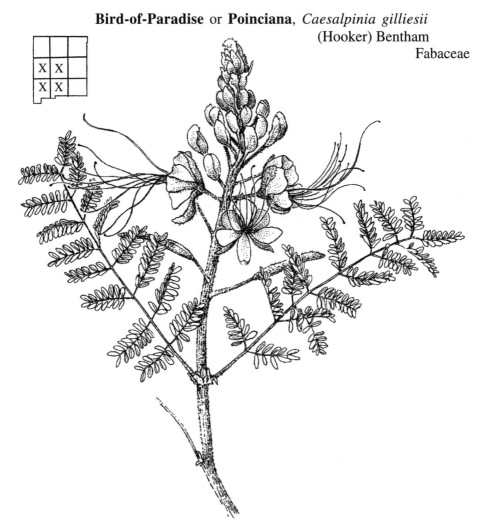

BIRD-OF-PARADISE or POINCIANA
*Caesalpinia gilliesii*

63.     Flowers pink to deep red, arranged in rather loose heads, stamens 20 or more, monadelphous, long and exserted; legumes silky pubescent with thickened margins, 3.0 to 8.0 cm in length and 0.4 to 0.6 cm in width; a low branching, prostrate shrub rarely reaching 30.0 cm in height at maturity and spreading by rhizomes. Records indicate this rare species occurs only in the southwest corner of New Mexico on dry, gravel slopes and mesas at 4,000 to 5,000 ft. (1,220 to 1,520 m) in elevation.

**Fairy Duster** or **Mesquitilla,** *Calliandra eriophylla* Bentham

Fabaceae

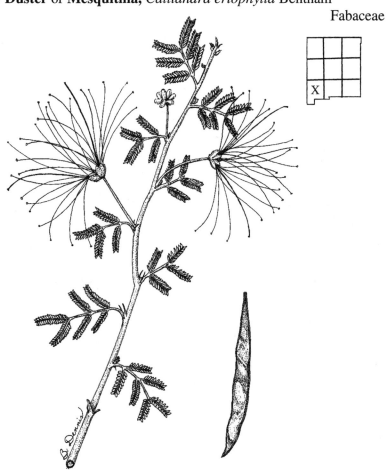

FAIRY DUSTER or MESQUITILLA
*Calliandra eriophylla*

63.     Flowers white, creamy white or yellow, arranged in tight and congested heads; taller shrubs, commonly reaching 1.0 m or more at maturity ................................................................................................ 64.

64.    Plant a suffrutescent perennial, only slightly shrubby at the base, 50.0 cm in height at maturity, frequently decumbent and overlooked as a woody plant; leaves twice pinnately compound with many leaflets on 2 to 7 pairs of pinnae, with a small orbicular gland located between the lower pair of pinnae, commonly more than 74 leaflets per leaf; inflorescences arranged terminally in heads of white to pale green flowers; fruit flattened and 7.0 cm in length, producing several seeds, dehiscent very early. This locally common species occurs over the plains and mesas of New Mexico at 3,500 to 6,000 ft. (1,070 to 1,830 m) in elevation. (Please see couplet 30, page 447.)

**Bundle Flower,** *Desmanthus cooleyi* (Eaton) Trelease

Fabaceae

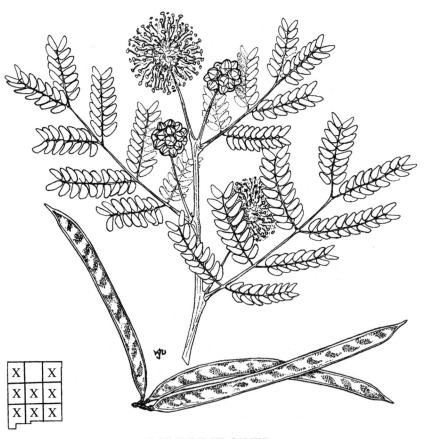

BUNDLE FLOWER
*Desmanthus cooleyi*

64. Plant woody throughout, a true shrub, commonly more than 1.0 m in height at maturity ............................................. 65.

65. Flowers white, in globose heads 1.0 to 1.5 cm in diameter; suffrutescent shrubs, with only the base and lower stems becoming woody at maturity, rarely over 1.0 m in height; this species unarmed, lacking thorns or spines; the fruit linear, flattened and only very slightly, if at all, constricted between the seeds, 5.0 to 7.0 cm in length and 0.5 to 0.9 cm in width. This infrequent species, with many varieties, is widely scattered over eastern and southern New Mexico at 4,000 to 6,000 ft. (1,220 to 1,830 m) in elevation. It flowers over much of the growing season and occurs over rocky hills and on grassy slopes in the mountains.

**Whiteball Acacia**, *Acacia angustissima* (Miller) Kuntze

Fabaceae

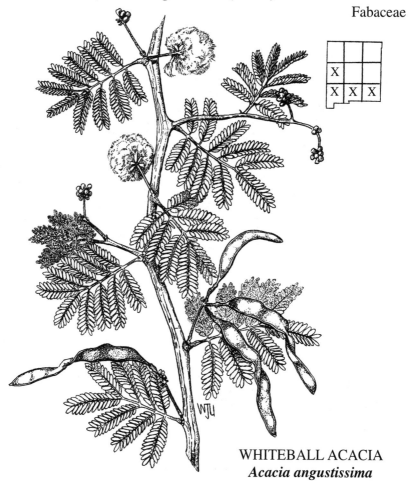

WHITEBALL ACACIA
*Acacia angustissima*

65.    Flowers yellow, in globose heads 0.8 to 1.0 cm in diameter; tall
       shrubs often reaching 3.0 to 5.0 m at maturity, white thorns rang-
       ing from 2.5 cm in length to <u>absent</u>, thus this species is identified
       here; the fruit linear, strongly constricted between the seeds and
       glabrous, 5.0 to 10.0 cm in length and 0.2 to 0.5 cm in width. A
       common and diverse species, it is widely scattered at 3,500 to
       6,500 ft. (1,070 to 2,000 m) in elevation over the southern half of
       New Mexico. Flowering over most of the growing season, it is
       abundant in dry, sandy soils and in drainage areas along streams
       and rivers. (Please see couplet 70, page 485 also.)

**Whitethorn Acacia** or **Mescat Acacia**, *Acacia constricta* Bentham

Fabaceae

WHITETHORN ACACIA
or MESCAT ACACIA
*Acacia constricta*

66. Leaflets averaging more than 2.0 cm in length; plant at maturity a large tree, commonly reaching to 15.0 or 20.0 m in height, the trunk often thorny, the thorns often reaching 5.0 cm or more in length; fruit 15.0 to 40.0 cm in length and 1.4 to 3.5 cm in width, often twisted and producing 6 to more than 20 seeds; leaves pinnately or bipinnately compound and often in clusters; plants polygamous or dioecious, the staminate flowers in many flowered racemes, the pistillate flowers on growth of the previous year and in racemes. The specific name "triacanthos" of this widely introduced species identifies the 3 sharp points commonly produced on each thorn. Escaping cultivation, this large tree tends to become a bottom lands species or may be found in open and wooded pastures or along fence rows.

**Honey Locust**, *Gleditsia triacanthos* L.          Fabaceae

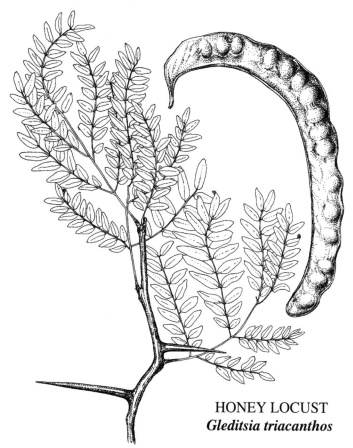

HONEY LOCUST
***Gleditsia triacanthos***

66.       Leaflets averaging less than 2.0 cm in length; plant at maturity a shrub or occasionally a small tree, rarely reaching 5.0 to 8.0 m, commonly less than 3.0 m in height, the spines and thorns rarely reaching 4.0 cm in length; fruit less than 18.0 cm in length and less than 1.5 cm in width ..... 67.

67.       Stamens numerous, more than 10 per flower and free; shrubs. genus. *Acacia* ................................................................................ 68.

67.       Stamens 10 per flower or fewer; shrubs or small trees. genus *Prosopis* or genus *Mimosa* ................................................. 71.

68.       Spines curved or hooked; flowers cream-colored or white; fruit 1.0 to 2.0 cm in width at the widest point and 4.0 to 14.0 cm in length ................................................................ 69.

68.       Spines straight (or absent); flowers yellow; fruit 0.2 to 0.5 cm in width at the widest point and 4.0 to 10.0 cm in width ................................................................................ 70.

69.       Flowers in elongate spikes; leaflets 3.0 to 6.0 mm in length; leaves bipinnate, averaging less than 5.0 cm in length; fruit 1.2 to 1.8 cm in width and 4.0 to 10.0 cm in length, the margins contorted around the seeds and irregular. Commonly forming thickets at 3,500 to 5,500 ft. (1,070 to 1,680 m) in elevation, this common shrub or small tree may reach to 20 ft. in height and can make walking difficult. It occurs from the dry gravelly mesas to the banks of streams and arroyos over the southern half of the State. A tea made from the flowers and leaves of *Acacia greggii* is used medicinally as an anti-inflammatory for stomach and esophagus in nausea, vomiting and hangover. It is said to have a distinctly sedative effect.

**Catclaw Acacia**, *Acacia greggii* A. Gray              Fabaceae

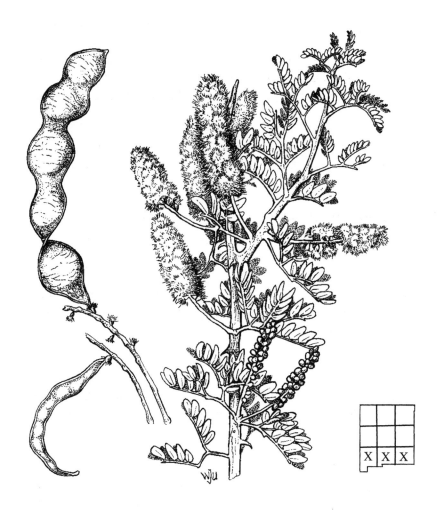

CATCLAW ACACIA
*Acacia greggii*

69. Flowers in globose heads; leaflets 6.0 to 11.0 mm in length; leaves bipinnate, averaging more than 5.0 cm in length; fruit 1.5 to 2.5 cm in width and 5.0 to 12.0 cm in length, the margins regular and only slightly contorted around the seeds, generally with smooth margins. This infrequent species may be found locally abundant on limestone bluffs and gravelly hills at 3,500 to 4,500 ft. (1,070 to 1,370 m) in elevation in the southeastern corner of New Mexico. Flowering in early spring, late March through May, this species has only been collected in Eddy County.

**Roemer Acacia**, *Acacia roemeriana* Scheele            Fabaceae

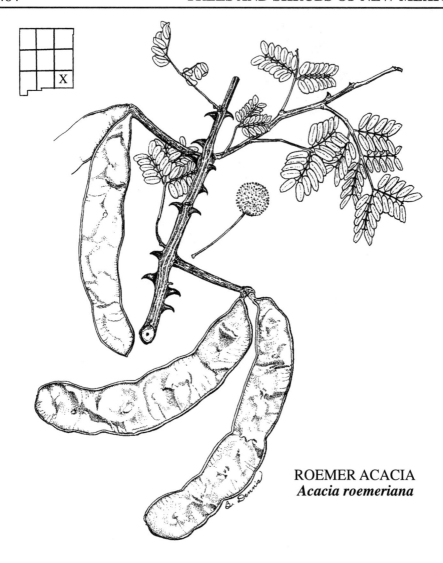

ROEMER ACACIA
*Acacia roemeriana*

70. Leaflets and young stems glandular-viscid; leaflets averaging less than 1.5 mm in length; pinnae 1 to 3 pairs per
leaf; leaves 1.0 to 2.5 cm in length at maturity; spines
straight, but often short, seldom reaching 2.0 cm in length.
This thorny, common shrub of southern New Mexico may
reach 2.0 m in height. Flowering in spring, it occurs at
3,500 to 5,200 ft. (1,070 to 1,600 m) in elevation and in
dry gravelly soils. The specific name, *neovernicosa*, refers to the shiny, almost varnished, appearance of the new
wood and fruit.

**Viscid Acacia**, *Acacia neovernicosa* Isley          Fabaceae

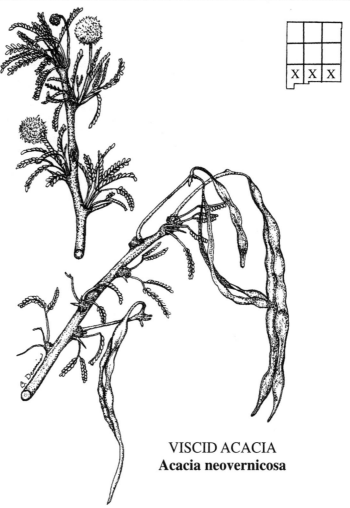

VISCID ACACIA
**Acacia neovernicosa**

70. Leaflets and young stems not glandular-viscid, sometimes slightly glandular-dotted; leaflets averaging more than 1.5 mm in length; pinnae 3 to 7 pairs per leaf; leaves 2.5 to 5.0 cm in length at maturity; spines variable, straight and slender, reaching 1.0 to 3.0 cm in length, or sometimes absent. Confined to the southern and southwestern counties at 3,500 to 6,500 ft. (1,070 to 2,000 m) in elevation, this abundant and often dangerous appearing shrub may reach more than 2.0 m in height. Common to the dry plains and hills, it can survive extremely dry conditions, flowering when water becomes available. (Please see couplet 65 for further description and illustration on page 480.)

**Whitethorn Acacia** or **Mescat Acacia**,
*Acacia constricta* Bentham                    Fabaceae

71.     Flowers in spikes or racemes, 3.5 to 8.0 cm in length, yellow to
        yellow-green or pale green in color, anthers with apical glands;
        stems armed with straight, needlelike, solitary or paired stipular
        spines ...................................................................................... 72.


71.     Flowers in globose heads or short spikes, 3.0 to 5.0 cm in length,
        white to pink to pale red in color; anthers lacking apical glands;
        commonly shrubs to 1.0 or 2.0 m, seldom reaching 3.0 m; stems
        and, in some cases, the legumes armed with short, straight to
        recurved, scattered, flattened prickles ............................................. 73.


        72.     Legumes tightly coiled in a spiral of uniform diameter;
                leaflets 4 to 8 pairs per pinna; leaves 3.5 to 8.0 cm in
                length, petioles shorter, averaging 1.5 cm or less in length;
                shrub or small tree, seldom over 8.0 m in height. This
                infrequent species occurs in alluvial soils along the Rio
                Grande and its tributaries in central and southcentral New
                Mexico, and desert washes in southwestern New Mexico
                at 3,500 to 4,500 ft. (1,070 to 1,370 m) in elevation.

                **Screwbean Mesquite** or **Tornillo**, *Prosopis pubescens*
                                       Bentham                  Fabaceae


        72.     Legumes straight to falcate, never in a spiral or uniformly
                twisted; leaflets 8 to 14 per pinna; leaves 6.0 to 18.0 cm
                in length, petioles longer, averaging more than 1.5 cm in
                length; shrub or small tree, seldom over 3.0 m in height.
                This common and abundant species is widely scattered in
                a wide range of life zones from the northeast corner over
                the southern two-thirds of New Mexico at 3,000 to 5,500
                ft. (910 to 1,680 m) in elevation. It flowers in the spring
                and may flower later in the growing season as water be-
                comes available. The invasion of *Prosopis* ssp. into former
                grasslands of the Southwest is the result of overgrazing a
                century ago when a military presence was sent to combat
                the Apaches (1865-1890). The seeds were spread through
                cattle droppings.

                **Honey Mesquite,** *Prosopis glandulosa* Torrey          Fabaceae

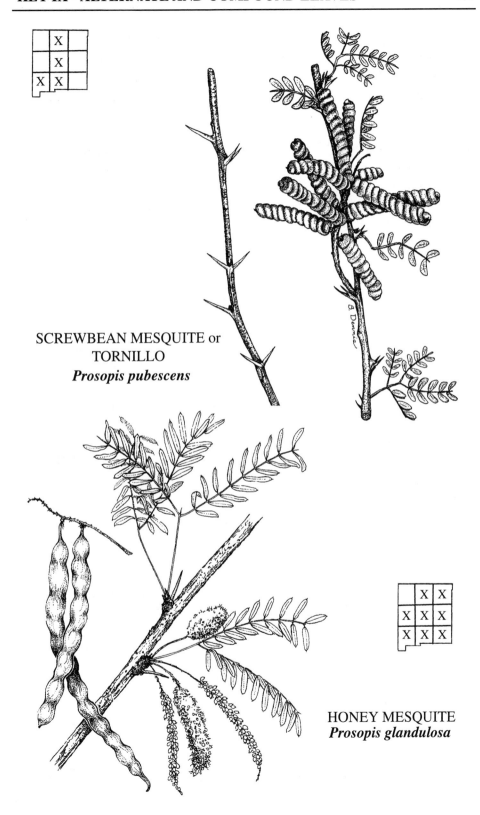

SCREWBEAN MESQUITE or
TORNILLO
*Prosopis pubescens*

HONEY MESQUITE
*Prosopis glandulosa*

73. Inflorescence a cylindrical spike, 3.0 to 5.0 cm in length; flowers pink to lavender, fragrant and showy; fruit linear, often prickly along the margins, to 5.5 cm in length, falcate and constricted between the seeds; twigs brown to yellow and villous to velvety. This attractive Mimosa is restricted to the southern one-third of New Mexico at 3,500 to 6,500 ft. (1,070 to 2,000 m) in elevation, in dry, rocky and sandy soils and along washes and arroyos. It tends to flower with the season and available moisture.

**Velvetpod Mimosa**, *Mimosa dysocarpa* Bentham    Fabaceae

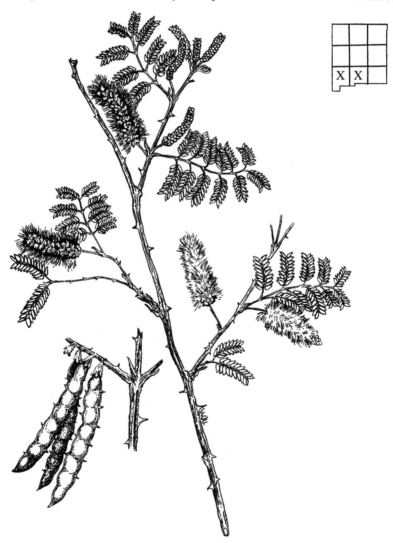

VELVETPOD MIMOSA
*Mimosa dysocarpa*

73.     Inflorescence a globose head, less than 2.5 cm in diameter .............. 74.

74.     Pinnae 1 to 3 pairs per leaf; flowers in showy, pink, gla-
        brous heads; stems armed with prickles that are straight
        or curved, solitary and stout; fruits linear, 2.5 to 5.0 cm in
        length, unarmed or armed with several stout, curved, flat,
        sharp prickles, falcate to straight and constricted between
        the seeds. This common shrub is widely scattered over
        eastern and southern New Mexico, on gravelly and lime-
        stone hills at 3,600 to 6,000 ft. (1,100 to 1,830 m) in el-
        evation. Reaching a height of 1.0 to 2.0 m at maturity, it
        can form thickets that make walking extremely difficult.

**Fragrant Mimosa**, *Mimosa borealis* A. Gray        Fabaceae

FRAGRANT MIMOSA
*Mimosa borealis*

74.    Pinnae commonly 4 to 10 pairs per leaf ............................... 75.

75.    Mature leaflets 3.5 to 6.0 mm in length; fruit 2.0 to 3.0 cm in
       length at maturity, not constricted between the seeds, linear and
       flattened; flowers white to pink in loose axillary globose heads.
       This uncommon species is confined to dry slopes and mesas in
       the southwest corner of New Mexico at 4,500 to 6,000 ft.(1,370
       to 1,830 m) in elevation. It grows only 50.0 to 80.0 cm in height
       and is more common to Arizona where several varieties have
       been described.

**Graham Mimosa**, *Mimosa grahamii* A. Gray               Fabaceae

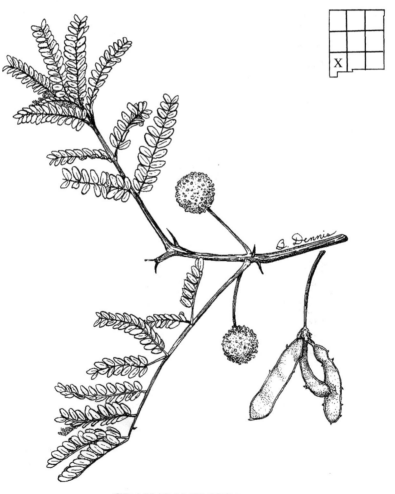

GRAHAM MIMOSA
*Mimosa grahamii*

75. Mature leaflets 1.0 to 3.5 mm in length; fruit 2.0 to 4.0 cm in length at maturity, constricted between the seeds, curved to straight, with curved or straight sharp prickles or unarmed; flowers white to pink, in small globose heads. This genetically and ecologically confusing species has been defined and redefined several times. It is widely scattered over the southern two-thirds of New Mexico at 3,500 to 6,000 ft. (1,070 to 1,830 m) in elevation, forming true brier patches. Flowering dates are as diverse as the variation in the species, with available moisture being the limiting factor.

**Wait-A-Bit** or **Catclaw Mimosa**, *Mimosa aculeaticarpa* var. *biuncifera* (Bentham) Barneby
Syns. *M. biuncifera* Bentham
*M. lindheimeri* A. Gray
*M. warnockii* B. L. Turner
Fabaceae

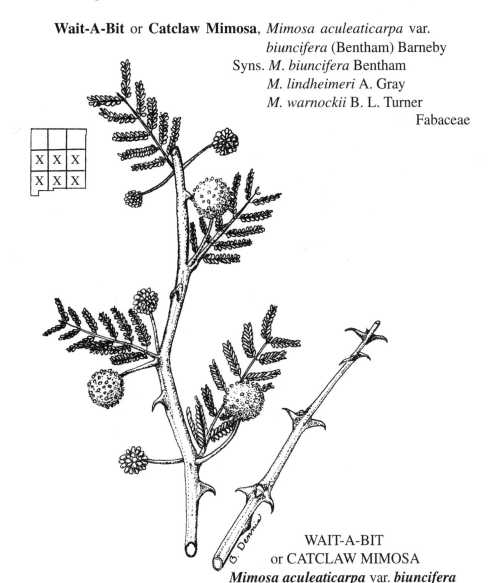

WAIT-A-BIT
or CATCLAW MIMOSA
*Mimosa aculeaticarpa* var. *biuncifera*

## GLOSSARY

*abortive* - rudimentary, arrested in development, unsuccessful, fruitless

*acaulescent* - without a stem, or the stem so short that the leaves are apparently all basal

*accrescent* - becoming larger with age, as a calyx which continues to enlarge after anthesis

*achene* - a small, dry, indehiscent fruit with a single locule and a single seed attached to the ovary wall at a single point (see Plate V)

*actinomorphic* - radially symmetrical, so that a line drawn through the middle of the structure along any plane will produce a mirror image on either side (compare zygomorphic)

*acuminate* - generally tapering to a sharp point and forming concave sides along the tip (see Plate III)

*acute* - tapering to a pointed apex with more or less straight sides (see Plate III)

*adnate* - fusion of unlike parts, as the stamens to the corolla

*aggregate (fruit)* - densely clustered; a group of small fleshy fruits originating from a number of separate pistils in a single flower as in the clustered drupelets of the raspberry

*alkaline* - material that is basic rather than acidic, having a pH greater than 7.0

*alternate* - borne singly at each node, as leaves on a stem (compare opposite) (See Plate I)

*ament* - see catkin

*anther* - the apical, pollen bearing portion of the stamen

*anthesis* - the flowering period, when the flower is fully expanded and functioning

*apex* (pl. *apices*) - the tip; the point farthest from the point of attachment

*appressed* - pressed close or flat against another organ

*areole* - a small, well-defined area on a surface, as the region of a cactus bearing the flowers and/or spines

*aristate* - bearing an awn or bristle at the tip

*attenuate* - tapering gradually to a narrow tip or base (see Plate III)

*awl-shaped* - short, narrowly triangular, and sharply pointed like an awl (see Plate II) *axil (or axile)* - the point of the upper angle formed between the axis of a stem and any part (usually a leaf) arising from it (see Plate I)

*axillary* - positioned in or arising in an axil

*axis* (pl. *axes)-* the longitudinal, central supporting structure or line around which various organs are borne, as a stem bearing leaves

*banner* - largest petal of a papilionaceous flower, as in peas

*barbed* - with short, rigid, reflexed points, like the barb of a fish-hook

*basal sheath* - closely imbricated bud scales at the base of a fascicle or cluster of needles

*beak (fruit)* - a narrow or prolonged tip, as on some fruits and seeds

*berry* - a fleshy fruit developing from a single pistil, with several or many seeds, as the tomato (see Plate V)

*bi-(prefix)* - a prefix meaning two or twice

*bipinnate* - twice pinnate; with the divisions again pinnately divided

*biternate* - twice ternate; with the ternate divisions again ternately divided

*blade* - the broad part of a leaf or petal (see Plate I)

*bloom* - a whitish, waxy, powdery coating on a surface; the flower

*bract* - a reduced leaf or leaflike structure at the base of a flower or inflorescence

*bristly* - covered with short, stiff, strong hairs

*bud* - an undeveloped shoot or flower (see Plate I)

*bud scar* - mark indicating former attachment of a bud (see Plate I)

*bundle scar* - scar left on a twig by the vascular bundles when a leaf falls (see Plate I)

*calcareous* - containing calcium and/or calcium carbonate

*callous* - hardened or thickened; having a callus

*calyx* - the outer whorl of modified leaves or sepals at the base of a flower (see Plate V)

*campanulate* - shaped like a bell

*canescent* - covered with dense, fine, grayish-white hairs

*capitate* - in heads; formed like a head in a dense cluster

*capsule* - dry, dehiscent fruit derived from two or more carpels (see Plate V)

*carpel* - a component or highly modified leaf comprising the female reproductive part of a flower

*carpellate* - with carpels

*catkin* - a specialized, scaly, spike-type inflorescence, often pendulous of apetalous and unisexual flowers as in the birches and willows

*caudate* - forming a tail or taillike tip or appendage

*caudex* -a short, thickened, often woody base of a perennial plant, usually subterranean or at ground level

*cauline* - of, on, or pertaining to the stem, as leaves arising from the stem above ground level

*cespitose (caespitose)* - growing in dense tufts

*ciliate* - with hairs protruding from the margins

*clasping* - partly surrounding the stem or other structure

*cleft* - indentations or incisions cut about half-way to the middle or base

*coetaneous* - with the leaves and flowers developing at the same time

*compound* - composed of two or more like parts; in leaves, with leaf divided into two or more segments (see Plate IV)

*cone* - in gymnosperms, the fruit consisting of a stiff axis and leaf-like scales bearing ovules or pollen

*conical* - cone-shaped, with the point of attachment at the broad end

*cordate* - heart-shaped, referring to the shape of a leaf or leaf base

*coriaceous* - with a leathery texture

*corolla* - whorl of petals, located above the calyx (see Plate V)

*corymb* - a flat-topped or convex inflorescence or cluster of flowers in which the pedicels, or flower stalks, are of unequal length with the lower stalks longer (see Plate VI)

*crenate* - shallowly ascending, round-toothed margin, teeth cut less than one-eighth the distance to midrib or midvein (see Plate III)

*crenulate* - diminutive of crenate; teeth cut less than one-sixteenth the distance to midrib or midvein

*cultivars* - a plant originating under cultivation

*cuneate* - wedge-shaped, triangular and tapering to a point at the base (see Plate III)

*cupule* - a cup-shaped involucre, as in an acorn

*cylindric* - cylinder-shaped; elongate and round in cross section

*cyme* - a flat-topped or rounded inflorescence or cluster of stalked flowers in which the central flower is the oldest

*deciduous* - persistent for one growing season; falling off, as leaves that are shed in autumn *deflexed* -bent abruptly downward

*dehiscent (fruit)* - opening at maturity to release contents, as a fruit or an anther (see Plate V)

*deltoid* - broadly triangular, length:depth ratio 1:1 (see Plate II)

*dentate* - margins with rounded or sharp, coarse teeth that point outward at right angles to midrib or midvein, teeth cut to one eighth the distance of midrib or midvein (see Plate III)

*denticulate* - diminutive of dentate, teeth cut to one-sixteenth the distance to midrib or midvein

*depressed* - pressed down, flattened vertically

*diadelphous* - stamens united into two often unequal sets by their filaments

*didynamous* - with two pairs of stamens of unequal length

*diffuse* - loosely branching or spreading; of open growth

*dioecious* - plants with imperfect flowers, but staminate and pistillate flowers borne on separate plants

*disjunct* - occurring in widely separated geographic areas

*disk* - in flowers, an enlargement of the floral axis developed near the base of the pistil or the ovary; in tendrils, a flattened portion of tendril, usually adhesive (see Plate VI)

*disk flower* - a regular flower of the composite or Asteraceae family, as distinquished from the ray flowers in the head

*dissected* - deeply divided into many narrow segments

*disturbed (habitat)* - habitats that have been interferred with, interrupted, or broken up, as in cultivated fields, railroad right-of-ways, roadsides, dry, waste places or rubbish heaps

*divaricate* - diverging or spreading apart

*downy* - covered with fine, soft hairs

*drupe* - a fleshy, indehiscent fruit with a stony inner fruit wall, as in cherries (see Plate V)

*drupelet* - a small drupe, as in the individual segments of a raspberry fruit

*ellipsoid* - a solid body elliptic in long section and circular in cross section

*elliptic* - a longer than wide shape with the widest axis at the midpoint of the structure and with margins symmetrically curved (see Plate II)

*entire* - without indentations or incisions on margins; smooth (see Plate III)

*epidermis* - outermost layer of cells of a nonwoody plant organ

*evergreen* - bearing green leaves throughout the winter, leaves persistent two or more growing seasons *exocarp* - the outer layer of the pericarp of a fruit

*exserted* - projecting above or beyond the surrounding parts

*exudate* - a substance excreted from a plant

*falcate* - sickle-shaped; hooked; shaped like the beak of a falcon

*fascicle* - cluster or bundle often with commonly attached parts (see Plate IV)

*fasciculate* - arranged in fascicles

*filament* - the stalk of the stamen which supports the anther

*filiform* - thread-like; filamentous (see Plate II)

*fleshy* - in fruits, having a firm pulp; thick and pulpy; succulent

*floccose* - bearing tufts of long, soft, tangled hairs

*foliaceous* - leaflike in color and texture; bearing leaves; of or pertaining to leaves

*follicle* - a dry, dehiscent fruit derived from one carpel that splits open along one suture or seam, as a milkweed pod (see Plate V)

*fruit* - a ripened, mature ovary, sometimes including other floral parts which are attached and ripen with it

*fusiform* - broadest near the middle and tapering toward both ends

*glabrous* - smooth; lacking hairs or pubescence

*glandular* - covered with minute blackish to translucent glands

*glaucous* - covered with a "bloom" or smooth, waxy coating

*globose* - round, spherical in form

*globular* - nearly globose

*glochid* - a barbed hair or bristle, as the fine hairs in *Opuntia*

*glossy* - having a smooth, shiny, polished surface

*granular* - composed of granules or grains

*granule* - a small grain-like particle or spot

*habitat* - native environment; region where a plant or animal naturally occurs

*haustorium* - a specialized root-like organ used by parasitic plants to extract water and minerals from the host

*head* - a dense inflorescence of sessile or subsessile flowers on a short or broadened compound receptacle (see Plate VI)

*heartwood* - a nonliving and commonly dark-colored wood in which no water transport occurs; found at the core of the wood and surrounded by sapwood

*hemispheric* - shaped like half a sphere or globe

*herbaceous* - like an herb, not woody; soft and succulent

*hirsute* - pubescent with coarse, stiff hairs

*hispid* - covered with long, stiff bristles or hairs

*hull* - the outer covering of a seed or fruit, as in the pod of peas *husk* - the dry, outer covering of various fruits or seeds, as in an ear of corn

*hypanthium* - fused or coalesced basal portion of floral parts (sepals, petals, stamens) around the ovary (see Plate V)

*imbricate* - with overlapping edges or margins like tiles on a roof

*imperfect* - flowers with either stamens or pistils absent; unisexual flowers

*incised* - margins sharply or deeply cut, usually irregularly (see Plate III)

*indehiscent* - not opening at maturity along definite lines or by pores (see Plate V)

*inedible* - not edible; unfit to eat

*inferior* - floral arrangement in which the ovary is situated below the point of insertion of the other flower parts (see Plate V)

*inflorescence* - an arrangement or cluster of flowers on the flowering axis

*infrastipular* - on the stem below the leaves, below the stipules

*internode* - portion of the stem between two adjacent nodes, usually lacking leaves and buds (see Plate I)

*involucre* - a whorl of bracts subtending an inflorescence or flower cluster

*keeled* - sharply creased or ridged

*lanceolate* - shaped like the head of a lance; elongate with widest axis below middle and with margins symmetrically curved (see Plate II)

*lateral* - borne on the side of a structure

*leaf scar* - mark indicating former attachment of a leaf (see Plate I)

*legume* - a usually dry, dehiscent fruit derived from one carpel that splits along two sutures, as a pea pod (see Plate V)

*lenticel* - a slightly raised, often lens-shaped area on the surface of a young stem (see Plate I)

*ligulate* - with a ligule

*ligule* - a tongue-shaped, flattened part of the ray corolla common in the Asteraceae

*linear* - long and narrow with parallel margins, length:width ratio greater than 10:1 (see Plate II)

*lobe* - a partial division of a leaf or other structure; any, usually rounded, segment or part of the perianth

*lobed* - large, round-toothed, cut one-eighth to one-fourth the distance to midvein (see Plate III)

*locule* - cavity or compartment within an ovary or anther (see Plate V) *loment* - legume which is constricted between the seeds

*lustrous* - glossy, shiny

*mealy* - powdery, dry and crumbly

*-merous* (suffix) - meaning parts of a set. A 5-merous corolla would have five petals.

*midrib, midvein* - the central rib or vein of a leaf or other structure (see Plate I)

*monadelphous* - stamens united by the filaments

*monoecious* - plant with all flowers imperfect, but staminate and pistillate flowers borne on same plant

*mucronate* - tipped with a short, sharp, abrupt point

*multiple fruit* - fruit derived from several flowers crowded on a single axis, as in mulberries or figs

*naked* - lacking organs or parts, e.g., a naked bud lacks scales

*net-veined* - with veins forming a network

*nodding* - bent to one side and downward

*node* - region on stem where a leaf, leaves or branches arise (see Plate I)

*nut* - a one-seeded, dry, indehiscent fruit with a hard fruit wall, as in acorns or walnuts

*nutlet* - a small nut

*obcordate* - inversely cordate, with the attachment at the narrower end; sometimes refers to any leaf with a deeply notched apex

*oblanceolate* - inversely lanceolate; elongate with widest axis above middle (see Plate II)

*oblique* - having an asymmetrical base (see Plate III)

*oblong* - elongate with more or less parallel margins, length:width ratio usually less than 10:1 (see Plate II)

*obovate* - inversely ovate; egg-shaped with the widest axis above the middle (see Plate II)

*obovoid* - inversely ovoid, with the attachment at the narrower end

*obtuse* - blunt with margins straight or convex, forming a terminal angle greater than 90 degrees (see Plate III)

*opposite* - two leaves or other structures per node, on opposite sides of stem or central axis (see Plate I)

*orbicular* - flat with a circular appearance (see Plate II)

*oval* - broadly elliptic, the width over one-half the length (see Plate II)

*ovary* - expanded basal portion of the pistil that contains the ovules (see Plate V) *ovate* - egg-shaped; with widest axis below middle and margins symmetrically curved (compare ovoid) (see Plate II)

*ovoid* - a 3-dimensional, egg-shaped figure with the widest axis below middle and margins symmetrically curved

*ovule* - embryonic seed; structure that develops into the seed after fertilization (see Plate V)

*palmate* - lobed, veined, or divided from a common point, like the fingers of a hand (see Plate IV)

*panicle* - a branched inflorescence with flowers maturing from the bottom upwards (see Plate VI)

*papilionaceous* - having an irregular corolla shaped somewhat like a butterfly, also see *zygomorphic*

*papillae* (pl.) - short, rounded nipplelike bumps or projections

*papillate* - having papillae

*pappus* - the modified calyx found in the Asteraceae, consisting of awns, scales or bristles at the tip of the achene

*parallel* - extending in the same direction and at the same distance apart at every point

*parted* - indentations or incisions cut one-half to one-fourth the distance to the base or the midrib (see Plate III)

*pedicel* - individual flower stalk

*pedicellate* - with a pedicel or flower stalk

*peduncle* - main stalk for the entire inflorescence

*peltate* - shield-shaped; having the stalk or petiole attached underneath near the center of the underside of structure or leaf blade (see Plate II)

*pendulous* - hanging loosely or freely downward

*perfect* - with both stamens and pistils present; bisexual

*perianth* - refers to the calyx and the corolla collectively; combined sepals and petals (see Plate V)

*pericarp* - the wall of the fruit

*persistent* - remaining attached; not falling or shedding

*petal* - a corolla member or segment; a unit of the corolla, usually colored or white (see Plate V)

*petiolate* - with a petiole or leaf stalk

*petiole* - a leaf stalk (see Plate I)

*petiolule* - stalk of a leaflet of a compound leaf (see Plate I)

*phyllary* - an involucral bract in the Asteraceae family; several phyllaries commonly surround the head (see Plate VI)

*pilose* - with long, soft, straight hairs

*pinna* (pl. *pinnae*) - one of the primary divisions or leaflets of a pinnate leaf *pinnate* - arranged on both sides of a common axis; arranged like a feather (see Plate IV)

*pinnatifid* - pinnately lobed half the distance or more to the midrib, but not reaching the midrib

*pistil* - the female reproductive part of a flower typically composed of a stigma, style and ovary (see Plate V)

*pistillate* - with pistils or carpels only in the flower; lacking stamens

*pith* - centermost tissue or region of a stem or root (see Plate I)

*plumose* - feather-like, as a plume

*pod* - the hull or seed case of peas, beans and other legumes

*polygamo-dioecious* - mostly dioecious, but with some perfect flowers

*pome* - a berry-like fruit fused to a fleshy receptacle with a bony or leathery inner fruit wall, as in apples (see Plate V)

*precocious* - with the flowers developing before the leaves

*prickle* - a sharp-pointed outgrowth from the epidermis or bark

*primocane* - the first-year, usually flowerless cane or shoot of *Rubus*

*procumbent* - prostrate, trailing; lying flat upon the ground but not rooting at the nodes

*prostrate* - lying flat on the ground

*pruinose* - with a waxy, powdery, usually white coating (bloom) on the surface, like a prune

*puberulent* - minutely pubescent; with fine, short hairs

*pubescent* - covered with dense or scattered hairs, usually straight and slender

*punctate* - covered with minute impressions or with translucent, sunken glands or with colored dots

*pyramidal* - a 3-dimensional, short, triangular figure, with length:depth ratio 2:3 to 1:3 or more; tetrahedral

*raceme* - an unbranched, elongated inflorescence with stalked flowers maturing from the bottom upward (see Plate VI)

*rachis* - the major axis within an inflorescence

*radiate* - parts spreading from a central point as in the Asteraceae

*ray flower* - strap-shaped or ligulate flowers, common in head inflorescences of the Asteraceae (see Plate VI)

*receptacle* - the extended portion of the floral axis which bears and supports the flower parts (see Plate V)

*reflexed* - directed backward, bent or turned downward

*resin duct* - a tube-like, intercellular space secreting or containing resin

*resinous* - having a yellowish, sticky exudate or discharge *reticulate* - netted

*revolute* - margins or outer portion of sides rolled backward or downward toward the dorsal surface; margins rolled under

*rhizome* - a horizontal underground stem

*rhombic* - with widest axis at midpoint of structure and with straight margins; diamond-shaped (see Plate II)

*rosette* - a circular cluster of leaves, petals or other structures

*rotate* - wheel-shaped, with a short tube and wide lobe at right angles to tube

*rotund* - rounded or rounded-out; plump

*rudimentary* - incompletely or imperfectly developed; vestigial

*rugose* - wrinkled

*saccate* - pouch-like, bag-shaped

*saline* - salty; containing or characteristic of salt

*salverform* - with a slender floral tube and an abruptly spreading and flattened apex

*samara* - a dry, indehiscent, winged fruit (see Plate V)

*scabrous* - having a harsh surface, rough to the touch

*scale* - small, protective non-green leaf on outside of bud; overlapping thin, flat, flaky or plate-like structures

*scaly* - covered with or composed of scales

*scape* - a naked peduncle; a naked flowering stem with or without a few scale leaves

*scapose* - flowers borne on a scape

*scurfy* - covered with small, branlike scales

*secund* - arranged only on one side of the axis

*seed* - a mature ovule

*sepal* - a calyx member or segment; a unit of the calyx (see Plate V)

*septicidal capsule* - a capsule that dehisces longitudinally through the septa or dividing wall

*sericeous* - with long, soft, slender, silky, appressed hairs

*serrate* - saw-toothed; teeth sharp and ascending, cut one-sixteenth to one-eighth the distance to the midrib or midvein (see Plate III)

*serrulate* - toothed along the margin with minute, sharp, forward-pointing teeth

*sessile* - attached directly, without a petiole, petiolule or stalk

*sheath* - portion of an organ which surrounds, at least partly, another organ, as the leaf base of a grass surrounds the stem

*shiny* - lustrous, polished, glossy

*simple* - undivided; not composed of more than one structurally
    equivalent unit

*sinus* - space or recess between two lobes or partitions of a leaf

*smooth* - without any configuration; lacking projections or rough-
    ness

*solitary* - simple, without others; one flower; not an inflorescence
    (see Plate VI)

*spatulate* - oblong or obovate apically with an attenuate base (see
    Plate II)

*spicate* - arranged on a spike

*spike* - an unbranched, indeterminate, elongate inflorescence with
    sessile flowers (see Plate VI)

*spine* - sharp-pointed petiole, midrib, vein or stipule; a sharp, slen-
    der, rigid outgrowth

*spinose* - bearing spines

*spur* - a short shoot on which flowers, fruits or leaves are borne; a
    tubular or pointed projection from the perianth

*stamen* - a floral organ that bears the pollen in flowering plants;
    the male reproductive part of a flower (see Plate V)

*staminate* - the stamens only in the flower; lacking pistils

*staminode* - a modified stamen which is sterile and produces no
    pollen

*stellate* - star-shaped

*stigma* - the tip of the pistil that receives the pollen, attached di-
    rectly to the style (see Plate V)

*stipule* - paired scales, spines, glands or blade-like structures at
    the base of a petiole (see Plate I)

*striate* - with longitudinal lines

*strigose* - bearing straight, stiff, sharp, appressed hairs

*style* - attenuated portion of pistil between the ovary and the stigma
    (see Plate V)

*sub-*(prefix) - meaning almost, slightly; e.g., "subcordate", slightly
    cordate; prefix meaning almost, e.g., "suborbicular", almost
    circular in outline

*subcapitate* - almost capitate

*succulent* - having juicy or pulpy tissues, as in cacti

*suffrutescent* - somewhat shrubby or only slightly woody at the
    base

*superior* - flower arrangement in which the other floral organs are
    attached below the ovary (see Plate V)

*symmetrical* - having a similarity in form or arrangement

*tendril* - a long, slender, coiling branch adapted for climbing (see Plate IV)

*terete* - round in cross section; cylindrical

*terminal* - at the tip or end of a branch or other structure

*ternate* - occurring in threes, as a leaf which is divided into three leaflets (see Plate IV)

*tesselate* - in a checkered pattern

*thorn* - a stiff, woody, modified stem with a sharp point

*thyrse* - a compact, cylindrical or ovate panicle

*tomentose* - covered with dense, interwoven hairs

*trailing* - prostrate and creeping but not rooting

*translucent* - shiny, partially transparent as in frosted glass; allows light to pass through but diffuses it so that objects cannot be distinguished clearly

*trifoliate* - a compound leaf with three leaflets (see Plate IV)

*triternate* - with three orders of leaflets, each ternately compound (see Plate IV)

*truncate* - cut straight across; ending abruptly almost at right angles to midrib or midvein

*tube* - the hollow, cylindrical part of a united corolla or calyx

*tubercle* - a mound which is fundamentally an enlarged leaf base, each bearing an areole or several spines

*tuberculate* - bearing tubercles

*tubular* - cylindrical

*twining* - twisted around a central object; coiling around an object

*umbel* - a determinate or indeterminate, flat-topped or convex inflorescence with the pedicels arising from a common point, like the struts of an umbrella (see Plate VI)

*umbellate* - resembling an umbel

*undulate* - wavy in a vertical plane, with a series of vertical curves at right angles to the central axis (see Plate III)

*unisexual* - with only one sex in each flower; with stamens or carpels absent in the flower

*utricle* - a small, bladdery or inflated, one-seeded, dry fruit

*valvate* - having margins of adjacent structures touching at edges only; not overlapping

*vein* - any vascular bundle forming the framework of a leaf blade

*veinlet* - a small vein

*ventral* - inner face of an organ; upper surface of a leaf ; adaxial

*villous* - covered with long, soft, crooked hairs

*vine* - an elongate, weak-stemmed, often climbing plant

*viscid* - sticky or gummy

*warty* - with lumps, like warts

*whorl* - a cyclic or acyclic group of leaves, petals, sepals or other structures; a group of three or more leaves or other structures per node (see Plate I)

*wing* - a flattened extension, projection or appendage

*woody* - hard and lignified

*zygomorphic* - bilaterally symmetrical, so that a line drawn through the middle of the structure along only one plane will produce a mirror image on either side (compare actinomorphic)

# Plate I

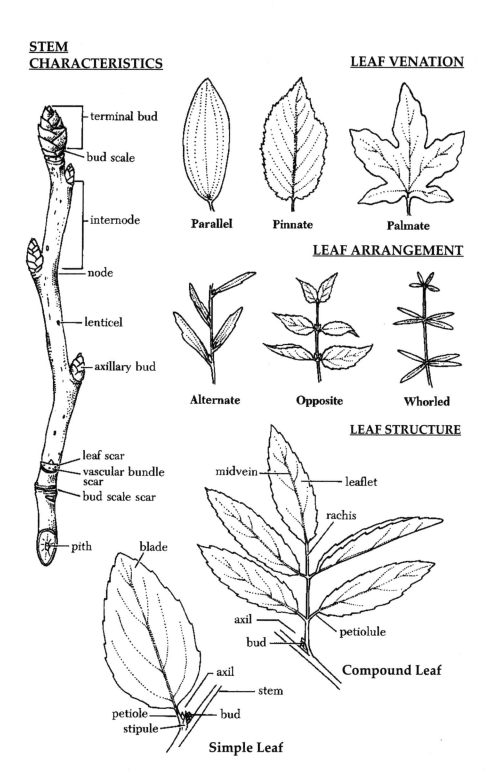

<u>STEM CHARACTERISTICS</u>

- terminal bud
- bud scale
- internode
- node
- lenticel
- axillary bud
- leaf scar
- vascular bundle scar
- bud scale scar
- pith

<u>LEAF VENATION</u>

**Parallel**  **Pinnate**  **Palmate**

<u>LEAF ARRANGEMENT</u>

**Alternate**  **Opposite**  **Whorled**

<u>LEAF STRUCTURE</u>

midvein — leaflet
rachis
axil — petiolule
bud

**Compound Leaf**

blade
axil
stem
petiole — bud
stipule

**Simple Leaf**

## Plate II

**LEAF SHAPES**

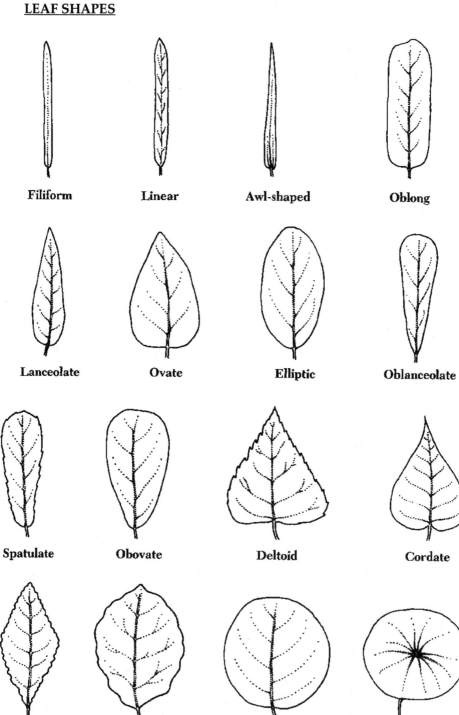

Filiform        Linear        Awl-shaped        Oblong

Lanceolate        Ovate        Elliptic        Oblanceolate

Spatulate        Obovate        Deltoid        Cordate

Rhombic        Oval        Orbicular        Peltate

## Plate III

### LEAF APICES

   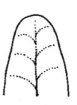 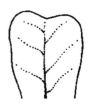

Acuminate   Caudate   Acute   Obtuse   Cordate

### LEAF BASES

  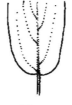 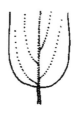 

Attenuate   Cuneate   Obtuse   Rounded   Oblique

### LEAF MARGINS

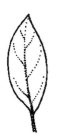  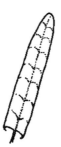 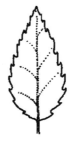  

Entire   Undulate   Revolute   Serrate   Biserrate   Dentate

  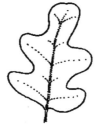  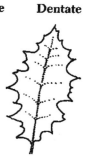

Crenate   Lobed   Divided   Incised

## Plate IV

### LEAF MODIFICATION

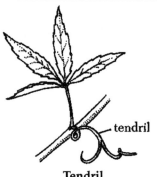

Tendril

Scale-like

Needle-like

### COMPOUND LEAVES

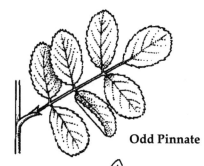

Odd Pinnate

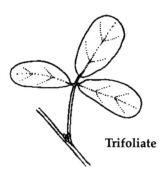

Even Pinnate

Palmate

Trifoliate

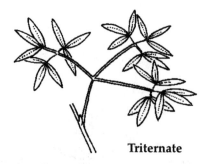

Triternate

Plate V

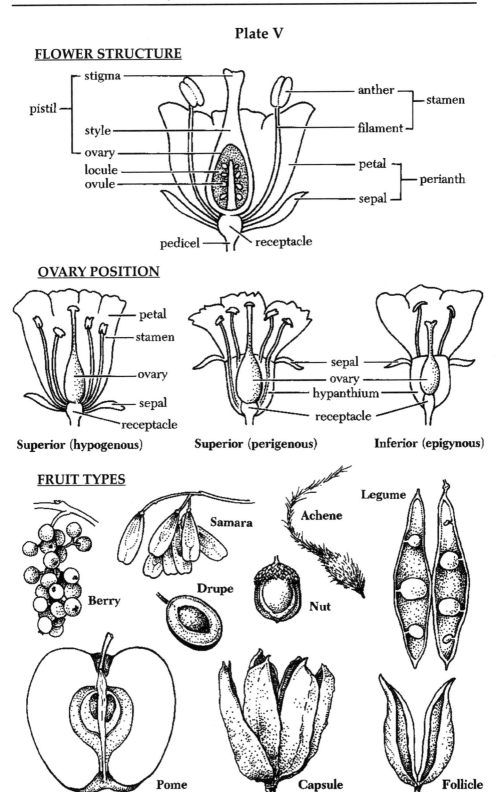

## FLOWER STRUCTURE

- stigma
- pistil
- style
- ovary
- locule
- ovule
- anther
- stamen
- filament
- petal
- perianth
- sepal
- pedicel
- receptacle

## OVARY POSITION

- petal
- stamen
- ovary
- sepal
- receptacle

**Superior (hypogenous)**

- sepal
- ovary
- hypanthium
- receptacle

**Superior (perigenous)**

**Inferior (epigynous)**

## FRUIT TYPES

Samara

Achene

Legume

Berry

Drupe

Nut

Pome

Capsule

Follicle

## Plate VI

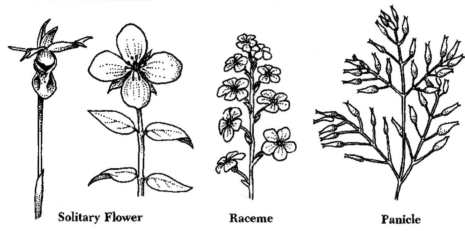

Solitary Flower          Raceme                Panicle

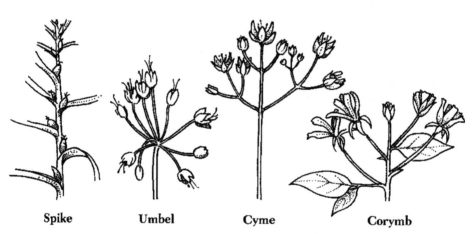

Spike          Umbel          Cyme          Corymb

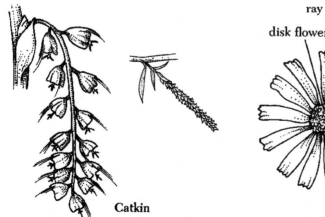

Catkin

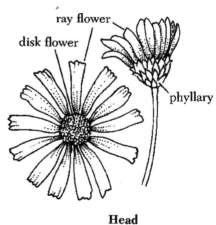

ray flower

disk flower

phyllary

Head

Adams, R. P. & T. A. Zanoni. 1979. The Distribution, Synonymy and Taxonomy of Three Junipers of Southwestern United States and Northern Mexico. *Southwestern Naturalist* 24:323-329.

Anderson, Loran C. 1995. The *Chrysothamnus-Ericameria* Connection (Asteraceae). *Great Basin Naturalist* 55(1): 84-88.

Argus, George W. 1995. Salicaceae Willow Family, Part Two: *Salix* L. Willow. *Journal of the Arizona-Nevada Academy of Science* 29: 39-62.

Benson, Lyman. 1982. *The Cacti of the United States and Canada.* Stanford University Press.

Benson, Lyman & Robert A. Darrow. 1945. *Trees and Shrubs of the Southwestern Deserts.* The University of Arizona Press.

Bowers, Janice Emily. 1993. *Shrubs and Trees of the Southwest Deserts.* Southwest Parks and Monuments Association.

Burgess, T.L. 1979. *Agave* - Complex of the Guadalupe Mountains National Park, Putative Hybridization Between Members of Different Subgenera. In Genoways, H. H. and R. J. Baker, *Biological Investigations in the Guadalupe Mountains National Park.* National Park Service, Proceedings Series Number Four.

Carter, Jack L. 1988. *Trees and Shrubs of Colorado.* Johnson Books.

Correll, Donovan Stewart & Marshall Conring Johnston. 1970. *Manual of the Vascular Plants of Texas.* Texas Research Foundation, Renner, Texas.

Denham, Bob. 1996. Key to the Taxa of *Cercocarpus* in New Mexico. *The New Mexico Botanist* Number 4: 3-5.

Dick-Peddie, William A. 1993. *New Mexico Vegetation: Past, Present and Future.* University of New Mexico Press.

Eckenwalder, James E. 1992. Salicaceae Willow Family, Part One: *Populus. Journal of the Arizona-Nevada Academy of Science* 26: 29-33.

Elmore, Francis H. 1976. *Shrubs and Trees of the Southwest Uplands.* Southwest Parks and Monuments Association.

Fletcher, Reggie A. 1987. Willows (*Salix*) of Arizona and New Mexico. USDA Forest Service, Range Management Staff, Southwestern Region, Albuquerque, New Mexico.

Gentry, H. S. 1982. *Agaves of Continental North America.* University of Arizona Press, Tucson.

Gleason, H.A. 1952. *The New Britton and Brown Illustrated Flora of Northeastern United States and Adjacent Canada. Vol. I-III.* New York Botanical Garden.

Harrington, H.D. 1954. *Manual of the Plants of Colorado.* Sage Books.

Harris, James G. & Melinda Woolf Harris. 1994. *Plant Identification Terminology: An Illustrated Glossary.* Spring Lake Publishing.

Hawksworth, Frank G. & Delbert Wiens.1972. *Biology and Classification of Dwarf Mistletoes (Arceuthobium).* USDA Forest Service, Agriculture Handbook No. 401.

Hickman, James C. (Editor). 1993. *The Jepson Manual: Higher Plants of California.* University of California Press.

Ivey, Robert DeWitt. 1995. *Flowering Plants of New Mexico.* Published by the Author.

Kartesz, John T. 1994. *A Synonymized Checklist of the Vascular Flora of the United States, Canada, and Greenland. Vol. I-II.* Timber Press.

Kearney, Thomas H. & Robert H. Peebles. 1951. *Arizona Flora.* University
    of California Press.
Kindscher, Kelly. 1992. *Medicinal Wild Plants of the Prairie: An Ethno-
    botanical Guide.* University Press of Kansas.
Lamb, Samuel H. 1971. *Woody Plants of New Mexico.* New Mexico
    Department of Game and Fish.
Lamb, Samuel H. 1989. *Woody Plants of the Southwest.* Sunstone Press.
Landrum, Leslie R. 1993. Fagaceae Oak Family. *Journal of the Arizona-Nevada
    Academy of Science* 27: 203-209.
Little, Elbert L., Jr. 1950. *Southwestern Trees: A Guide to the Native Species
    of New Mexico and Arizona.* USDA Forest Service, Agriculture
    Handbook No. 9.
Manor, Paul S. 1993. Foliar Trichome Variation in *Quercus* Section
    *Protobalanus* (Fagaceae). *Sida* 15(3): 391-403.
Martin, W.C. & C.R. Hutchins. 1980. *A Flora of New Mexico. Vol. I-II.*
    A.R. Gantner Verlag K.G. (J. Cramer).
McGregor, Ronald L. (Editor). 1986. *Flora of the Great Plains.* University
    Press of Kansas.
Moore, Michael. 1979. *Medicinal Plants of the Mountain West.* The Museum
    Of New Mexico.
Morin, Nancy R. (Editor).1993. *Flora of North America, Vol. 2.* Oxford
    University Press.
Powell, A. Michael. 1988. *Trees and Shrubs of Trans-Pecos Texas.* Big Bend
    Natural History Association, Inc.
Roalson, Eric H. & Kelly W. Allred (Editors). 1995. *A Working Index of
    New Mexico Vascular Plant Names, Edition 1.* Range Science
    Herbarium, Dept. of Animal and Range Sciences, New Mexico
    State University, Las Cruces, New Mexico.
Simpson, Benny J. 1988. *A Field Guide to Texas Trees.* Gulf Publishing Company.
Stephens, H.A. 1973. *Woody Plants of the North Central Plains.*
    The University Press of Kansas.
Vines, Robert A. 1960. *Trees, Shrubs and Woody Vines of the Southwest.*
    University of Texas Press.
Weber, William A. 1976. *Colorado Flora, Eastern Slope.* University Press
    of Colorado.
Weber, William A. & Ronald C. Wittmann. 1992. *Catalog of the Colorado
    Flora: A Biodiversity Baseline.* University Press of Colorado.
Weber, William A. & Ronald C. Wittmann.1987. *Colorado Flora, Western Slope.*
    University Press of Colorado.
Welsh, Stanley L., N. Duane Atwood, Sherel Goodrich & Larry C. Higgins (Editors).
    1987. *A Utah Flora.* Great Basin Naturalist Memoirs, Number 9,
    Brigham Young University.
Williams, Kenneth B. & Charles D. Bonham. 1972. Leaf Variations in *Vaquelinia
    Californica* Populations of Arizona. *Arizona Academy of Science* Vol. 7,
    No. 2: 47-50.

Illustrations are referred to in boldface type

Illustrations are referred to in boldface type

# A

## Index to Families